FIELD BOOK OF
NATURE ACTIVITIES
AND CONSERVATION

FIELD BOOK OF NATURE ACTIVITIES AND CONSERVATION

BY WILLIAM HILLCOURT

Illustrations by FRANCIS J. RIGNEY

G. P. PUTNAM'S SONS   NEW YORK

CONTENTS

PART I
ACTIVITIES IN THE WHOLE FIELD OF NATURE

PART II
SPECIFIC ACTIVITIES PROJECTS

PART III
CONSERVATION PROJECTS

To GRACE

and all others

who share her

curiosity, wonder, and love

of nature

INTRODUCTION

NATURE has a way of speaking to all of us, of calling us out under the open sky to listen to her "various language." The way we accept her message and act upon it depends on ourselves—our background, our temperament, our ambition.

To the born scientist, her call is a challenge—to know and to probe. To woodsmen and campers, she is a friend providing materials and food to use in woodcraft. To each of us, she suggests things to do in the out-of-doors. To those among us who think beyond the immediate present, she is a rich heritage to conserve and protect for generations to come.

> KNOWING nature—
> PROBING nature—
> USING nature—
> DOING nature—
> CONSERVING nature

five major approaches to nature and her ways—not, by any means, separate and clearly definable, but closely related and interwoven. There is no end to the possibilities that nature presents to you! By which door will you enter into the whole vast field of nature? That is the question. . . .

Books will point the way to you.

The books that deal with *knowing,* or identifying, nature are almost without number. They range from tiny booklets, through pocket-size field books, to weighty tomes illustrated with marvelous color reproductions.

Textbooks in biology, scientific books, and journals concern themselves with *probing* nature—the study of structure and functions, of reactions and behavior patterns.

In the field of *doing,* the number of books is meager. There have been books in certain, specialized phases of it. But few attempts have been made to cover the broad aproach to the whole field, to suggest a variety of activities from which those with the greatest appeal could be chosen.

7

The literature on the subject of *conserving* nature is growing by leaps and bounds. At last, we are awakening to the tremendous importance of conservation to the future of our nation and the world. But the majority of books published on conservation deal mainly with the crying necessity for it—only a few attempt to present a program of action with which the average person might associate himself.

It is to fill the need for a book on specific suggestions for *doing* things in the outdoors and for *conserving* nature that this *Field Book of Nature Activities and Conservation* was written.

Each activity of this *Field Book* is aimed toward creating an understanding of some phase of nature, and, through understanding, a desire to protect and conserve nature. Through nature activities you can lead others to a realistic approach to conservation—not only in terms of contouring, terracing, flood control, and similar broad aspects, but also in terms of what each of them as individuals can do for the protection of nature.

By awakening a love of nature in those whom you are guiding, you are working toward the ultimate goal of all conservation: the wise use and systematic replenishment of natural resources that can be renewed—forests, grasslands, and wildlife; the planned protection and proper utilization of our soil and waters; and the prudent expenditure of those resources which once gone are gone forever—our mineral wealth.

It is my hope that this *Field Book of Nature Activities and Conservation* will become your constant companion, as you set out to use some of its suggestions. My aim in writing it will have been accomplished if its ideas give to you some of the same joy and happiness that I myself have found in learning about nature and her ways.

A book of this type is never completed. Every day new ideas spring up. In working with nature, it is possible that *you* may discover or invent a new activity that may appeal to others who are interested in the out-of-doors. If you do, I sincerely trust that you may want to share it with me, and in that manner help me to improve this field book of *ours*.

—WILLIAM HILLCOURT

PART I

ACTIVITIES IN THE WHOLE FIELD OF NATURE

1. YOUR PERSONAL PURSUITS
IN NATURE

THE golden rule for your personal pursuits is this: *Pick a nature activity that will give you enjoyment and satisfaction.* Start out in a spirit of adventure, and make up your mind to have a good time.

There is a nature pursuit for *every taste.*

There are simple things you can do alone, complex activities that require the co-operation of many people. Nature gives you a chance for artistic or literary self-expression, for easy, leisure-time recreation or intensive study. Your early friendly familiarity with nature may become a thorough scientific knowledge that will enable you to add to our understanding of wildlife. The beauty and order of nature may open your mind to the Guiding Force behind it all.

There is a nature activity to fit *every age.*

If you are young, there is a vigorous life before you in the out-of-doors, exploring the unknown, bringing home with you the results of your excursions. Your interest in nature may possibly lead you into your life's work.

If you are an adult, a nature activity will help you get more out of life. Most people hurry through life only half alive. They have no ears to hear the songs of the birds, no eyes to look at a nodding flower. They lead lives of "quiet desperation" engulfed in a thousand worries. Their tension might be broken by a vigil under the open sky, by watching the quiet, enduring things in nature.

If you have reached your prime, there are still many years of nature fun ahead of you. An interest, an absorb-

11

ing hobby, is your best life insurance. Throw yourself into a nature activity to "stay alive after sixty-five."

There is a nature hobby for *every pocketbook*.

Many nature activities require no equipment and no expense. On the other hand, if you have the money, spend it on whatever supplies you feel you need to get the most out of your favorite interest.

ON SETTING OUT—*You* require enjoyment and satisfaction from your nature activity. What does *it* require of you, in turn?

It requires *curiosity*—a mind that is open to the What? When? Where? Why? and How? of nature. Without wonder, your nature pursuit is meaningless.

It requires *keenness of observation*. You must learn to observe things—not just with your eyes, but also with your ears, your nose, your palate, your fingers. All your senses come into play—including that important sixth sense, common sense, which makes it possible for you to comprehend, to figure out the meaning of what you have observed with the other five.

It requires *patience*. You cannot hurry things in nature. It takes time for the seasons to roll around, for flowers to open and trees to grow. It takes time and vigilance to follow the lives of birds and mammals and insects.

It requires *honest effort*. Your ultimate satisfaction will depend to a great extent on the effort you have made, the neatness and finish of your workmanship.

If you live up to these requirements, your rewards will be great. Your eyes will be opened to the marvels of nature, your life will be filled with rich experiences—and you will have a wonderful time!

Field Trips

The one nature activity, above all others, is the *field trip*. It is in nature that you learn nature—not by hearsay, but by actual experience and your own observations.

If you like to walk, nature walking will add a new meaning to your outdoor excursions. If walking is not as yet in your blood, take yourself out in the open whenever an opportunity presents itself. You will soon catch the bug and enjoy your outdoor hours.

FIELD EQUIPMENT—For most field trips, little equipment is required.

CLOTHING—Any sturdy outdoor clothing will do. Dress for the season and the weather. Bring along a sweater or other warm covering for cool mornings and evenings, a raincoat for a rainy day.

Proper footwear is of special importance. If you are accustomed to low shoes, use them. Some outdoorsmen prefer 8-inch or 10-inch boots. The important thing is that they be old acquaintances. New shoes may cause blisters. Get them broken in before you use them on a field trip.

NOTEBOOK—In one of your pockets, carry a notebook and a pencil. Keep a record of each of your field trips—date, place, weather—and of the things you see.

FIELD BOOK—For identification purposes, bring along a field book on the subject in which you are particularly interested—whether birds, mammals, insects, trees, and so on. The titles of recommended books will be found in each of the chapters of Part II of this book.

EATS—For an all-day trip carry one or more pocket meals. Sandwiches may be your most logical choice. Or you may develop your own field ration of chocolate bits, raisins, nuts—separate or in mixture. A canteen of drinking water will prove a blessing if you aren't certain of finding potable water in the field.

OTHER EQUIPMENT—Be prepared to take care of cuts and scratches with a minimum of *first-aid* items—a few bandaids and a couple of iodine ampules. Take mosquito lotion along in areas where you expect to run into insect pests. Be prepared for chiggers where they prevail, with sulphur powder or Sulfafoam.

For almost all field trips you will want to bring a strong *pocketknife*. Best model is probably the popular Scout knife with its small and large blades and variety of tools.

Specialized field trips require *special equipment*—binoculars for bird walking, insect net, plant press, and so on. Such equipment is dealt with in detail in chapters throughout the book.

If your equipment is rather extensive, tote it in a *side bag* (musette bag) in a strap over one shoulder, or in a small *knapsack* on your back.

WHEN TO GO—TIME OF YEAR—If you are interested in a certain field of nature, you must watch the time of

Equipment for a field trip is quickly assembled. Be prepared for emergencies with a minimum of first-aid items.

year. If all of nature is your oyster, there is no closed season for your activities.

SPRING is ushered in by the chorus of peepers. It is the time of awakening life—of early flowers and bursting buds, of returning birds, of nest building and young animals.

During SUMMER, the long, drowsy days hum with the song of the cicada in green trees and wide over flowering meadows. When twilight falls, animals roam through woods and over fields, katydids tune up their fiddles, and fireflies flash in the darkness.

FALL brings a brilliant display of dying leaves and a vast array of autumn flowers. Bird visitors leave for the south—there is the honking at night of high-flying wedges of wild geese. It is a season of seeds and fruits, of nature getting ready for its winter sleep.

In WINTER the trees stand like dark silhouettes against the sky. In the north, snow covers the ground—its smooth surface broken only by the hieroglyphics of tracks of animals and birds. Plants are at rest, ready to be called back to active life when the lengthening days return.

TIME OF DAY—Unless you are a professional naturalist, or a retired businessman, you will have to fit your nature activities into your daily work schedule, giving them whatever time you can manage. The best way—and probably the only way—of finding that time is by careful planning. Set aside some minutes in the morning, and some hours on definite evenings during the week. Plan to use certain week-end hours for field trips or intensive work at home.

DAWN—If your main interests are in the fields of bird and animal life, early morning, around dawn, is your best time of day. Those are the hours when the bird chorus is at its loudest, and when most mammals are abroad.

For many other nature activities, it pays to be an early riser. The air is bracing; the smell of the good earth stimulating. There is a feeling of expectancy all around you, as if all nature were waiting for the coming of the new day. Then the first rosy blush in the eastern sky, fading stars overhead, and finally a golden sun above a far horizon. You haven't experienced nature at her best until you know the magic of the dawn.

EVENING AND NIGHT—From early twilight to full darkness is your next best time of day for studying the life of wild animals.

You hear the rustle of their footfalls among dry leaves. You can watch them as they come to their watering places. As darkness falls, bats sweep overhead and nightflying insects appear; brilliant-hued moths are attracted to your sugaring places. And high above you, the constellations of the season form their ageless patterns.

DAYTIME—The height of day is your best time if your nature interests involve flowers and trees, insects and water life. For nature photography, sunlight is preferable to any of its weak imitations.

WHERE TO GO—Nature, like charity, begins at home. From there, you can expand your horizons in all directions.

YOUR BACK YARD—The distance of your field trip is immaterial. Many famed naturalists—Fabre, Mendel, and others—never went beyond their own immediate surroundings. In your own back yard or your garden there may be the ingredients for a lifetime's study, in the fields of insects and plants, birds and small mammals.

SPECIFIC AREAS—The investigation and natural history survey of a local park, a camp site, the school grounds may be of great value to yourself and to others. The next step is to get out through your countryside to find out about its wildlife communities—fields and woods, marshes and swamps, streams, lakes, or ocean shore. You may want to spend your time at one specific location—like Thoreau at his Walden Pond—or make your whole parish or county your theater of operation—like Gilbert White in his Selborne.

YOUR NATURE TRAVELS—With modern transportation you have a chance to travel to faraway places. By automobile or train, ship or plane, the whole country and our whole world can become your field. You can travel to a certain spot of unusual features—like Muir into California redwood territory—or circumnavigate the globe in search of knowledge—following in the wake of the *Beagle* that carried Darwin around the world.

FIELD TECHNIQUES—The field techniques for specific phases of nature are described in the chapters of Part II of this book. In all cases, a few simple rules apply.

Be methodical—Decide in advance what you want to do and what you expect to accomplish. Your earliest field trips may be reconnaissance expeditions, to learn the lay of the land and to discover its wildlife communities. When this job has been done, be specific: Lay out a plan of action for each field trip, and bring along the necessary equipment and note-taking material.

Be leisurely—You are not out to break records, but to discover and observe. You can only do this if you take your time. Get to your starting point quickly, then slow down. Get into the habit of walking Indian style—gliding, rather than striding, with a smooth rhythmic movement of the whole body, arms hanging loosely at your sides.

Be quiet—Avoid unnecessary noise—talking, stepping on dry twigs, or crunching gravel. You will be quietest if you travel alone. There are times when that is the only way you can gain your objective. But you will probably enjoy your field experience more if you have along a congenial companion—a good friend, a sweetheart, or your life partner. Bring such a companion, if you like, but be certain that he or she shares your nature interest and knows when to speak and, more important, when to fall quiet. Four eyes are better than two—but four feet make more noise than two, and a companion gabbing at the wrong time may mean the difference between seeing the bird or animal you came for, or missing it altogether.

Be alert—Walk with all senses keen. Scan the landscape around you, from your immediate surroundings to the farthest distance. Stop completely from time to time to listen, moving your head around to find out from what direction sounds come.

Be inquisitive—The way to find things is to look for them. A movement in the underbrush—was it an animal? Investigate. A bird flies up suddenly—from its nest? Locate it. A flat rock on the ground—what life does it hide? Turn it over. A purple flower among the black-eyed susans—which is it? Find out.

Recording Your Findings

NATURE NOTES

The moment you set out on a nature activity, start your nature notes at the same time. Get into the habit of jotting down your observations and your thoughts about nature.

You may think them unimportant. Well, perhaps they are—but maybe not. Some of our richest treasures in the whole field of nature have come from men who observed and made a record of their observations—men like White, Thoreau, Muir, Hudson, Burroughs, Fabre, Jefferies, and, in our own day, Peattie and Teale. They were unknowns at first, but their work has added immeasurably to our understanding of nature.

NOTEBOOKS—Many types of notebooks have been used in the past; countless others will be used in the future. Pick the kind that fits your own idea and style.

Many naturalists use a small, pocket-size booklet, 3x5 inches or slightly larger, for their entries, transferring them afterwards into larger books. Others like the loose-leaf method, writing their observations on each phenomenon on a single page, afterwards taking out the sheets and filing them according to subjects.

For special research, it often pays to have pages made up with headings and columns that make it easy to insert the findings. Such pages may be mimeographed, photo-offset, or printed, at a very reasonable price.

NOTE TAKING—The most important point in your note taking is that you *write down what you see*. The literary style matters little as long as your notes are correct, exact, and clear. Several approaches are feasible.

RECORDS—Keep a record of each field trip you take—of date, route, destination, weather, fauna and flora observed. Such records supply the minimum data for your work.

LOGS—Expand your field trip records to include detailed accounts of what you see. Add sketches, maps of territory covered, photographs.

DIARIES—Many naturalists have kept copious diaries of their comings and goings, their observations and musings. Try it. It may prove the method that suits you best.

OBSERVATIONS—The most important notes you can make are the detailed descriptions of observations of the activities and behavior of wildlife. While much is known about birds, mammals, reptiles, insects, and so on, much is still obscure. Your own, exact observations may cast a new light on natural phenomena and may become accepted facts when corroborated by the findings of other naturalists.

NATURE SKETCHING

Your nature notes will be greatly enhanced if you are able to accompany them with simple sketches.

If you have already done life drawing, the step to nature drawing is comparatively simple. If drawing is a new venture for you, get hold of a good book on nature sketching, secure the help of a local artist, and go to work. You may never become an Audubon or a Tory Peterson, a Livingston Bull or a Bransom, a Schuyler Mathews or an O'Keeffe—but you can try!

BOOKS ON NATURE SKETCHING—Arthur Zaidenberg. *How to Draw Wild Animals*. Abelard-Schuman Limited, N. Y.

John Skeaping. *Animal Drawing*. Studio Publications, N. Y.

Raymond Sheppard. *How to Draw Birds*. Studio Publications, N. Y.

Fredric Sweney. *Techniques of Drawing and Painting Wildlife*. Reinhold Publishing Corp., N. Y.

Victor Perard. *Drawing Flowers*. Pitman Publishing Corp., N. Y.

Frederick I. Garner. *How to Draw Trees*. Foster Art Service, Laguna Beach, Calif.

To a great extent, nature drawing—any drawing, for that matter—is a question of courage. Observe, then put on paper what you see, to the best of your ability. Draw without hesitation—long, confident lines. Try to catch the feeling of your subject. Don't aim for details in the beginning—beginners see too many of them and try to get them all in. To prevent this common fault, close your eyes to narrow slits, and look out from under the lids—in this way, details are blurred, and you see your subject as masses of light and shade.

It is, of course, not possible here to go very deeply into the techniques of nature sketching, but a few hints may prove helpful:

BIRDS—Think of the egg from which the bird came. The general body shape of the adult bird is almost the same. Begin your sketch by suggesting this egg-shape— rounded or lengthened, depending on the bird you are sketching. Add head, tail, legs. Then indicate the feathers —not individual feathers, but feather masses. The feathers are not scattered over a bird, but are arranged in a well-defined pattern.

ANIMALS—Practice side views until you can do them readily, then try other views. For side view of long-legged animals—deer, elk, moose—start with a square. One top corner is the shoulder, the other the rump; one bottom corner is the fore foot, the other the hind foot. Draw in two circles, one to indicate the ribs, the other the hind-quarters. Connect them, and you have the general basis for your drawing. For side view of short-legged animals, begin with a rectangle of the proper proportions, add the two circles, and go on from there.

In drawing an animal in motion, remember that the four legs move independently of each other. Study the action of walking and running animals until you get the rhythm right.

FISH—Probably the easiest creatures to draw. First the long arc of the back, then the usually flatter arc of the belly. Fins and tail—finally the details of gills and head.

INSECTS—Insects are generally sketched from the top. Keep in mind that insects—like most other creatures— are bilaterally symmetrical: One side of the body is a mirror picture of the other. This suggests your procedure: Draw one half of the body, then copy this for the other half.

FLOWERS—Flowers have the advantage that they keep their pose. You can study them from all angles and arrange them for best effects. Flower sketching calls for a certain daintiness in execution to catch the personality

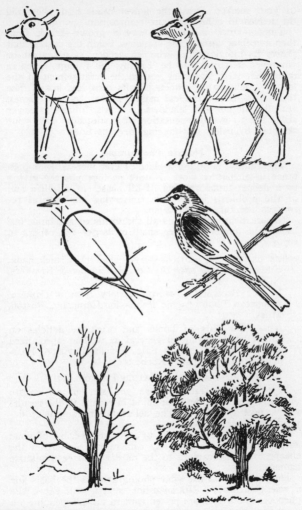

In drawing mammals, a square or a rectangle is your basic pattern. The egg is the starting pattern in bird drawing. When drawing a tree, think of the way in which it grows: trunk first, then major branches, smaller branches, leaf masses.

of your models. Draw the flower heads first, then add the leaves to complete your composition.

TREES—Draw a tree the way it grows—trunk first, then sweeping up into the branches. Catch the outline that shows its individuality—whether slender, vase shaped, or whatever it happens to be. Finally, the foliage. Keep in mind that large branches govern the arrangement of the leaves—each major branch has its own leaf mass. The trick is to show these leaf masses in their various planes, with highlights and shadows. A tree's foliage is never still; try to get the sensation of restlessness into your sketches by using fast-moving, nervous lines.

Nature Photography

The camera is taking a place of ever increasing importance in all nature work. Nature photographs are giving us a deeper understanding of all phases of wildlife and of the problems involved in conserving our natural resources for future generations

Nature photography has all the thrills of the hunt, but leaves the game—whether small or large—for others to enjoy.

BOOKS ON NATURE PHOTOGRAPHY—Allan D. Cruickshank, Editor. *Hunting with the Camera*. Harper & Brothers, N. Y.

L. W. Brownell. *Natural History with a Camera*. American Photographic Publishing Company, Boston, Mass.

Note—For lists of books and magazine articles on nature photography in general as well as specialized subjects, drop a line to Sales Service Division, Eastman Kodak Company, Rochester 4, N. Y.

YOUR APPROACH TO NATURE PHOTOGRAPHY

WHY PHOTOGRAPH?—Before you set out on nature photography, make up your mind in regard to the results you expect to achieve. The selection of equipment depends on your decision.

Are you interested mainly in a personal record of your nature pursuits? Almost any camera will do—from the cheapest folding camera to the most expensive miniature camera.

Do you want to use your photographs as the basis for a scientific study? No snapshot camera will serve the purpose, but a medium-priced camera may, depending on your requirements.

Do you expect to show your photographs to a larger audience than your immediate family, and possibly use them for educational work? In that case, you need to investigate the idea of taking color slides or movies.

Do you hope to have nature photography assist you in earning money for the further pursuit of your nature hobbies? Is it your ambition to see your nature photographs occupy honored positions in national exhibitions? Then buy the kind of equipment that will produce clear, crisp enlargements of professional quality, and learn to use it to the limit of its capacity.

MARKETS FOR NATURE PHOTOGRAPHY—The nature magazines listed on page 30 are in the market for suitable photographs.

Photo Market Guide. Published by D. R. Nephews Co., Brooklyn, N. Y.

Photographic section, *The Writer's Market.* Writer's Digest, Cincinnati, O.

ANNUAL SALONS OF NATURE PHOTOGRAPHS—Among others: Buffalo Museum of Science, Buffalo 11, N. Y. Kentucky Society of Natural History, University of Louisville, Louisville, Ky. Natural History Society of Maryland, Baltimore Museum of Art, Baltimore, Md. Chicago Natural History Museum, Chicago, Ill. Cranbrook Institute of Science, Dearborn, Mich. Write for particulars.

WHAT DO YOU INTEND TO PHOTOGRAPH ?—Every season of the year presents a multitude of opportunities for outstanding nature photography.

You may like the idea of becoming a free lancer in all of nature, photographing whatever comes your way of special interest and human appeal. On the other hand, there may be a specific subject in which you want to specialize.

Your decision in this respect also will have a direct bearing on the equipment you need to purchase. You will readily realize that the equipment required for ultra close-up insect photographs will have to be somewhat different from the kind that you can get along with in photographing tree silhouettes.

The most profitable procedure, therefore, before you buy your equipment, is to check the general suggestions presented in the following pages, and to add to them the recommendations contained in the chapter of this book that treat the subject you want to cover.

WORKING WITH OTHERS—Instead of learning nature photography solely "by guess and by golly," learn from the experiences of others as well.

Very possibly, a photographic club already exists in your locality. Find out how to join it, from your photographic dealer.

If your specialty is motion pictures, join a branch of the Amateur Cinema League, and get the added benefit of direct advice from the technicians of the national headquarters of this association.

ASSOCIATIONS—Check with your local photographic dealer to learn the names and addresses of Camera Clubs in your vicinity.

Amateur Cinema League, Inc. Hdqrs.: 420 Lexington Avenue, New York 17, N. Y. Periodical: *Movie Makers*.

STILLS

Stills in black-and-white, and as color transparencies, have the greatest variety of uses, from general study material and corroboration of observations made in the field, to printed reproductions and visual aids.

CAMERA AND LENSES—Suitable cameras for nature work fall in four categories:

ROLL-FILM CAMERAS—The usual amateur roll-film camera has a limited use for nature photography. It can be used "as is" for distant shots of landscape features, trees, and for large subjects up to its minimum focusing distance of 3½ or 4 feet.

By slipping an extra lens or "portrait attachment" over the camera's regular lens, it is possible to get closer to a subject and, in this way, secure a larger image on the negative. Portralens 1+, for instance, permits you to get within about 21 inches of your subject; the 2+ lens to within 13½ inches; the 3+ lens to 10 inches. The focusing must be done by measuring distances and fields according to focusing tables that accompany the lenses.

The speeds of roll-film cameras range up to 1/100 second, and in some instances, to 1/200 second. The most popular negative sizes are 1⅝×1⅝ inches, 2¼×2¼ inches, and 2¼×3¼ inches.

BOOK—*How to Make Good Pictures*. Eastman Kodak Company, Rochester, N. Y.

35 MM CAMERAS—The 35 mm miniature camera—Leica type—is, as the name implies, small and compact. For most purposes, you focus it through a coupled range finder. For close-ups, the camera is used in conjunction with a reflex housing, or a special focusing device—Focaslide or Speed-O-Copy—which provides knife-sharp focusing on ground glass.

More accessories for specialized photography are available for miniature cameras than for any other type of camera. The standard lens, with a focal length of 50

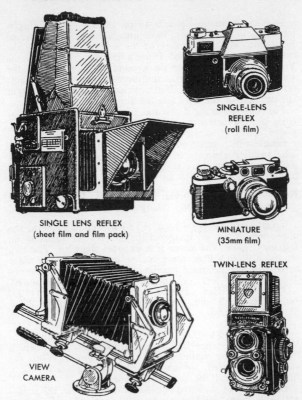

SINGLE-LENS
REFLEX
(roll film)

SINGLE LENS REFLEX
(sheet film and film pack)

MINIATURE
(35mm film)

TWIN-LENS REFLEX

VIEW
CAMERA

Cameras vary greatly in suitability for nature photography, as well as in size and cost. Pick a camera to fit your needs.

millimeters, is interchangeable for long-distance work with telephoto lenses of 90, 125, 150, 200 mm focal length, varying somewhat with brand of camera and manufacture of lens. For close-ups, you have a choice of extension tubes, ranging from a length of 7 mm to 90 mm. These tubes can be used singly or in combination.

Miniature cameras have speeds up to 1/1000 second. They use 35 mm film and produce 1×1½-inch black-and-white negatives or color transparencies.

BOOK—Willard D. Morgan & Henry M. Lester. *The Leica Manual*. Morgan & Lester, N. Y.

REFLEX CAMERAS—SINGLE-LENS REFLEX—In a single-lens reflex camera you look into a hood on a ground glass onto which an image of the subject, as seen by the camera lens, is reflected from a mirror, right side up. You focus the picture on the ground glass and follow the action of the subject until the moment you trip the shutter. As you press the shutter release, the reflex mirror springs out of the way and the film is exposed.

For long-distance shots and for close-ups, the regular lens, on the better cameras, can be replaced with telephoto lenses of varying lengths.

Single-reflex cameras have speeds up to 1/1000 second. The smaller cameras use roll film—35 mm or No. 120. The larger, commercial types—Graflex—use sheet film or film packs, 3¼×4¼ or 4×5 inches.

BOOK—Willard D. Morgan & Henry M. Lester. *Graphic Graflex Photography*. Morgan & Lester, N. Y.

TWIN-LENS REFLEX—In a twin-lens reflex camera, the upper lens forms an image of the subject for focusing on a ground glass, the lower lens exposes the film. The two lenses, although 2 or more inches apart, cover the same area by a synchronized parallax correction. For close-ups (closer than 3 feet), special close-up lenses are required.

Twin-lens reflex cameras, with speeds up to 1/1000 second, use roll films for making 1⅝×1⅝-inch or 2¼× 2¼-inch negatives.

VIEW CAMERAS—The view camera—Graphic and professional view type—has a ground-glass back on which the image of the subject appears, upside down. When the subject is focused, the ground glass is replaced with a film holder, and the exposure made.

By using the standard lens—normally 101 or 127 mm and extending the bellows, you can get close enough to a small subject to take a full size photograph of it. The magnifying power of the lens can be increased by the use of extension tubes—metal tubes of varying lengths that screw in between lens and camera.

For long-distance shots, the view camera can be provided with the same kind of telephoto lenses as used for reflecting cameras. These lenses are equally important for close-ups.

View cameras have speeds up to 1/1000 second. They use 3¼×4¼- or 4×5-inch sheet film or film packs.

BOOK—*Graphic Graflex Photography*. See above.

OTHER EQUIPMENT—TRIPOD—For most nature photography, you need a steady tripod. Pick a telescoping model that will make it possible for you to set it at a low height, as well as at 5 feet. A tilting head for the tripod greatly simplifies its use.

EXPOSURE METER—An exposure meter is well-nigh indispensable. You may be able to get along without it for average outdoor photography, by using the exposure guides that come with the various films. But you will need it for close-up and color photography.

FLASH EQUIPMENT—For daylight photography in poor light and for night photography, you may want to secure flash equipment synchronized for your camera. For best results, purchase the flash equipment specifically designed for your camera.

FILMS—Your selection of films depends on your objects and the light conditions under which they are to be photographed.

BLACK-AND-WHITE FILMS—COLOR SENSITIVITY—In the early days of photography, a deep blue sky photographed pure white, an orange flower solid black. By adding certain dyes to the emulsion, film manufacturers have succeeded in developing films that more nearly express the relative brilliance of the colors in nature. *Orthochromatic films*—such as Verichrome—respond to green and yellow : *Panchromatic films*—Panatomic-X, Isopan IFF, and others—to orange and red as well. Because of its higher color sensitivity, it is advisable to use one of the panchromatic films for black-and-white nature photography.

Tip—An outdoor shoot can often be further enhanced by the use of a filter. A light to medium-yellow filter (Wratten K1 and K2) will darken a sky background, and lighten red and yellow objects. A deep-yellow filter (G filter) is used to increase the texture of outdoor objects.

SPEED—Stationary objects can be photographed with slow film. Fast-moving objects, on the other hand, require fast films—Plus X Pan or Isopan ISS, or even Tri X Pan or Isopan Ultra.

In using high-speed film, remember that with extra speed comes increased graininess in the negative. This is of little consequence when negative is large, but may show up unpleasantly in a magnification of a 35 mm negative.

COLOR—Color slides or transparencies have become strong competitors to movies for visual instruction and entertainment. They have also caused increased use of the 35 mm miniature camera, although color film is available for other cameras as well, in sheet form.

Five color films lead the market : Kodak's Kodachrome, Ektachrome, and High Speed Ektachrome ; and Ansco's

Anscochrome and Super Anscochrome. They come in two types: Daylight Type for use in the outdoors and Tungsten Type for use under artificial light.

NATURE MOVIES

The taking of nature movies is considerably more difficult than shooting nature stills. It takes far more planning, more skill in approaching wildlife, and imagination in editing the scenes into a unified whole. But the result is often breath-taking, especially when shot in color.

Before starting on movies, decide on your aims. Is your main purpose to produce shots that will please your family and friends, or is it your hope to reach a larger audience?

In the first case, 8 mm movies will do. They can be successfully projected in your living room.

But if you want to show your efforts before a larger group of people, you will have to use 16 mm, taking your scenes at 16 frames a second for silent projection, or at 24 frames a second, if you intend to have sound dubbed on to your movies.

BOOKS—*How to Make Good Movies.* Eastman Kodak Company, Rochester, N. Y.
ACL Movie Book. Amateur Cinema League, 420 Lexington Avenue, New York 17, N. Y.

CAMERA AND LENSES—Whether you settle for 8 mm or decide on 16 mm, by all means pick a camera that makes exact focusing possible—in other words, a magazine-loading 8 or 16, or if you are beyond the amateur class, an advanced camera such as the Cine-Kodak Special. For focusing, you open up the magazine camera, remove the film magazine, and insert in its place a ground-glass focusing finder. Through this you will see exactly what the lens sees. You can compose your shot knowing that neither top nor bottom will be cut off in shooting. Take out focusing finder, put in the magazine, and shoot.

For long-distance shots and for extreme close-ups, the standard lens can be replaced by a telephoto lens.

In the 8 mm field, several telephoto lenses are now available, to take the place of the regular 13 mm lens. Your dealer can tell you which lenses will fit your 8 mm camera.

For a 16 mm camera, you can replace the standard 25 mm lens with any of several telephoto lenses—50, 63, 75, 102, 152 mm and others. If you decide to purchase one telephoto lens only, you will find that the 75 mm or 102 mm lens is of greatest use. The image, when you use such a lens, is three or four times, respectively, that of a shot taken with the standard 25 mm lens.

Tip—Curiously enough, a wide-angle lens can often take the place of a telephoto for close-up photography. The Kodak Wide-Angle Lens for 16 mm cameras, for instance, can be focused at close range to cover a field only 3⅝ inches wide.

OTHER EQUIPMENT—Tripod—A few movie makers get along without a tripod—their movies show it! There are occasions when you have to shoot without one, but for perfect shots you do need a tripod. Get a model with sturdy, telescoping legs and with a tilting and panoraming head—not that you will ever want to panoram, but so that you will be able to swing the camera easily into position.

Exposure meter—By all means! While the exposure guides packed with each roll or magazine of motion picture film are adequate for ordinary amateur shots, they do not have the answer for all the exposure problems you will run up against in nature photography. The meter has.

FILMS—Black-and-white film for movies is still on the market, but the comparatively small extra cost of color film has turned almost all amateurs toward color.

Black-and-white—For 8 mm and 16 mm cameras, Plus-X for ordinary shooting and Tri-X for shooting under poor light conditions and indoors.

Color—For both 8 mm and 16 mm cameras, Kodachrome and Ansco Moviechrome—Daylight Type for outdoor shooting, Type A Kodachrome or Tungsten Ansco Moviechrome for indoor use under artificial light.

You need a good camera and a steady tripod. Telephoto lenses are used for long-distance shots and for extreme close-ups.

Tip—If it is necessary for you to shift repeatedly from outdoor to indoor shots, use Type A or Tungsten type throughout, with outdoor filter when shooting in the open.

Your Nature Collection

A nature collection is far more than a gathering of in-animate objects. It is a record of your nature activities, supplementing your nature notes, sketches and photographs. In addition, each item is a reminder of interesting hours spent in the field, and often also of pleasant moments at home, preserving the specimen.

You will want to be proud of your nature collection. You will be if it is well developed and well kept. A great portion of this *Field Book* is devoted to the methods involved in making collections. If you follow the suggestions, you will have a collection of professional quality.

EQUIPMENT AND SUPPLIES

Each type of collecting requires its own type of equipment. You will get most out of your hobby if you make the equipment yourself. You will find detailed suggestions for doing so in the chapter of this book dealing with your nature specialty.

Certain equipment and supplies cannot be made at home. Some of them may be improvised from materials in neighborhood shops. The rest may be purchased from biological and scientific supply houses.

SUPPLY HOUSES—General Biological Supply House, Inc. (Turtox Products), 761-763 East 69th Place, Chicago 37, Ill.

Ward's Natural Science Establishment, Inc., 3000 Ridge Road East, Rochester 9, N. Y.

Central Scientific Company, 17000 Irving Park Road, Chicago 13, Ill.; 79 Amherst Street, Cambridge 42, Boston, Mass.; 441 Clinton Avenue, Newark 8, N. J.

New York Scientific Supply Co., 28 West 30th Street, New York, N. Y.

Cambosco Scientific Co., 37 Antwerp Street, Boston, Mass.

Carolina Biological Supply Co., Elon College, Elon, N. C.

Southern Biological Supply Co., New Orleans, La.

South-Western Biological Supply Co., P. O. Box 4084, Station A, Dallas 8, Tex.

Powers and Powers, Denver 1, Colo.

College Biological Supply Co., 9230 Woodlawn Avenue, Seattle 3, Wash.

California Biological Service, 1612 West Glendale Blvd., Glendale 1, Calif.

Your Nature Workshop

If at all possible, set aside a separate room in your home for a nature workshop. The great advantage of this is that you can leave whatever project you are working on spread out on table and desk without worrying about having it disturbed.

But whether you can manage a separate nature shop or must use a corner of the living room, the main feature of your layout will be your *work table*. Select one of a size to fit the job you are doing. It can be comparatively small if you specialize in insects, but you need plenty of elbow room for preparing a herbarium. For some jobs, you will be most comfortable seated; for other work, standing may be more efficient. Pick your table height accordingly.

A *cabinet* for equipment and supplies is the next requirement. Provide it with a lock if any of your supplies contain poisons—such as the cyanide jars used in insect collecting.

Storage facilities should be developed to suit your specific needs. For some collections, cabinets with shelves are suitable. For others, drawers are preferable. Design your storage units to a standard pattern so that more can be added as needed. Make doors and drawers as airtight as possible to exclude insect pests.

And then, of course, a *book shelf* for your technical books, notebooks, and scientific periodicals.

Helps in Your Nature Pursuits

"No man is an iland, intire of it selfe . . ." You do not stand alone. The work of naturalists before you is available to you, and many institutions and associations are ready to welcome you and help you.

Your Nature Library

BOOKS—There are nature books by the thousands. Choose those that will be of greatest value in your work.

Your minimum needs—To get a satisfactory experience out of any phase of nature, you need *two good books* in that field: a book that will give you a basic knowledge of your specialty, and a field book for the identification of specimens.

Throughout the following chapters, titles of such books are given. An earnest attempt has been made to include only titles that are in print. In referring to publishers, where no address is given, it is New York City, N. Y.

Other books—You would hardly stop with two books. From that small start, your nature library will grow by leaps and bounds as your interest increases.

In most instances, your first two books will contain bibliographies that will lead you on to others.

Check with your local library and find out what books it has in the field in which you are interested. Some of those books may appeal to you so much that you will want to own them. If still in print, they can be purchased through your regular bookstore. If out of print, a second-hand bookstore or a "book hunter" may be able to locate them for you.

At the same time, keep your eyes open for new books in the book columns of your newspaper and in the book section of nature periodicals.

PAMPHLETS—Our Federal Government publishes a great number of pamphlets on wildlife and plant life of interest to naturalists throughout the country. In addition, your own state has probably published pamphlets on your local fauna and flora and problems connected with their protection and management.

Write to the agencies involved for a list of their publications, and secure those that relate to your interests.

ADDRESSES—U. S. Department of the Interior, Fish and Wildlife Service, Washington 25, D. C.

U. S. Department of Agriculture, Washington 25, D. C.

State Department of Conservation—your state capital.

State Fish and Game Commission—your state capital.

State Museum—your state capital.

State Agricultural Extension Service—your state agricultural college.

PERIODICALS—In addition to the specialized bulletins of scientific associations, a number of excellent nature periodicals aimed at a wider audience are published regularly. They pick their subjects from the whole wide field of nature and are profusely illustrated, mostly with photographs.

Besides providing you with enjoyable reading and excellent pictures, each of these magazines will help you to keep up with new discoveries, new methods of studying nature and new books.

PERIODICALS—*Natural History.* American Museum of Natural History, Central Park West at 87th Street, New York, N. Y.

Outdoors Illustrated. Audubon Society of Canada, 177 Jarvis Street, Toronto 2, Ontario, Canada.

Audubon Magazine. National Audubon Society, 1130 Fifth Avenue, New York 28, N. Y.

Hobbies. Buffalo Museum of Science. Humboldt Park, Buffalo, N. Y.

The Scientific Monthly. American Association for the Advancement of Science, 1515 Massachusetts Avenue, N.W., Washington 5, D. C.

Occasional nature articles: *National Geographic Magazine,* National Geographic Society, Washington, D. C.

PERSONS AND INSTITUTIONS

PERSONS—There is almost certainly somebody in your "neck of the woods" already interested in the same or a similar type of nature activity as the one on which you are concentrating. Trouble is that most such people go about their work in a quiet manner, and it is hard to find out who they are.

Contact your nearby high-school biology teacher or college biology professor. In all probability, they will know of nature-interested people within the community and can suggest how you may meet them.

If this fails, you may want to strike up a correspondence with people outside your immediate vicinity who share your nature interest. To find out who they are, peruse the pages of *The Naturalists' Directory.* This directory contains the names, addresses, and special subjects of study of close to four thousand amateur and professional naturalists of North and South America, and of countries around the world.

REFERENCE—*The Naturalists' Directory.* Jerrold Oakley, Publisher, Armonk, N. Y.

INSTITUTIONS AND OFFICES—In addition to individual naturalists, find out what local institutions and offices deal with subjects related to your nature interest, such as:

Natural history museum, or college nature exhibit—Zoological garden—Aquarium—Botanical garden—Observatory—State or National park or sanctuary—State or federal forester, fish, game, or wildlife representatives—Agricultural county agent.

Make the acquaintance of curators, wardens, or agents. They will gladly give you their technical assistance.

NATURE ASSOCIATIONS

Your luckiest break will be a chance to join a local nature club or branch of a national nature association. The great advantage in belonging to such groups is the opportunity to get together with like-minded people for indoor meetings with talks and discussions, and, more important, for field trips under expert guidance. The best known association is probably the *National Audubon Society.* While its main specialty is bird study, it deals with all other phases of nature as well.

ASSOCIATIONS—National Audubon Society. Hdqrs.: 1130
   Fifth Avenue; New York 28, N. Y. Periodical: *Audu-
   bon Magazine*.
   American Nature Study Society. Hdqrs.: Beth Schultz,
   Dept. of Biology, Western Michigan Univ., Kalama-
   zoo, Mich. Periodicals: *Natural History;* Cornell
   Rural School Leaflets.

The names and addresses of associations and clubs that
specialize in certain subjects will be found in the chapters
describing these subjects. Many of these associations are
members of the *American Association for the Advancement of Science*. In joining this association, you will meet
scientists and amateurs with whom you can discuss your
nature hobby.

ASSOCIATION—American Association for the Advancement
   of Science. Hdqrs.: 1515 Massachusetts Avenue, N.
   W., Washington 5, D. C. Periodicals: *Science*
   (Weekly), and *The Scientific Monthly*.

NATURE CAMPS AND SCHOOLS

If you can possibly manage to do so, plan to spend
some time—a couple of weeks or more—with other
naturalists, in pursuit of your nature interests.

There are a number of nature camps in various sections
of the country, with two-week periods of intensive work
—among them the Audubon Nature Camps in Maine,
Connecticut, Wisconsin, and California.

REFERENCES—For information on the Audubon Nature
   Camps, write to National Audubon Society, 1130 Fifth
   Avenue, New York 28, N. Y.

Many universities, teachers' colleges and biological laboratories provide graduate and undergraduate courses in
various fields of nature. Several of these courses are open
to the general public. Some of the institutions make their
facilities available to people who wish to do independent
study and special research.

REFERENCES—*Biological Field Work*—Directory of Nature
   Summer Camps and Biological Stations. General Bio-
   logical Supply House, 761-763 East 69th Place.
   Chicago 37, Ill.

2. GETTING OTHERS INTERESTED

IN NATURE

AS YOUR own interest in nature deepens, you may want to awaken in others the same curiosity, wonder, and love that you feel. If you are a parent, or a youth leader, or a scientist, it may be your desire to do so. As a teacher or camp counselor, it may be your responsibility.

Nature Leadership

Your success as a nature leader will depend on your personality, your understanding, and your approach.

YOUR PERSONALITY—You can't get others enthusiastic about nature, unless you are genuinely enthusiastic yourself. A bubbling, contagious enthusiasm is your best ally for catching the interest of others—not the artificial slap-on-the-back kind, but the kind that is the result of a deep love for nature in all her forms. The sincerity of your enthusiasm will be evident to all who come in contact with you—they will soon catch some of it themselves.

But enthusiasm is not enough. You need a certain amount of leadership ability to go with it. Almost any person who knows where he is going can become a leader. It is a matter of having a program that you believe in, and the ability to present it simply and sincerely.

YOUR UNDERSTANDING—It is of great help if you have a good general understanding of nature—not necessarily the deep insight of an expert, but rather the knowledge of the interested amateur. You need not be a walking encyclopedia. On the contrary, it will prove of far greater importance to the people with whom you deal, if you can get them to seek out the information for themselves, in field books and pamphlets, rather than have the answer pat for them the moment they ask you. There is no question which of the attitudes is better when, for example, a youngster brings you a wiggling snake and you have the choice between, "Well, well, what have we here? Let's see if we can find out what it is!" and "That's a garter snake! Next!"

One of your big objectives is to inspire others to become self-active, self-observant, and self-reliant. But that requires far more than an understanding of subject matter. It requires an understanding of the people you are attempting to lead—a realization that any one of them is as important as any one else. Remember that each has his own interests and is trying to pursue them to the best of his ability, gropingly, perhaps, and needing a helping hand.

If you can make each person feel your sincere interest in him, you will have little difficulty in inspiring him to do his best toward broadening his own knowledge and toward advancing the work of the group.

YOUR APPROACH—Your relationship to the people you are to lead will determine your approach.

FOR THE PARENT: *Example and Exposure*—The best way for a parent to instill a nature interest in a child is to keep his or her own interest in nature before the child, as an ever-present example. What the child sees it will try to imitate. Through imitation comes understanding and the desire for repetition. The repeated action may then eventually become a habit that will follow the child through adolescence into adulthood.

If you are interested in birds, what would be more normal than to let your children help you as you go about feeding birds in winter, help you put up bird houses in the spring, go with you to look for them in field and forest all summer long, watch with you the flocks that gather for southward flight in the fall?

You will succeed most easily if your own nature interest is a natural part of your life, if you cannot help observing the things that happen around you, and if you have a deep-rooted love for all living things. Your children will early begin to feel and share that love and will eagerly follow your nature leadership if you keep their nature pursuits on a happy, enjoyable basis.

FOR THE YOUTH LEADER AND CAMP COUNSELOR: *Exploits and Excitement*—In dealing with Scouts, campers, and other young people, your main problem is to catch them long enough to influence them. At best, you have them for a hike a month and a few weeks in camp. They come with their own ideas of what they want to do. To many of them nature is "sissy-stuff." You must prove to them that it is virile and vital. This cannot be done by setting a morning or an afternoon period aside for "Nature." It must be done by correlating nature with the rest of the program, making use of opportunities as they come along, creating experiences—infiltration, if you like.

Hiking along some twilight hour, you may happen upon a deer. A quiet warning silences the group. "How close can we get to it?" There's a thrill to stalking a deer through dew-laden grass. There may be a beaver dam somewhere near camp—an evening's vigil watching the colony at work will never be forgotten. Climbing for a squirrel's nest, diving for samples of life from the lake bottom, gliding silently in a canoe close to a kingfisher's perch, getting up before the break of dawn to listen to the bird chorus—there's excitement and challenge to each of these exploits.

Excitement in the beginning to the few, perhaps—but you want to reach them all. You want them all in on the fun. How interest the others? By *souvenirs* brought home from the trips—beaver-gnawed branches, a live snake, a praying mantis, an ant-cleaned animal skull. By publicizing the unusual on the *bulletin board* of camp or meeting room. By creating *nature trail* and *trailside museum*. By short *nature reports* around the council fire. By making the uninitiated feel the mysterious fraternity that somehow exists among nature enthusiasts, and making them eager to join it.

You can catch youth through a great number of the activities described in the following chapters. The trick is to spring the right activity at the right time, keeping at it as long as it thrills—then shifting to another before the interest wanes. A little here, a little there—it takes time and effort and patience to teach a youngster to walk woodsmanlike through nature, aware of the teaming life around him.

REFERENCES—Betty Price. *Adventuring in Nature*. Association Press, 291 Broadway, New York 7, N. Y.
Marie E. Gaudette. *Leader's Nature Guide*. Girl Scouts, 830 Third Avenue, New York 22, N. Y.
William Gould Vinal. *Nature Recreation*. McGraw-Hill Book Company, N. Y.
William Hillcourt. *Boy Scout Handbook*. Boy Scouts of America, New Brunswick, N. J.
William Hillcourt. *Scout Field Book*. Boy Scouts of America.

FOR THE TEACHER:—*Excursions and Experiments*—
The days when nature study to a science teacher meant
book learning and blackboard outlines only are gone forever—and good riddance! It is no longer a matter of
cramming a certain number of pages into the brain of the
students, but rather of arousing curiosity and establishing
a desire in pupils to find out about nature for themselves
—each person according to his or her own interest and
inclination.

Whenever possible, study nature in nature. Take the
class outdoors on excursions as often as it can be arranged. Use the field trip techniques described on page
39, varying the methods somewhat to suit the age of
the participants. For an older group, feel the pulse of the
pupils, figuratively speaking, and be ready with suggestions for nature projects (see page 42) that may
appeal to them collectively or individually. For a group
of young children, make use of occasional nature games
(page 43).

Much of the schoolwork must, of necessity, take place
within the four walls of the schoolroom. The trick here is
to bring nature indoors in the form of experiments—trying out things, finding out about things. Projects started
outdoors on an excursion may be continued indoors—collections, terrariums, and so on. Individual students or
small teams may be encouraged to engage in projects,
bring in their nature finds, and report on their nature discoveries. From the great number of projects described in
the following pages, a series of activities may be scheduled
to fit all seasons of the school year.

BOOKS—J. A. Partridge. *Natural Science through the
Seasons.* The Macmillan Company of Canada; avail-
able through The Macmillan Company, New York,
N. Y.

A. B. Comstock, *Handbook of Nature-Study.* Comstock Publishing Company, Ithaca, New York.

Margaret M. Hutchinson. *Children as Naturalists.* The
Macmillan Co., N. Y.

PERIODICALS—*The Science Teacher.* Official Magazine of
the National Science Teachers' Association, 1201 Six-
teenth Street, N. W., Washington 6, D. C.

The American Biology Teacher. Official Magazine
of the National Association of Biology Teachers,
Bryan City Schools, Bryan, Ohio.

The Science Counselor. The Duquesne University
Press, 901 Vickroy Street, Pittsburgh 19, Pa.

FOR ADULTS: *Experiences and Exchange*—Almost every
adult has some interest in nature. In a few, it finds ready

expression. In others, it may be hidden in the back of their minds, waiting to be called to the fore. Still others are too shy, or too sophisticated, ever to admit the interest —yet may become strongly stirred in close contact with nature.

The simplest means of getting adults interested in nature is through shared experiences and the exchange of ideas. A walk with a few intimate friends through the woods at twilight, a camping expedition, a fishing trip, the showing of a nature movie—any of these may be the kind of experience that may send an adult into a life-time nature hobby.

NATURE CLUBS

Your aim in nature leadership is to get people interested in nature. You may succeed in establishing a *general* interest in many, an *intense* interest in a few. It may prove worth your while to give the intensely interested more of your time, even to the point of helping them to get themselves organized into a nature club, for the purpose of digging deeper into their particular fields.

WHO MAKE UP THE CLUB?—Whether the club consists of youngsters or of adults, keep in mind that the club belongs to its members. You may be willing to sponsor it, and may be of great help in getting the club under way, but the moment it is started, it is important that each member accept a definite responsibility in the club and be encouraged to carry it out.

It is usually best to start a club with relatively few members, then increase the number as others want to join.

THE CLUB CONSTITUTION—To get everything off in a businesslike manner, spend some time during the first meetings developing a constitution for the club. It need not be elaborate. Its main purpose will be to establish rules for membership and decide on the aims of the club. The following form may prove suitable:

Constitution of the .... Nature Club

ARTICLE I—NAME
The name of this club shall be ....

ARTICLE II—PURPOSE
The purpose of this club shall be as follows:
Sect. 1. To foster and keep alive an interest in ....
....
Sect. 2. To increase our knowledge in the special field of ....
Sect. 3. ....

ARTICLE III—MEMBERSHIP, DUES

Sect. 1. Membership in this club shall be open to .....
Sect. 2. Dues shall be $...... (monthly) (yearly),
payable ....

ARTICLE IV—OFFICERS

Sect. 1. The officers of this club shall consist of President, Vice-president, Secretary, Treasurer and ....
Sect. 2. The officers shall be elected by ballot and majority vote, for a term of ....
Sect. 3. The duties of the officers shall be as follows:
....

ARTICLE V—MEETINGS

Sect. 1. Regular meetings shall be held on ...... day,
.... month.
Sect. 2. The order of business at regular meetings shall be as follows: Roll Call—Reading of the Minutes—Unfinished business—Committee reports—New business—Main program feature—Project work—Announcements—Adjournment.
Sect. 3. Special meetings may be called by ....
Sect. 4. The annual meeting of this club shall be held on ....

ARTICLE VI—AMENDMENTS

Sect. 1. This constitution may be amended by vote of two-thirds of the members.

THE WORK OF THE CLUB—With the club established, the members go to work.
The first order of business is to lay out the program of the club so that its aims may be fulfilled. If it is a project on which all members can get busy, well and good. If the project divides itself into a number of phases, form as many separate committees as necessary, each committee responsible for the work in one of the phases. The committee chairmen together may make up a "steering committee" that will keep the project as a whole moving along smoothly.
"Action" is the key word to success in a nature club. You will have no luck keeping a club alive on business discussions and talks. Members join a nature club for outdoor activities, not for indoor gabfests. If you are a sponsor of a club for youngsters, help them stay on the active line with field trips and projects. If you are working with adults, make your voice heard and do your part to make your nature club a club of the out-of-doors.

GUIDE BOOKS—Science Clubs of America, *Sponsor Handbook*. Science Service, 1719 N Street, N. W., Washington, D. C.

Audubon Junior Program—Audubon Teachers' Guide.
National Audubon Society, 1130 Fifth Avenue, New
York 28, N. Y.

Co-operating with Existing Agencies

Instead of starting a separate Nature Club, you may
be inclined to make your abilities available to established
youth organizations that include nature pursuits as part of
their regular program. They will most certainly welcome
your services.

Look in your telephone book or check with a local
schoolteacher to find out what groups of boys or girls
are found in your vicinity. Then make the necessary contacts and discuss the type of activities that may be
developed.

In some instances, your help may be needed in direct
work with the youngsters. In other cases, you may be
of even greater assistance in training their leaders in a
dynamic nature program—not just for camp, but for year-
round use.

ADDRESSES—*Boys*—Boy Scouts of America, New Bruns-
wick, N. J.
Boys' Clubs of America, 381 Fourth Avenue, New
York 16, N. Y.
YMCA, YMHA—see local directory.
Girls—Girl Scouts of U. S. A., 830 Third Avenue,
New York 22, N. Y.
Camp Fire Girls, 16 East 48th Street, New York,
N. Y.
YWCA, YWHA—see local directory.
Boys and girls—4-H Club, U. S. Department of Ag-
riculture, Washington 25, D. C.

Field Trips

The field trip is your best means of imparting to others
a love for nature, of giving them an understanding of the
interrelationship between all living things, of teaching
them to observe and to know nature.

Whether you are undertaking a field trip for a group
of adults, a school class, nature club, or Scout Troop, it
is important to plan it well in advance, to use an effective
field technique, and to provide for a follow-up to evaluate
the results.

Planning

The preparation for a field trip of a small group of five
to eight people will take less planning than for a larger
group, and the participants will each get more out of the
experience. The larger group requires stronger leadership
and closer supervision. For greatest effectiveness it is
generally advisable to divide a large group into sub-

groups, each with a well-liked student leader, along the lines of the Patrol Method used in Scouting.

WHAT?—Before you set out, arouse the interest of the participants and make them clearly aware of what you expect to accomplish. The What? may be the discovering of the main wildlife communities along the route, looking for birds or animals, finding facts to substantiate statements in textbooks, learning the economic aspects of the territory, exploring a specific destination, collecting specimens. Unless there is a definite reason for going, known to all, some will look upon a field trip as a picnic, others will come along "for the ride," and the result will be meager.

WHERE?—The Where? should be picked to provide maximum opportunity for the investigations that are the aim of the trip. Some of the students may be able to make specific recommendations, or a map may show the possibilities. It pays for the leader to make a personal reconnaissance hike over the route, in advance of the field trip, to make certain that it suits the purpose. If you are not too familiar with the subjects that may open up on the trip, you may want to ask a specialist to come along.

WHEN?—Set the *date* in conference with the participants. Determine the *time for starting,* and figure out from the length of the route the approximate *time for the return.*

HOW?—Get *permission* in advance from owners of property you may want to cross. In case of youngsters, get parents' permissions, and, for school children, the permission of principal and superintendent as well.

Figure out what *equipment* to take and make some of the participants responsible for bringing it along.

Each person will bring his or her own *luncheon* if the trip extends for the whole day. Bring water in *canteens* if you do not expect to pass places where safe drinking water is available.

Take a small amount of *first-aid supplies*—mostly bandaids and iodine ampules. Teach the participants what poisonivy looks like and warn them against touching it or brushing against it.

Arrange for *transportation* to a suitable starting point —by private cars, public carriers, or chartered bus.

FIELD TRIP TECHNIQUES

Each type of field work has its own techniques—bird hiking requires one method, animal study another, investigating pond life still another. Detailed techniques are described in the chapters that follow. Certain procedures apply to all kinds of group field trips:

Follow the leader while traveling—The leader sets the

pace and the directions; the participants follow closely behind. In that way, they have a chance to see what the
leader sees, and can be assembled quickly.

Obey signals—To get close to wildlife on a field trip,
it is necessary to proceed in silence. This is not feasible
for most groups, and not necessary all the time. Instead,
establish a simple system of silent signals: hand held
up for "silence," hand swung in circle for "gather round,"
hand pushed up repeatedly from shoulder height for
"come here."

Practice good outdoor manners—Stay on the trail;
keep it narrow. Obey "no trespass" signs. Leave no debris
for others to pick up. If a luncheon fire is built, make
POSITIVE it is out before leaving.

> "Let noone say—and say it to your shame—
> That all was beauty here until you came."

Don't pour in—draw out!—Encourage the participants
to learn by observing and questioning. Don't attempt to
lecture on the trail. When occasion suggests, and the trail
opens up sufficiently, gather the group in horseshoe formation, and discuss what you have seen. Ask questions,
give as many of the participants as possible a chance to
tell what they have noticed. When a question is asked,
don't snap out the answer—ask another question of the
whole group: "Does anyone know the answer?" If it is
finally up to you to provide the answer, give it, if you
know it. If you don't, be frank about it: "I don't know.
Let's find out." The field book in your knapsack will probably have the information.

Work from base—From time to time, stop and establish a base. Give everyone a chance for independent
roaming and exploration before the group gathers and
sets out again.

Take it easy—Take a short rest occasionally. Make
the lunch hour a time for happy relaxation—for a young
group, throw in a few nature games.

FOLLOW-UP—After a field trip, arrange a *discussion*
of the shared experiences: "What did we accomplish?"
"Did we reach our aim?" "Where do we go from here?"
Again, make use of questioning to draw out each par-
ticipant.

Collect results—Encourage the making of reports of
the field trip as a whole and of specific observations. Get
them accompanied by drawings, map sketches, photographs, if possible.

Prepare collections—If specimens have been collected,
get them properly prepared.

Send thank-you-notes—Mail out notes as promptly as

possible to thank the people who may have helped to make the experience a success.

Nature Projects

A nature project is a nature activity with a specified, tangible end result. "Make an insect collection" is a nature activity as long as life itself. "Make a collection of 100 local insects" is a project within the ability of any interested person.

The right kind of projects will keep the nature interests of a club, a camp, a class, or a youth group alive and humming.

SELECTING THE PROJECT—To help you in proposing and developing nature projects for any season of the year and any type of group work, a special *Projects Index* accompanies the regular index of this *Field Book,* starting on page 419. The information necessary for carrying out the projects is contained in this volume.

The projects vary in difficulty from the pressing of plants and the making of an aquarium to the taking of a bird nesting census and the planting of a community forest. Some of the projects can be handled effectively by a single person or by a buddy team, other projects require the co-operation of large groups and a certain amount of equipment and expenditure. Still other projects are combinations of a number of procedures.

PRESENTING THE PROJECT—In a nature club, a project may be proposed "from the floor" or suggested by an officer or a committee. In a school or youth group, a project should be presented, listing its possibilities to make the group enthusiastic about attempting it. For greatest effectiveness, the main part of the planning for any project should be done by the members of the group. The work connected with it should be self-imposed, not assigned. Only then will the project have its full significance and provide its maximum training potential.

CARRYING OUT THE PROJECTS—The individual project needs little organization. Group projects must be handled differently. The following methods suggest the approaches to two types of group projects—one, an easy one, the other more complex:

"Let's make a simple camp museum." What shall it contain? Quick discussion among camp members, then specific suggestions put down on cards: Make up an exhibit of five kinds of soil; collect and exhibit ten insects; make a display of six common rocks; make four plaster casts of animal tracks; plant six different tree seedlings in cans and identify them; make a rearing cage and inhabit it with six caterpillars; collect ten twigs and mount them for display; make a terrarium; find five shells—and

so on. "Who will do what?" Campers, singly or as bud-
dies, volunteer, and the cards are distributed. A time
limit is set for the completion of the project—an hour or
an hour and a half. A moment later, the campers are on
their way. You wind up with the nucleus of a camp
museum that can be further developed.

"Let's make a survey of our school ground." What is
involved? Map sketching—who will do it? Locating the
trees and taking their measurements—who? Identifying
the specimens—who are our experts? Someone to take
photographs of the more important trees, someone for
sketching, someone for leaf printing, someone for wood
samples. Volunteers and still more volunteers!

When a project is finished, it should be "tied up" neatly,
and those working on it credited with its successful completion. If feasible, develop a report of the accomplishment for future use by the group.

REFERENCE—Ramond Tifft Fuller. *Nature Quests and
Quizzes: A Nature Seeker's Handbook.* John Day Co.

Nature Games

All work and no play . . . In working with young
people, remember that even the most eager nature student
needs moments of relaxation. The wise nature leader in-
tersperses periods of study with periods of games. Sometimes, games of a purely recreational nature are in order.
Most of the time, you can use games that will add to the
nature experience of the player.

BOOKS OF NATURE GAMES—Elmo Stevenson. *Nature Game
Book.* Greenberg Company, N. Y.

Paul W. Nesbit. *Instructive Nature Games.* Published
by author, Estes Park, Colo.

The games that follow are designed mostly for young
people, but many of them can be used with older groups
as well. Even nature experts will enjoy matching themselves against Nature Questions, Nature Art Gallery, I
Know Me, Who Am I?, and others.

OUTDOOR GAMES

NATURE FAR-AND-NEAR—Make a list of twenty or
thirty items to be found along the route, with a score for
each—such as "Bird's nest, 10 points—Live snake, 15
points—Monarch butterfly, 5 points—Frog, 10 points—
Animal track, 5 points—Flying crow, 5 points." First
player to observe one of the items and report to the leader
scores.

LISTEN!—On sign from leader, players remain perfectly
still for three minutes, listening and writing down the

sounds they hear : Bird songs, insect "songs," tree rustles, and so on. Player with most complete list wins.

NATURE HUNT—Leader announces an item to be collected. First player to bring it in scores 5 points. Continue as long as desired.

NATURE MEMORY HUNT—Teams study for two minutes a display of thirty nature specimens—leaves, flowers, shells, insects, etc.—trying to memorize them. They then set out to duplicate the exhibit. Team scores 5 points for each item collected, loses 5 points for each thing collected that was not in the original exhibit.

LEAF HUNT—Teams are given ten minutes to gather *one* leaf only from as many different trees as they can find. When brought in, the leaves are arranged on the ground, and slips of paper with names are placed next to them. Team with the most leaves correctly identified wins.

LEAF MATCHING—Start as for LEAF HUNT. Instead of labeling, proceed as follows : One team holds up a leaf, identifies it, scores 5 points. First other team to hold up similar leaf scores 10 points, other teams that have leaf score 5 points each. Team first to identify holds up next leaf, and so on. If a team identifies incorrectly the leaf it holds up, it scores nothing, but the team first to correct mistake scores 10 points extra.

UNNATURAL NATURE—In a small area, "doctor-up" a number of plants—tie oak leaves on tulip tree, pine cones on spruce, black-eyed susan on thistle, and so on. Send out teams to discover these freaks. Team bringing back report of greatest number of oddities within certain time limit win. Score extra if team identifies both original plant and unnatural addition.

TREE TAGGING—Give each team twenty pieces of 1-inch gauze bandage, 12 inches long, with numbers from 1 to 20 written on them, in a different color for each team. Object is to tie gauze bandages on as many different trees as possible, within 100 feet of starting point. One team member keeps list of trees tagged. Team tagging most trees correctly within time limit wins.

NATURE SCAVENGER HUNT—Give each team sealed letter: "Our Indian chief has not slept for twenty nights. The witch doctor of our tribe has promised to cure him with his famous sleeping brew, but needs your help. Bring him the following ingredients within one hour from the moment you read this : ten dandelion seeds—two bird feathers—four dead flies—bit of rabbit fluff—ten white pine needles—live frog or toad—two caterpillars . . . (and so on, around twenty items)." Team bringing in largest number of items within time limit wins.

NATURE TREASURE HUNT—Each team gets sealed envelope. On signal, envelopes are opened. Inside is card

reading: "Go to tallest hemlock you see from this point."
At hemlock is sign: "Follow direction of largest branch
to patch of cattails at water's edge." Here is another
message: "Follow shore toward setting sun to second
alder." A number of arrows scratched in the ground lead
from alder to large boulder; in a crevice is a message:
"To oak." There is a solitary oak out in the field—must
be it. And so on, until the last message: "Look under
dead pine." Here the winning team finds the treasure:
Candy, peanuts, or what-have-you.

QUIET GAMES FOR INDOORS OR OUT

WHO AM I?—Prepare a set of file cards with the name
of a bird, a tree, etc., on each. Pin name card on back of
each player without letting the player know what name
he has. Players circulate and ask each other questions
that can be answered by "yes" or "no" or "don't know."
Only three questions may be asked of one person. Each
player learning his identity within a time limit scores.

NATURE KIM'S GAME—Teams gather around table covered with a cloth. Cloth is lifted for one minute to reveal
about twenty to thirty nature items. Teams go into hud-
dle and attempt to make a complete list of items. Team
with largest number wins.

MUSEUM—Arrange a number of specimens on table or
ground. Each specimen has a number on a file card.
Players write down numbers and names of items they
recognize. When time is up, player with most correct
identifications wins.

NATURE ART GALLERY—Fasten twenty or more pictures, without names, of birds, OR trees, OR flowers, etc.,
on the wall. Number the pictures. Players move around
with pencil and numbered sheets, and try to recognize
the pictures. They write down the names on their sheets and
turn in sheets at certain time limit. Player with most
correct names after the time limit wins.

THIS AND THAT—Secure pictures of animals and of
animal tracks, of birds and of bird nests, of trees and of
tree leaves—or, even better, animal pictures and track
casts, bird pictures and feathers, tree pictures and winter
twigs—and so on. Place items on display, each item numbered. Object is for players to write down numbers of
matching pairs.

IDENTIFICATION—Each team has field book on the subject in question. Leader shows a not-too-common specimen of tree, flower, insect, and so on. First team to
identify it correctly from field book wins.

SCRAMBLED NAMES—Give to each team a list of fifteen
or more scrambled names of birds, OR trees, OR flowers,
etc., such as: "1. MOSITETU 2. NIDRALAC 3. CUJON 4.

PODOWKRECE." First team to bring in correct unscrambled list wins: "1. TITMOUSE 2. CARDINAL 3. JUNCO 4. WOOD-PECKER."

TRUE OR FALSE—Leader reads list of statements, some of them true, others false. Such as: "Poisonivy is not an ivy, all bats are blind, toads cause warts, deer chew cuds, ants have no wings, all animals have hair, spiders are insects . . ." First player to yell correctly "True" or "False" scores.

NATURE QUESTIONS—Similar to familiar party game, *Twenty Questions*—but not necessarily restricted to twenty questions: Leader assumes identity of tree, bird, animal, or whatever, without revealing the name. He answers, with "yes" or "no," questions put to him by the players trying to find out what he is, such as: "Are you a plant?" "No." "Are you an animal with four legs?" "No." "With wings?" "Yes." "Are you a large bird?" "No." And so on. May be played as team game: Each team interrogates a separate leader. All leaders have the same identity. First team to get the name wins.

I KNOW ME—Leader reads a series of graded statements leading toward the identity of some specimen—bird, tree, etc. Player first to yell the name scores according to number of statement, from 8 points to 1, as for instance: "8. I am one of the tallest trees in the forest in North-East America. 7. My leaves drop in the fall. 6. My wood is soft, white. 5. My bark is light gray, furrowed. 4. My trunk is straight, like a column. 3. My fruits fall apart into many pieces. 2. My leaves look as if the tips were cut off with scissors. 1. My flowers resemble a well-known garden flower. I am the TULIP TREE."

Nature Trails

It is not always that you or some other leader are available to take a group of nature enthusiasts on a trip through the wilds. In working toward the creation of a nature trail you solve this problem by providing absentee leadership. The thought behind this is to give a person a chance to take a self-guided walk over a clearly defined path, marked with occasional signs that tell the story of the more important natural-history features along the way.

The spirit of the nature trail was well expressed by Dr. Frank E. Lutz—who may be considered the father of the modern application of this idea—at the entrance to one of his early trails:

"A friend somewhat versed in Natural History is taking a walk with you and calling your attention to interesting things."

The best location for a nature trail is a park, a camp, a grove adjacent to the school grounds. Get permission of the proper authorities for laying out the trail, and secure the help of others for doing the work.

GENERAL RULES—Follow these rules in establishing a nature trail:

1. *Keep the trail narrow.*
2. *Keep it natural*—don't destroy, tear up, fake.
3. *Keep it woodsy*—office labels and baggage tags do not belong in nature.
4. *Keep it simple*—don't attempt to say too much about too many subjects. Give facts—whimsey will be misunderstood. Present some of the facts in a humorous vein.
5. *Keep it protected*—no ax scars, no nails. Make it a sample of good conservation.
6. *Keep it growing*—add to it and change it with the seasons.
7. *Keep it beautiful.*

REFERENCES—William H. Carr. Several pamphlets: *Blazing Nature's Trail; Trailside Action; Trailside Family; Trailside Interdependence; Trailside Transformation; Ten Years of Nature Trails.* American Museum of Natural History, Central Park West, New York, N. Y.

Enjoying Nature. National Recreation Association, 8 West 8th Street, New York 11, N. Y.

Roger T. Peterson. *Nature Trails,* National Audubon Society, N. Y.

TRAINING TRAIL

The training trail is a general trail, aimed at creating an interest in all phases of nature.

LAYING OUT THE TRAIL—To be successful, the entrance to the trail should be readily accessible. The trail should not be too long—half a mile or so is a good distance—and it should return to a spot close to the starting point or end at a suitable destination announced at the entrance.

The trail should run through as many types of wildlife communities as possible. To do this, it will probably have to be rather rambling. For this reason, it will seldom be feasible to make use of established paths—a new trail has to be created.

Before laying out the trail, walk back and forth, cross-country through the location. Get a clear picture of the spots that should be incorporated in the trail and decide on their sequence. Then take a walk along the trail-to-be with a helpful companion: a ball of twine. Tie an end to a tree at the starting point, then unwind the twine to mark the trail. After the trail is marked in this manner, it is possible to distribute groups of helpers all along the trail for the clearing job.

Use only hand sickles and hand axes for clearing. Make your coworkers aware that the rule *"keep the trail narrow"* means "keep it so narrow that it must be followed single file."

MARKERS—The cheapest way to mark a nature trail is with paraffin-dipped linen tags or file cards. Such marking is apt to make the trail "cheap" in more ways than one. Better use markers that suggest more permanency and fit into the spirit of the woods. Place them about twenty steps apart, or just so far that you can sight the next one.

WOOD MARKERS—Cut pieces of ¼-inch plywood 5×7 inches or larger. Paint with leaf-green or light brown oil paint. Screw to rustic posts, pointed at one end.

Tip—Excellent for wood markers—and usually free— are slabs and ends of orange crates and apple boxes.

SHEET-TIN MARKERS—Cut sheet tin, or better, sheet aluminum, into suitable pieces. Nail to posts, or make two holes in each marker by which they can be wired to trees and shrubs.

Tip—Instead of painting names on sheet-tin markers, the top and bottom may be turned over so that removable cardboard markers can be inserted.

LIFTING MARKERS—People like to touch things—the lifting marker gives them the chance. This is simply the ordinary wood marker, with another piece of wood of the same size hinged to it at the top. The front is lifted to reveal the legend of the marker.

SWINGING MARKERS—Bend a piece of strap iron into a U. Cut a wood marker to fit in the U and suspend it by two nails through holes bored in the uprights of the U-frame. Part of the legend is on the front, the rest can be read only by swinging the marker over.

PAINTING THE MARKERS—To protect the markers against rain and sun, they should be painted with a good quality paint, and varnished.

CARDBOARD MARKERS—Cut the cardboard to size, and write the legend on it with India ink. Use a Speedball pen —no. B-5 for light lines, no. B-2 or B-3 for heavier lines. When the ink has dried thoroughly, cover the cardboard front and back with two coats of varnish.

Markers for nature trails may be made from metal or wood, simple (top), or designed for lifting or swinging (bottom).

Tip—For added attractiveness, use poster cardboard in several colors—one color for flowers, another for trees, and so on.

WOODEN MARKERS—Cover with a primer, then paint with one or two coats of outdoor flat paint in whatever color you prefer. Letter the markers with diluted oil paint or artists' colors in a color to contrast with the color of the markers. Use a fine, pointed brush. Cover with a coat of varnish when completely dry.

Tip—India-ink pen-lettering does a quicker job than painting. To prevent the ink from running, abrase the surface slightly by rubbing it with a finger or a cloth dipped in fullers' earth or talcum. Varnish when ink is dry.

METAL MARKERS—Metal marker should be primed, then covered with two coats of outdoor paint before lettering. Be certain to use a primer specifically made for priming metal, to insure firm bonding. Otherwise, the paint will soon start peeling.

LABELING—The wording on the markers should be short and catchy—more than names, lots of information in a small "nugget"—with no pretentious scientific approach. The way to get the proper wording is to write it on the spot. As Lutz expresses it: "Desk-written labels are apt to be desky." A classic example is the chatty:

> This lead-pencil tree—Red Cedar—is the favorite wood for making pencils. It is also used for cedar chests. Smell it.

as against the "desk" label:

> Red Cedar, *Juniperus virginiana,*
> Northeastern United States.

The labels can be straight IDENTIFICATION:

> W-H-I-T-E Pine—five letters to the name, five needles to the cluster.
> Bark like alligator skin? It's Dogwood.
> Leaflets three—let it be! Poisonivy.

They may suggest USES:

> Wild Grape and Staghorn Sumac—fruits for refreshing drinks.
> Early pioneers used the hardwood of Dogwood for skewers or "dags"—hence its name.
> American Hornbeam wood is as tough as the "muscular" branches suggest!

They may be an invitation to LOOK or to LISTEN:

> Along this deer run, Virginia Deer roam down for water.
> Silence—would you hear the Thrush
> Bell-like in the evening hush.

They may be HUMOROUS:

> Happy are Cicadas' lives
> For they all have voiceless wives.
> Touch me today—I'll itch you tomorrow.

And they can be TEASING, such as this on one side of a swinging label:

> Pat yourself on the back IF . . .

and this on the other side:

> . . . you noticed the Robin's nest in the Choke Cherry you just passed.

OTHER FEATURES—PICTURES—Pictures of birds, plants, trees, may be cut out of Audubon cards or five-and-ten cent store booklets and pasted on some of the signs. Protect with Valspar. Tree markers may be provided with oil-paint or ink leaf prints (see page 304).

INSECT CAGES—Insects may be displayed on their feed plants in transparent, cylindrical cages (see page 185).

STUMP DETECTIVE—If there is a prominent stump along the trail, put up a Stump Detective sign (see page 293).

TESTING TRAILS

The testing trail is developed in the usual manner, but instead of giving information, it asks for it. A person wanting to test his nature knowledge enters the trail with a piece of paper and a pencil. As he walks along, he jots down his answers. At the end of the trail he checks their correctness against the right answers, posted on a bulletin board.

A testing trail may be a NUMBERED TRAIL, with number markers next to specimens to be identified. Or it can be a QUESTION TRAIL with labels with questions based on the training trail labels: "Which is the tree with alligator skin?" "How many leaflets has the poisonivy?" "Do female cicadas 'sing'?" and so on.

Nature Museums and Workshops

A museum has an important part to play in spreading the nature gospel. Here is displayed the experiences and finds of numerous field trips, arranged in such a way that "he who runs may read"—and may possibly hesitate long enough to pick up some interest in nature. Here are things to arouse the curiosity of the youngster, a place where the advanced naturalist may succeed in instilling in others some of his own enthusiasm.

The large museum is often a place of imposing halls, with quiet onlookers. The small museum should be a living, functioning workshop, with participants sharing in its creation and upkeep.

Pointers are useful on the testing trail: log with sighting holes, arrow pointer, numbered marker with string to subject.

That word "sharing" is the secret of a successful nature museum. Someone—teacher, camp counselor, youth leader, Scoutmaster, club member, naturalist—must want to share his or her nature enjoyment with others and get students, campers or people of the community excited about joining in the efforts.

TYPES OF NATURE MUSEUMS—The most important function of the small nature museum is as a *nature headquarters*—a place where youngsters and adults can come to look at various types of nature exhibits and collections and find out what methods were used in their development—where they can come after a field trip to work on their collections, where they can get help in identifying their specimens, and where they can meet with others to discuss their problems and tell of their successes.

In the *school,* the school science room may be built into such a museum. If no science room is available, a corner in a class room may do, or an attic room or basement room may be turned into a nature den.

In the *Troop* or *club room,* a wall may be set aside for nature displays.

In *camp,* a couple of sturdy tables may be put up and protected by canvas tarps, or by a permanent roof. In a larger camp, a rustic shelter or small building may be erected to serve as nature headquarters.

In some communities, nature groups have established *trailside museums* in conjunction with nature trails through parks or community forests.

Private citizens have, in many instances, opened up their *homes* for the purpose of sharing their nature interests with youth groups and nature club members.

The perfect arrangement would involve facilities that are well-lighted—with shelves and wall space for displays, cabinets or drawers for storage of equipment and supplies, and work tables large enough to provide adequate space for group work.

DEVELOPMENT AND MAINTENANCE—As far as possible, the exhibits should be developed by nature students, and maintained by them. Only in this manner will the museum have its maximum educational effect.

If a nature club is already in existence, it would be logical for such a club to take over the responsibility, electing a curator and assistant curators. In other groups, nature enthusiasts may offer their services.

The curators will develop the general plan for the exhibits, will encourage others to bring in their finds, help in their arrangement and labeling, and be responsible for the order and general tidiness of the museum.

 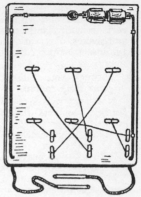

Wiring diagram for electrified chart. For simplicity's sake, chart has only six pictures, instead of usual twenty or more.

A nature museum should be a growing thing. The *making* of it is more important than the *looking* at it. The exhibits should therefore be worked at, changed, improved upon, in many instances, replaced regularly—partly to keep up with the seasons but, more important, to get other hands to work. Replacement is particularly important where the groups change from time to time, such as in the organizational summer camps and in school.

MUSEUM EXHIBITS

The size of the museum and the ambition of the curators govern the types of exhibits that can be included.

PICTURES—Make use of the artistic talent in the group to create an interesting frame for the main exhibits. Bring in original nature sketches, paintings, and photographs, as well as clippings from magazines. Develop nature maps of the surrounding area, showing location of important trees, animal homes, and so on. Paint posters or even murals.

SOURCES OF INEXPENSIVE PICTURE MATERIAL—Drop a line to U. S. Department of Agriculture for Miscellaneous Publication No. 60, *List of Available Publications.* Contains list of posters and pictures available free or at low cost.

U. S. Department of Interior. Fish and Wildlife Service, Washington 25, D. C. Request list.

National Geographic Magazine. School Service Department, Washington 6, D. C. Request list.

National Audubon Society, 1130 Fifth Avenue, New York 28, N. Y. Audubon Bird Cards.

LIVE EXHIBITS—Include only if regular care can be given: aquarium with native fish and water plants, terrariums with plants and amphibians, cages with mammals and snakes, observation bee hives, "anthill," rearing cages for insect larvae. All described in subsequent chapters.

Tip—Loan exhibits of live animals may be available through your State Conservation Department. Write your state capital.

NON-LIVE EXHIBITS—Bird nests, bird houses, mounted feathers, contents of pellets. Animal-track casts, animal-gnawed things, scat. Snake skins, preserved snakes. Mounted fish. Shells. Insect collections. Pressed flowers, spore prints, leaf prints, wood samples, twig and seed collections. For instructions for making them, see chapters throughout the book.

MODELS AND DIORAMAS—Miniatures of animal homes, wildlife communities, conservation practices. Large models of flower parts, insects, water animals.

HOW-TO-MAKE EXHIBITS—Display of equipment and steps in making nature collections—leaf prints, track casts, and so on.

RECORD PLAYER—With records of bird songs, the calls of frogs and toads, and "songs" of insects.

BOOK SHELF—Field books for identification, reference books, nature magazines.

BULLETIN BOARD—For questions and answers, clippings, announcements.

In addition to the main exhibits, gadgets that have a special appeal for youngsters may be included:

ELECTRIFIED CHART—In its simplest form, this consists of a large chart with a number of unnamed pictures of animals, birds, plants. The names appear in a special panel at the bottom of the chart. At each picture and each name is a metal knob. Attached to the chart in long wires are two brass rods. When one rod is touched to the knob under a picture, and the other to the correct, corresponding name, a bulb lights up, or a buzzer sounds.

The chart itself may be made of plywood or wallboard. The knobs can be brass paper fasteners. On the back of the chart, the prongs of the fasteners are connected in pairs—picture and name—with bell wire. The wires from the two rods run to two doorbell batteries, or flashlight batteries, and to a buzzer or a flashlight bulb (see wiring diagram, page 53).

"WHAT IS IT?" SHELF—On a small shelf, have a daily exhibit of an unidentified object found by a student. Or place on it some items to be brought to the students' attention. Special recognition may be given to the first person identifying the object.

PART II

SPECIFIC ACTIVITIES PROJECTS

3. BIRDS

BIRDS are the most beloved of all living wild creatures. They appeal to young and old alike.

Who does not thrill to the sight of a clutch of downy fledglings in a nest, to the soaring sweep of a bald eagle, to the song of the hermit thrush at dusk, to the flashing beauty of the hummingbird halting before your delphinium on whirring wings?

The flight of birds has been the envy of man through the ages. "Free as a bird in the air . . ." is still considered the ultimate in liberty. It is birds that symbolize happiness, peace, strength.

Poets have written odes in their praise, artists have painted them, scientists have studied them. But you need be neither poet, nor artist, nor scientist to enjoy them. A little patience and quick eyes are all that are required.

If you like, you can travel afar looking for birds—into field, marsh, and woodland, and along the seashore. You will see them far out over the expanses of the widest oceans. You will find them nesting in deserts and near mountain summits. Birds and their songs will follow you almost everywhere you go in the great out-of-doors.

And if you don't go, they will come to you. Sit quietly on your front porch some summer morning, and they will congregate on your lawn. Feed them in the winter, and grateful juncos and chickadees, nuthatches and woodpeckers will keep you company. Many valuable observations of bird life have been made through the window panes of sickrooms.

You will get a certain amount of casual satisfaction out of seeing a beautiful bird on the wing or of listening to its song. A much greater satisfaction comes to you when the color or shape or sweep of a bird tells you what it is, and when bird songs become as familiar to you as well-loved old tunes.

You reach the peak in your bird-watching career when your observations shed light on some of the mysteries that still abound in our knowledge of birds.

BOOKS ON BIRD LIFE—Arthur A. Allen. *The Book of Bird Life.* D. Van Nostrand Company.

L. W. Wing. *Natural History of Birds.* Ronald Press.

T. Gilbert Pearson, Editor. *Birds of America.* Garden City Publishing Company.

WORKING WITH OTHERS

You can get much enjoyment out of solitary bird walks. But as your interest in birds mounts, you will want to share your excitement with others. Also, you will want to take advantage of all the help that is available, thus further increasing your own enthusiasm.

Right in your own immediate vicinity, there are bound to be several other people interested in birds, with whom you can discuss your discoveries. They may help you in identification, assist you in solving your problems.

Every state and county has amateur bird clubs— branches of the Audubon Society or of an ornithological society. Their members go on bird walks under expert guidance. They meet to hear talks on various phases of bird life, and to watch some of the magnificent films and color slides of birds that are taken in ever increasing numbers. Many of these local clubs publish their own small magazines and bulletins.

All of these groups are eager to take in new members who are genuinely interested in birds and their conservation. Your local librarian or biology teacher should be able to put you in contact with the nearest group. If not, simply drop a post card to the National Audubon Society or to one of the ornithological clubs.

SOCIETIES—National Audubon Society. Hdqrs.: 1130 Fifth Avenue, New York 28, N. Y. Periodical: *Audubon Magazine.*

The American Ornithologists' Union. Hdqrs.: U. S. National Museum, Washington 25, D. C. Periodical: *The Auk.*

The Wilson Ornithological Club. Mostly Middle West. Hdqrs.: Aaron Bragg, Farm Street, Dover, Mass. Periodical: *The Wilson Bulletin.*

The Cooper Ornithological Club. West and California. Hdqrs.: C. V. Duff, 2911 Antelo View Drive, Los Angeles 24, Calif. Periodical: *The Condor.*

Field Study of Birds

EQUIPMENT FOR BIRD STUDY

CLOTHING—As you will be doing your bird watching in the cool of early morning, or in the evening, you will need warm clothing. A wool sweater for summer use, and a parka-type coat with an outside layer of wind-resistant material for the cooler seasons of the year will serve you well.

Your clothing should be sturdy and water repellent as well as warm. It has to resist brambles and thorns and withstand all kinds of weather.

Pick a color that blends well with the surroundings. The actual hue is of little importance—it can be brown, green, blue, or even red. It is the tone that counts. A brilliant tone will attract the birds' attention to you and will disclose the slightest motion you make. A subdued tone will make you almost invisible.

Pay special attention to your footwear. Rubbers will protect you in the early morning dew. Use rubber "waders" if you intend to study marshland bird life.

> *Tip*—A good insect repellent to smear on exposed skin of face and hands may mean the difference between an enjoyable and a miserable morning walk.

STUDY EQUIPMENT—FIELD GLASSES—Your eyes may be strong—nevertheless, you will soon feel the need of a pair of field glasses for "pulling" the birds close to you. But there are field glasses and Field Glasses.

OPERA GLASSES—If you have a pair of opera glasses in the house, make use of them in the beginning. They generally magnify two to three times, are easy to carry and easy to handle.

FIELD GLASSES—The usual field glasses are enlarged versions of opera glasses. They contain a system of lenses that magnify the object four to five times. Higher magnification makes these "Galilean-type" glasses unwieldy because it necessitates greater length, therefore added weight.

PRISM BINOCULARS—Prism binoculars are ideal for bird watching. They consist of a combination of lenses and prisms that make great magnification possible with small size and weight.

A binocular is expensive. But since it is a lifetime investment, it pays to buy the best and most durable that is available. Before making the purchase know your needs, and check each of the following points:

Magnification—The magnification, or power, is indicated on the binocular by the figures "6$\times$", "7$\times$"—"six times," "seven times"—and so on. "6×" means that the object, viewed through the binocular, appears six times as large as it looks to the naked eye. The larger the magnification, the more difficult becomes the use of the glasses— the movement of an unsteady hand is magnified as many times as the object. Many experts prefer 8× or 9× for themselves, but recommend 6× for their students. You may want to compromise on 7×.

Relative brightness—In full daylight, a high relative brightness is not required, but when the binocular is to be

Prism binoculars are the ideal glasses for bird watching. Glasses with central focusing are particularly easy to use.

used in the early morning hours and in the dim light of evening, the extra brightness becomes important. To find the relative brightness of a binocular, first check the diameter of the objective lens—the lens farthest from your eyes. This is usually stamped in millimeters, next to the magnification, such as 7×,35. Divide the diameter by the magnification (in this case, 35 divided by 7). Take the result (5), and square it (25). The relative brightness is 25. Similarly, the relative brightness of 6×,30 is also 25, while the brightness of 8×,30 is 14.1.

"Coated" lenses increase the relative brightness.

Field of View—By field of view is meant the diameter of the "picture" you see through the binocular. A wide field makes it easy to locate your object and keep it in view without moving the glasses. The field should, preferably, be not less than 100 yards wide at a distance of 1000 yards.

Focusing—Two types of focusing are in use: *Individual focusing* that requires separate focusing of each eye piece, and *central focusing* by which the focusing of both lenses is done simultaneously. Central focusing is the simpler and quicker method, therefore the more popular. When focused, a good binocular will show a sharply defined picture from one edge of the lens to the other, no distortion, and no color fringes.

Tip—For further hints on the choice of a binocular, write to Bausch & Lomb Optical Co., Rochester, N. Y. for the free pamphlet, *Binoculars and How to Choose Them.*

BIRD BOOKS—A good bird book makes it possible for you to identify the birds you see—provided you know how to use it.

In most guides, the birds are arranged by families. It won't take you long to get accustomed to this arrangement. The bird bobbing on the lake's surface "looks like a duck." No doubt it is, so you notice its colors and markings and look it up in the section on "Ducks." A bird feeding on the ground has a short, stout bill and a "sparrowlike" build. You refer to the section that covers "Sparrows, finches, etc." Eventually, the classification of a bird and its family becomes almost second nature to you. You are well launched on your career as an expert bird watcher.

BOOKS FOR FIELD IDENTIFICATION—R. T. Peterson. *Field Guide to the Birds,* and *Field Guide to the Western Birds.* Houghton Mifflin Company.

Leon A. Hausman. *Field Book of Eastern Birds.* G. P. Putnam's Sons.

G. H. Pough. *Audubon Land Bird Guide, Audubon Water Bird Guide,* and *Audubon Western Bird Guide.* Doubleday & Company.

Wilfrid B. Alexander. *Birds of the Ocean.* G. P. Putnam's Sons.

Willard Ayres Eliot. *Birds of the Pacific Coast.* G. P. Putnam's Sons.

H. E. Jaques. *How to Know the Land Birds.* (Pictured-Key). Wm. C. Brown Co., Dubuque, Iowa.

NOTE-TAKING MATERIAL—No serious bird student is ever without a notebook—a pocket-size book in which you make notes of the field trips you take, including dates, weather, and locality, and of the birds you see and identify.

FINDING BIRDS

The first indication of the presence of a bird may be its song floating to you through the air. The rustle in dry leaves on the forest floor may tell you of another, motion among the branches in a treetop of still others. Dark silhouettes may soar above you in the sky or move across a sunlit lake.

To find birds, keep your eyes open wherever you are, and scan the whole wide out-of-doors—from sky to ground, the compass round.

WHERE?—Birds may be found almost anywhere.

HERE!—The place to begin looking for them is Here— on your own front lawn or in your back yard. Know your own birds well before you start looking in the other fellow's yard.

WILDLIFE COMMUNITIES—The next step is to become familiar with the wildlife communities in your vicinity— whether grassland or marshes, forests or mountains, deserts or ocean shores—and search out each territory for the bird life in it. By studying birds in relation to their surroundings, you will learn far more about them than by just walking cross-country listing whatever birds you see.

SPECIFIC SPECIES—Later on you may want to locate certain species. Then it is a matter of looking them up in your bird book, finding out in what kind of surroundings they live, and seeking them there.

REFERENCES—Olin S. Pettingill. *A Guide to Bird Finding East of the Mississippi* and *A Guide to Bird Finding West of the Mississippi.* Oxford University Press.

WHEN?—TIME OF YEAR—The number of different birds will fluctuate greatly with the seasons. Certain birds will be *permanent residents* in your section. In spring, a number of *summer visitors* may arrive from the south. They leave in the fall, to be replaced by *winter visitors* coming down from the north. In spring and fall, *transients* will stop by for a short stay during their migrations. And finally, there are the *accidental visitors* that may drop in, off their usual course.

WINTER—Winter is a good time to begin your bird study. Comparatively few birds are around, and there are no leaves or luxuriant weed growth to obscure them. Then, as spring and summer set in, you add new birds to your list daily, as they arrive.

NOW!—But the best time to start is right NOW— whether this be winter or summer—provided you don't insist on knowing every bird you see the first time you see it.

TIME OF DAY—The early bird catches the worm. The early watcher sees the birds.

DAYBREAK—Birds are active in greatest numbers around daybreak. So check the calendar for the hour of sunrise, and plan to be up and out about an hour earlier. Your best bird-watching time is from early dusk until the sun is four fingers above the horizon.

EVENING—Second best is the evening, from an hour before sunset until dusk turns into darkness.

WEATHER—The weather conditions will influence the

number of birds you see. You will see most on mornings
that are cool and clear. When the weather turns rainy
and gray, windy and raw, the birds remain in hiding.

Bird Walking

Set the alarm early for a spring or summer bird walk
—three o'clock A.M. (four o'clock for Daylight Saving
Time). Get up early enough to dress warmly and to eat
a bit of breakfast before you set out. There's little enjoyment in a bird walk, if you are shivery and hungry. Pick
up glasses, field book, and note book, and be on your way.

You may like to have a couple of companions along, or
even a small group of bird enthusiasts. More than half a
dozen is inadvisable, unless they are oldtimers in the art
of bird walking and know how to walk and act.

"Go West"—Greeley's old advice, "Go west, young man,
go west," might have been written for early morning bird
walkers. By planning your hike, as far as possible, so that
you will be going west, you will have the rising sun behind you, therefore its rays full on the birds in front of
you. Instead of seeing them as dark silhouettes, you will
be able to observe their colorings.

Walk briskly toward the territory that is the objective
of the morning's investigation. When you get there, slow
down and move forward softly, with smooth motions.

"Stop . . ."—"Stop, look and listen" is another fitting
slogan for bird walkers. Stop often, and scan the surroundings for movements that will betray the presence of
a bird. Stop long enough to let birds that may have become alarmed feel secure again and resume their singing.
You can then locate them by their song.

When you notice a bird, freeze in your tracks, and
bring your field glasses up to your eyes in a long smooth
motion. Any sudden, jerky motion is sure to scare the
bird. Move closer only when the bird seems to pay no
attention to you.

If you want to communicate your findings to your companions, or to get their assurance that your identification
is correct, do it in your normal tone of voice, as in ordinary conversation. Some birds pick up the hissing sounds
of whispering far more readily than they do the deeper
sounds of talking. Hausman sums it up very neatly:
"When among warblers, talk like a duck." But he adds:
"When among ducks, talk like a warbler." Birds with
low-pitched calls hear low notes but do not pick up the
high-pitched ones.

"Try squeaking"—If your bird is too far away for
good observation, you may be able to "squeak" it closer.
Purse your lips and place them against the back of your
hand or against a finger. Then draw in your breath in a

long squeaky kiss. Repeat a few moments later. The sound you produce resembles the distress signal of a bird in agony. The inborn curiosity of all birds does the rest.

An even more effective method of drawing a bird closer is an imitation of its song. Your early attempts may be crude, but they should improve with practice (see page 66).

"Take notes"—Keep the birds under close watch. Then, before you move on, get out your notebook and jot down your observations.

If the bird was not immediately identified, write down

Squeaking is an effective way for attracting birds to you. It is made by giving your hand a long-drawn-out squeaky kiss.

enough notes about it to make identification possible later. The six S's of field identification will suggest the necessary information: *Size—Shape—Shadings* (color and markings)—*Sound—Sweep* (movement among branches or while flying)—*Surroundings* (territory where observed).

> *Tip*—Don't let an expert companion tell you immediately the name of a bird unknown to you. Its name will stick far better if you have to make notes of it and work it out in your own field book.

If you come home from your bird walk knowing the birds of your locality a little better, and, possibly, one of them especially well, your efforts are well paid.

REFERENCE TEXT—Leon A. Hausman. *Bird·Hiking*. Rutgers University Press, New Brunswick, N. J.

BIRD SONGS

Then you hear a bird song, locate the singer and identify it. From that moment on, attempt to associate that song with that bird, that bird with that song. Eventually, you will be able to tell a bird by its singing alone.

HELPS FOR IDENTIFYING BIRD SONGS—The only really effective way of identifying a bird by its song is to see the bird so often while it is singing that sight and sound become inseparable. Unfortunately, few birds are accommodating enough to repeat their performance until you know the song by heart on first acquaintance. It may take you a number of field trips before you master a song. In the meantime, one of the following short cuts may help you:

RECORDINGS—A number of bird songs have been recorded on sound film and transcribed to records with great fidelity. Listen to repeated playing of these records until your memory retains some of the songs.

RECORDS—*American Bird Songs.* Cornell University Records, 124 Robert Place, Ithaca, N. Y.

R. T. Peterson, Arthur A. Allen, Peter Paul Kellogg. *Field Guide to Bird Songs* (with 2 records). Houghton Mifflin Company, Boston, Mass.

Flicker Records, Old Greenwich, Conn.

WORD ASSOCIATIONS—Your first impression of a bird's singing may be that it is buzzing, chirping, melodious, metallic, raucous, warbling, or what-not. Then, as you listen, the sounds begin to take on a certain coherence. It will help you to remember a bird's song if you can make the sounds spell out familiar words, or, better, phrases of related words.

Your bird field book may suggest that the song of the black-throated green warbler sounds like "zee-zee-zoo-zoo-zee." How much easier to remember if you hear it as "Trees, trees, murmuring trees"—or even as "Cheese, cheese, Limburger cheese"—depending upon the poetry in your soul. Check for yourself the olive-sided flycatcher's "whip-whee-wheer" against "Whoops! Three beers!"

It pays to develop your own system, and only depend on other people's inventions when they are as well established as "teacher, teacher, teacher" for the oven bird, "Madgie, Madgie, Madgie, put on your tea-kettle-ettle-ettle" for the song sparrow, and "Old Sam Peabody, Peabody, Peabody" for the white-throated sparrow—or "Oh Sweet Canada, Canada, Canada"—if you happen to live north of the border.

Some of these word associations have been so generally accepted that they have become the names of the birds. When a strong and vibrant "whip-poor-will" floats to you on the night air, you know immediately that a whip-poor-will is about. Similarly, you will have little difficulty in recognizing killdeer, peewee, bobwhite, chickadee.

MUSICAL NOTES—While some bird songs may be indicated by words, others can be represented by musical notes.

If you are musically inclined, you may see a bird song in your mind's eye as a regular piece of music and jot it down that way. This can be only approximate, since no instrument can faithfully reproduce the songs of birds.

BOOK ON BIRD SONGS—F. Schuyler Mathews. *Field Book of Wild Birds and Their Music*. Bird songs expressed by means of musical notes. G. P. Putnam's Sons.

SYMBOLS—Simpler than musical interpretation is a system of lines and figures representing notes, their length and quality. The pitch of a note may be indicated by the relative position of the sign, its duration by the length of the line that makes up the sign, its quality by the shape of it.

A number of methods have been suggested for putting the songs of birds in black and white, but the perfect method still waits to be developed—by YOU, maybe.

BOOK ON BIRD SONGS—Aretas A. Saunders. *A Guide to Bird Songs*. Bird songs shown by a system of lines. D. Appleton-Century Company, N. Y.

IMITATING BIRD SONGS—"Let's all sing like the birdies sing . . ." Would be swell if we could! It would be our best means of getting birds close to us for inspection and identification. We can't, because we have no syrinx. Nevertheless, with what we have, it is possible to give a fair imitation that will fool the less discriminating birds.

WHISTLING—Even without being an expert whistler, it should not take you long to learn to imitate the songs of chickadees, orioles, phoebes, and several other birds that have simple call notes. All that is needed is a straight outward or inward whistling through puckered lips.

LIP-TONGUE WHISTLING—For some bird songs you need to co-ordinate lips and tongue. Take the song of the robin, for instance. You can express it fairly well in words: "Cheerily, cheer-up, cheerily, cheer-up." Say those words aloud. Notice how the tip of the tongue flutters behind the upper teeth? Now, give a straight whistle. Next, combine whistle with the flutter of the tongue tip. Finally, get the correct pitch and timing by listening to a real robin. And there you are!

Numerous other bird songs may be imitated in this manner—by combining whistling, with steady or quivering lips, with the tongue action used for speaking the approximate sounds. Keep the lips in a tight pucker with a small opening for the high, reedy calls. For lower-pitched calls, open up the lips wider, and tighten your cheek muscles to create a sounding box.

OTHER IMITATIONS—For still other calls, you must be able to vibrate the soft palate in the back of your mouth. That's a trick you may master by drawing in your breath along the roof of the mouth. Now combine it with an inward whistle to effect the trill of many bird songs.

By combining quivering lips, fluttering tongue tip, vibrating soft palate, there's hardly a bird song you can't imitate. But it will take plenty of practice before you reach that point.

When imitating hollow and deep sounds, make a sounding box out of your cupped hands and blow down over your thumb knuckles.

USE OF HANDS—For imitating the hooting of owls, and the mournful moanings of doves and cuckoos, use a sounding box made by cupping your hands together. Wet your lips, place them against the knuckles of your thumbs, and blow down into the hollow between your hands, the way you blow down into a bottle to make it whistle. You can vary the pitch of the sound by wagging your fingers. With a little practice, you can turn your hands into an instrument on which you can produce numerous flutelike birdcall imitations.

MECHANICAL DEVICES—Many sporting-goods stores carry whistlelike devices for imitating certain birdcalls, specifically the calls of duck, goose, crow, hawk, and turkey. They are easy to use, even for a novice.

FINDING NESTS

Finding bird nests is like playing detective: The untrained sleuth finds his clues by stumbling over them, the trained detective knows where to look for them. You may locate your first few nests by accident, but when you become a skilled bird watcher, your eyes will be drawn almost automatically toward them.

WHEN?—Bird nests may be found throughout the year, but are most easily seen at certain seasons.

FALL AND WINTER—For the beginner, the best time to look for nests is late fall, winter, or early spring, when the leaves are off the trees and therefore do' not hide the nests. The trouble is that at that time of the year the nests are empty and therefore of little interest beyond their structure and location.

SPRING AND SUMMER—The perfect time to locate bird nests is spring and early summer. During nest construction, birds carrying nesting material will give the position of the nest away. Later, after the eggs are incubated, birds carrying food will do the same.

> *Tip*—Continue your nest hunting well into the summer—late July or early August. Some birds are late nesters: waxwings, goldfinches, among others. You may also find second broods—or even thirds—of birds you missed earlier.

WHERE?—It will help you immeasurably in locating nests if you let your bird field book tell you where to look for them. When you hear a singing towhee, then, you will know that there's no sense in looking high in the trees for its nest—towhees build on the ground. Similarly, when you see a Baltimore oriole, you will immediately look up and try to find its hanging nest among the drooping branches of a tall tree high above you.

As in all other bird watching, "Stop, look, and listen" is the key to finding nests—but place the emphasis on the listening. Singing indicates the presence of a male announcing its territorial rights, which, in turn, means a mate and a nest. Locate the singer in your field glasses, watch his actions, look for the female. Follow the two with your eyes until you discover the nest.

REFERENCES—*Audubon Bird Guide* (see page 61) gives clear description of nest localities.

Richard Headstrom. *Birds' Nests—A Field Guide* and *Birds' Nests of the West.* Ives Washburn, N. Y.

GROUND NESTS—Most ground nests are located by flushing the female off her eggs or young by walking zigzag through a field where you suspect a nest. The spot from which the female flies up may not necessarily be where the nest is located. The smarter birds "sneak" along the ground before flying up to draw your attention away from the nest.

> *Tip*—In the field, marsh, and meadow, you can make use of a "flushing line"—a 50- or 100-foot-long ¼-inch manila rope or clothesline. With a companion,

To do a systematical scanning job, sweep the field of your
binocular from left to right, then from right to left.

walk over the ground, with the rope between you in
such a way that it drags over the top of the grass.

LOW BUSH NESTS—Spread some of the branches apart,
carefully, and peer inside. Or shake or strike, gently, the
outside branches to flush possible birds off their nests.
Then study the interior.

TREE NESTS—Scan the trees systematically with your
binocular, sweeping its field slowly from left to right,
along the treetops, then further down from right to left,
still further down from left to right, from branch tip to
branch tip, until the whole location has been carefully
studied.

CAVITY NESTS—Some birds—woodpeckers, owls, flickers,
wrens, and nuthatches—nest in cavities in dead trees.
Locate a dead tree. Study the base of it for telltale chips
that indicate that holes have been expanded into suitable
nests. But chips or no chips, scrutinize every dead tree
in your binocular for possible nest holes. Watch the opening until the bird shows itself.

Tip—Rapping a tree lightly with a stick may scare
out some of the cavity dwellers. Strong pounding may
bring out others—not just birds, but possibly squirrels.

OTHER NESTS—Nests of certain birds must be looked
for in their own peculiar places: bank swallows by looking in burrows in sandy banks, marsh birds by wading

among the reeds in hip boots, barn swallows and phoebes by checking on top of crossbeams in barns and garages, sea birds by following sandy and rocky shore lines, herons, hawks, and eagles by climbing trees with steel climbers attached to your feet, and so on.

CAUTION—Be careful not to disturb vegetation that shades a nest. Also, do not return too often or go too close to a nest. The human scent you leave may cause one of the bird's enemies to investigate—to the detriment of the bird. Instead, do most of your nest watching from a distance, through field glasses.

BIRD WATCHING

When you begin to bird watch, you move from the general field of birds to the specific. The difference between bird walking and bird watching may be considered the jump from seeing *birds,* in the plural, to observing *bird,* in the singular. Or if not studying a single bird, at least concentrating more definitely on the *intensive* life study of certain species, or on definite problems that await solution. It is no longer a matter of listing birds, but of finding out how birds live. The very word "watching" suggests keen and patient observation. For lasting importance, it should be accompanied by careful and extensive note taking.

BLINDS—While much bird watching can be done with binocular, much more can be accomplished by using a blind. A blind is simply a structure, put up close to a bird's nest or at a spot where it feeds or bathes, in which you can hide, unobserved by the bird. The blind you want will depend on your needs and your imagination.

IMPROVISED BLIND—A blind may be of natural materials, found on the spot. Push a few sticks in the ground, in the form of a rectangle. Tie cross pieces to them. Then lean leafy branches or reeds against this crude framework.

Tip—A piece of five-foot chicken wire makes an excellent foundation for a blind made of native materials.

UMBRELLA BLIND—The umbrella blind was originally described by Dr. F. M. Chapman. In its simplest form it consists of an old beach umbrella, camouflaged with green or brownish-green canvas paint. The "handle" is pushed into the ground, or tied to a pole driven in at an appropriate spot. A piece of fabric, about seven feet wide, and slightly longer than the circumference of the umbrella, is attached, as a curtain, along the edge of the umbrella with hooks or safety pins. The bottom edge of the curtain is staked to the ground so that it does not flap.

By using a light-weight cambric, muslin, or percale dyed leaf green (olive green), it is possible to see out through the fabric, while the bird cannot see in. For unobstructed observation, cut slits at suitable places and hold them open with spreaders of thin wood.

Tip—Old, thin sheets make excellent blind covers when dyed.

TENT BLIND—The cheapest type of tent blind consists of a piece of burlap tacked onto a framework of four poles put up half-pyramid style. By using better material, cutting and sewing it into proper shape, and attaching it to four bamboo poles, you have a light-weight tent blind that can be put up in a moment (illustration, page 72).

For the study of field and shore birds, a low blind is advisable. A pup tent, or other prism-shaped tent, is suitable.

Tip—For comfort in a low blind, dig a knee-deep trench directly inside the wall through which you are observing. You can then stand up or sit down by placing your feet in the trench.

A tent blind may also be made from a framework of one-inch piping put together with plumbers' joints, and covered with material, or from a frame of 2×2-inch wood, hinged so that it can be folded up. Such blinds can be taken apart to occupy little space and can be quickly erected.

BOX BLIND—For observation over a long period, you may desire a more permanent structure. Several ornithologists have made use of blinds constructed from walls of waterproof plywood, with small openings at strategical places for observation, and with shelves attached to the inside for equipment—photographic and otherwise.

An old beach umbrella makes a good bird blind. Provide it with side curtains, staking them down firmly at the bottom.

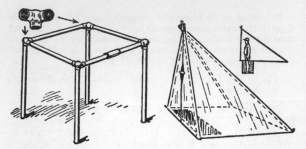

A frame for a bird blind may be made from one-inch piping or from 2x2's. A knee-deep trench will add to your comfort.

Tip—A furniture packing box can be turned into a usable box blind. Camouflage it with green or brown paint. Cover top with roofing paper.

USING THE BLIND—With the construction of the blind completed, you are ready to place the blind in position for use.

PLACING THE BLIND—For certain nest studies, as well as for photography, you will want to be within five feet of your bird, or, possibly, still closer. You will have little luck if you should abruptly dump the blind at this distance. You will, almost certainly, scare the bird away for good.

Instead, put up the blind thirty to forty feet from the nest. Leave it here for a couple of hours or longer, until the bird has become accustomed to this addition to the landscape. Then move it closer by half the distance and leave it again. Work for not more than ten minutes each time, then walk away to permit the bird to return to its nest. At long last, place the blind in its final position. If possible, leave it here for a number of hours, or, better, overnight, before you occupy it.

OCCUPYING THE BLIND—When you are ready for your observations, get the help of a companion to act as a decoy. The two of you approach the blind together. You step inside the blind, while your friend moves away from it. The bird seems to figure, "Something came, something went, coast is clear," and returns to its nest. Without the decoy you may have to wait for quite a while before the bird dares to come back to its nest.

While in the blind, move as little as possible. Use your observation slots carefully, opening them up slow motion. Keep the interior dark. The darker it is the harder it is for the bird to notice any movements in the blind.

When ready to leave use your friend again to convoy you away. Otherwise, your decoy ruse may not work the next time.

BIRD LISTS AND SURVEYS

As you become familiar with more and more birds, you will want to keep track of those you identify. You start listing the birds you see on your walks. Soon, bird listing becomes a sport you play with yourself and with your companions.

Eventually, carefully kept lists may become of scientific importance by throwing light on many things that are not yet clear—such as abundance of birds at certain times of the year, fluctuation in migration and so forth.

PERIODICAL—*Audubon Field Notes*—Bimonthly magazine devoted to results of bird watching. National Audubon Society, 1130 Fifth Avenue, New York 28, N. Y.

DAILY LISTS—Whenever you take a bird walk, jot down the species you see, and the number of birds of the different species.

DAILY FIELD TRIP CARD—Instead of writing down the names of the birds each time you can simplify the matter by using a printed "field trip card" listing the names of birds in your locality. Some of the national bird societies have these available at a penny or two apiece. A number of local bird clubs print their own.

FIELD LISTS—*Audubon Daily Field Card of Birds*. Separate cards for Eastern, Central, and Pacific States. National Audubon Society.

BIG DAY LIST—You may get a kick out of trying to beat your own previous record of number of birds seen. Your best chance comes during the height of the spring migration, in the middle of May. Get up before dawn, and stay out all day. Visit as many different habitats as possible—from wood-edged meadows and open fields, to forests and marshes. Return home after evening dusk has fallen.

Tip—Big Day Walks often have a strong appeal to clubs and youth groups. Organize the walk into a tournament of several teams.

CHRISTMAS BIRD COUNT—Every year the National Audubon Society sponsors a Christmas Bird Count. The count covers one calendar day during the period, approximately, December 25 to January 2. Any group interested in birds may organize a count within its own locality.

To prepare for the count, get a topographic map of your area. Draw a circle of 15-mile diameter of the specific territory you want to cover. Investigate the area in advance and decide on the most effective way of covering it.

A dawn-to-dusk investigation on the day of the count is of greatest significance. If that is not possible, at least seven full hours should be spent in the field.

Write up a report covering location, habitat, time, weather, species, and numbers seen, names of people participating. Mail the report so that it is in the hands of the Audubon Society not later than January 17th. Acceptable reports are published in the March issue of Audubon Field Notes.

Note—Write to *Audubon Field Notes,* National Audubon Society, for full particulars on making the Christmas Bird Count and on preparing the report.

YEAR LISTS—Bird lists become especially valuable when kept on a year-to-year basis.

YEARLY RECORDS—When you get home from a bird walk, transfer the information from the daily list to a permanent record book, to a loose-leaf notebook, or to separate file cards for each bird. In this way, you build up a list of birds seen the year round.

Two hundred species is a good score if you are located along the American coastline. An inland score of one hundred and fifty is excellent.

RECORD BOOK—H. E. Jaques. *Field Notebook for Studying Birds*. William C. Brown Company, Dubuque, Iowa.

BIRD CALENDARS—The dates on which certain birds arrive in the spring will take on special significance to you, in your yearly lists. When do you usually see your first robin? Is spring early or late this year?

With the listing of birds by the calendar, you enter the science of *phenology*—still another case where the "Greeks have a word for it," from *phainein,* to appear, and *logo,* to study: the study of the chronological appearance of things in nature.

Tip—The making of *Bird Calendar Charts* appeals to school children and youth groups. Make a chart with space for name of bird, when first seen, where, by whom. If possible, decorate chart with colored Audubon Society pictures or photographs of the birds.

BREEDING-BIRD CENSUS—During nest building and breeding time you may want to extend your bird interests

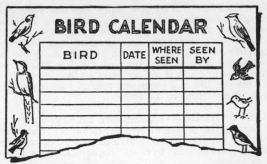

The making of a bird calendar appeals especially to school children and youth groups. Give credit to the observers.

into making a census of breeding birds within a certain territory.

The first time you try it, don't bite off more than you can chew: Make a census of your own garden, school campus or favorite camp site. For your next attempt: Pick a suitable, larger area for investigation. Since you will need to spend at least two mornings and an evening a week there during the census period from late May to the end of June, it is advisable to choose a territory close to your home. The area should be between 20 and 30 acres. A territory smaller than 20 acres will yield little information of significance, larger than 30 acres will be too difficult to cover.

In preparing for the census, secure a large-scale topographic map of the territory. Divide the map section of the main area into checkerboard squares with sides 208 feet long each, covering approximately one acre each. Lay out the identical squares in the field, marking the corners with prominent stakes, measuring the distances by pacing or with a steel tape. By using this grid method of clearly marked squares, you will be able to make a thorough survey of every acre—its individual briar patches, bushes, trees—and note down on copies of the orginal map the location of singing males and of nests actually seen.

Here again the Audubon Society is interested in your findings. Reports of this type of work appear yearly in the November "Breeding-Bird Census" issue of *Audubon Field Notes*.

Note—Write to *Audubon Field Notes*, National Audubon Society, for instructions on the taking of a Breeding-Bird Census, and for method of reporting it.

LIFE LISTS—Out of your daily lists and your yearly listings come the names of the birds you have seen throughout your career as a bird watcher.

KEEPING A LIFE LIST—The simplest way of keeping your life list is to use your bird guide book. Write in it, next to the description of the bird, the date and the place where you first saw it. As the years go by, your bird book will take on life as a permanent reminder of thousands of happy hours spent in the field.

BIRD BANDING—Through bird banding, we are able to unravel the secrets of bird migration and distribution, and find out the life span of birds, their mating habits, habitat preferences, territory requirements, and many other things.

Many a bird student considers federal and state permits to conduct a bird-banding station his top honors in ornithology. These permits are a recognition of his ability to identify and handle birds expertly. They constitute a challenge and an opportunity to work with other ornithologists the world around.

A bird-banding station can be set up in the field or operated in connection with an established feeding station or bird sanctuary. The project itself involves trapping of birds, attaching numbered metal bands to their legs, making complete records of individual birds banded, and submitting these station records periodically to the Fish and Wildlife Service of the federal government, which is in charge of the banding work in the United States.

REFERENCE—F. C. Lincoln. *Manual for Bird Banders.* Fish and Wildlife Service, U. S. Department of the Interior, Washington 25, D. C.

BANDING PERMITS—Before starting bird banding you need the two permits mentioned above. The federal permit is secured by applying to the Chief, Fish and Wildlife Service, Department of the Interior, Washington 25, D. C. Your application must be accompanied by full details of your qualifications for doing the work, certified by a reputable ornithologist, and by a description of the problem you want to investigate. A similar application for the state permit is sent to the conservation department of your own state.

When approved, the Fish and Wildlife Service provides you with the necessary bands and record blanks free of charge.

TRAPS—Traps are easily made, according to instructions in the *Manual for Bird Banders,* from no. 2 or no. 3 hardware cloth of galvanized wire, soldered over frames of no. 10 or no. 12 wire. They may be built to be tripped by the operator from a distance, or by the bird itself on entering.

TRAY TRAPS—The simplest trap is made in the form of an inverted tray or box, approximately 3×4 feet, with sides 10 to 12 inches high. Prop it up at one corner on a short stick. Tie a string to the stick and lead it to a spot from which you can observe the trap. When a bird has entered, trip the trap by pulling the string.

DOOR TRAPS—The door trap is made in the same shape as the tray trap, but with three sides only. The fourth side is replaced with a hinged or sliding door that can be tripped with a stick.

FUNNEL TRAPS—The funnel trap is self-operating. It is box shaped like the others, but has, instead of a door, a funnel-shaped entrance, with the small end to the inside of the trap. The bird walks in, stays because it can't find its way out.

All traps are provided with a small rear door through which you can reach in to take out the captured birds. Paint your traps dull green or brown, so that they will be as inconspicuous as possible.

Tip—As many as a dozen traps may be set up in a quarter-acre garden. Surround the trapping area with chicken wire to keep cats out.

BANDING—The bands are made of aluminum and come in varying sizes to fit birds of all sizes, from size 1, used for the smallest songbirds, through size 1A, 2, 3, 4, 5, 6, to X, used for geese, pelicans, eagles, and similar large birds. In requisitioning bands, specify the proper size for the birds you are studying.

The band is carefully fastened with a pair of pliers around the bird's leg directly above the toes. It should fit closely, yet turn easily. If too tight, it will injure the bird; if too loose, a twig may catch in it.

RECORDS—The record of the banded bird is entered immediately on one of the regular record sheets provided by the Fish and Wildlife Service. It should cover the name of the bird, band number, estimated age, sex, and date of original banding. Records of birds are kept until their season is over—winter birds in the spring, summer birds in the fall—then submitted to the Service.

OTHER METHODS OF MARKING—In addition to using metal bands, other marking methods are sometimes employed.

CELLULOID BANDING—For special studies, the Fish and Wildlife Service makes available celluloid bands in different colors. They can be placed on the legs of birds in numerous combinations—red on one leg, green on the other; blue over yellow on one leg, black over green on the other, and so on. They have the great advantage that they may be spotted through binoculars, so that the activities of the individual bird may be followed.

FEATHER MARKING—Still another method for field observation consists in cementing chicken feathers, dyed to brilliant hues, to the back of the birds, at the base of the tail feathers.

WORKING WITH OTHERS—Bird banding is a co-operative effort. The work of one man means little. It's many people working together in an organized effort that makes bird banding an important ornithological activity.

In the beginning, you will get your main help from the Fish and Wildlife Service. But as you continue the work, you will want to find out what other bird banders are doing and share your own findings and ideas with them. That is the time to join and take part in the meetings of your regional bird-banding association, and to subscribe to the quarterly *Bird-Banding* journal.

ASSOCIATIONS—Northeastern Bird-Banding Association (New England). Periodical: *Bird Banding*. Charles B. Floyd, 210 South Street, Boston, Massachusetts.

Eastern Bird Banding Association. (Eastern States outside of New England). Periodical: *Bird Banding*. Horace Groskin, 210 Glenn Road, Ardmore, Penn.

Inland Bird Banding Association. (Central States). James B. Cope, Earlham College, Richmond, Ind.

Western Bird Banding Association. (Pacific States). Miss Helen S. Pratt, 2451 Ridge View Avenue, Los Angeles 41, Calif.

FIELD OBSERVATIONS

While great steps have been taken in uncovering the secrets of bird life, today the complete life history is known for comparatively few birds, and there is room for much study of the broad subjects of territory, songs, nesting, migration.

The following list may contain suggestions for phases of bird study that you may want to investigate:

ARRIVAL OF MIGRANTS—Do males and females arrive together or separately? If separately, which arrives first? Do younger birds arrive before or after the older birds? Relationship between arrival and weather conditions, status of local vegetation and insect life.

PAIRING—Are birds paired on arrival, or does pairing take place afterwards? Evidences of courtship display observed.

TERRITORY—Do males establish and defend territories (by singing, fighting, pursuit) before or after pairing?

How large is territory? What are its characteristics—
forest, field, marsh, edge, or what? Do females assist in
territory defense? How? Distinction between breeding
and feeding territories? Are both defended?

SINGING—How many different types of calls and
songs? For what purpose used—summoning, scolding,
warning, no apparent purpose, etc? Is singing done in
flight, from ground, from nest, from perch? What time
of day? Do females sing? At what time of season does
singing end?

NEST BUILDING—Does male or female build the nest?
If both, which does most work? What time of day is nest
built? Full description of all steps—from selection of
spot to final nest, including list of materials used.

EGGS—How soon after nest building are eggs laid?
How long before clutch is completed? How many eggs?
Do male and female both set? For how long periods
each? What is the length of incubation period? How
many eggs hatch?

NESTLINGS—How do parent birds approach nest with
food? How many feeding trips are taken by males,
females, during the day? How do nestlings react? What
calls have they? How old are nestlings when they leave
nest? Do they leave by themselves, or are they encouraged
by parent birds? For how long after leaving are they fed
by parents?

NUMBER OF BROODS—Evidence of second brood? Third
brood? Is previous site used for nesting?

FALL MIGRATION—Do migrants disappear by couples,
small groups, flocks? Do other species join flock? What
maneuvering does flock perform before leaving? Relationship between departure and weather conditions, status of
local vegetation.

SPECIAL PROBLEMS—Testing intelligence and use of
senses. Feeding habits. Molting. Deformities, parasites,
and diseases. Enemies. Roosting of wintering birds.

REFERENCE TEXTS—Joseph J. Hickey. *A Guide to Bird
Watching*. Oxford University Press.

Olin Sewall Pettingill, Jr. *A Laboratory and Field
Manual of Ornithology*. Burgess Publishing Company,
Minneapolis, Minn.

Each issue of the periodicals of the various ornithological societies contains numerous suggestions for investigation and methods to use.

Birds around the House

Some bird lovers get their greatest thrill from watching
birds in their natural habitat—in fields and forests. You
may be one of them.

On the other hand, you may get your main pleasure out of attracting birds to your home—to have their singing and graceful beauty add charm to your grounds and garden. Your efforts will be comparatively small—whether they involve feeding, nesting helps, or special plantings—but your satisfaction will be great.

REFERENCE—John W. Baker, Editor. *The Audubon Guide to Attracting Birds.* Doubleday and Company.
    John K. Terres. *Songbirds in Your Garden.* Thomas Y. Crowell Co.
    Thomas P. McElroy. *The New Handbook of Attracting Birds.* Alfred A. Knopf.
    W. L. McAtee. *Attracting Birds.* Conservation Bulletin 1. Fish and Wildlife Service, U. S. Dept. of Interior. 10 cents from Superintendent of Documents, Washington 25, D. C.

BIRD FEEDING

The feeding you do in summer will be almost completely for your own enjoyment. Many birds will like the idea of an easy handout, even when native food is plentiful.

Done in the winter, the feeding will give you the added satisfaction that you are helping to conserve bird life, specifically through severe periods of ice and heavy snow. One thing is important: When you have once started winter feeding, be certain to keep it up regularly. You have made the birds depend on you, rather than on their own ingenuity, and it may prove a great hardship for them if you should fail in what, by your own action, has become your duty.

FOODS—The food you serve will depend on the birds you hope to attract. Woodpeckers, nuthatches, and other insect eaters will be attracted by fats—animal or vegetable. Sparrows, juncos, cardinals, and finches stick almost exclusively to a diet of seeds, while chickadees and titmice prefer variety. Robins, mockingbirds, and cedar waxwings are mostly fruit eaters. Hummingbirds are famous for their preference for flower nectar.

FATS—Suet, fat trimmings from beef and other meats are eagerly accepted by many insect eaters. So are bacon rinds and chopped meat—even bones with a few shreds of meat left on them. Nut meats are also in demand, especially peanuts, chopped or as peanut butter.

SEEDS—There is a great diversity of acceptable seeds. Hemp and millet rank high on the list. They are followed by sunflower seeds, and the seeds of the cucumber family —squash, pumpkin, cantaloupe, watermelon. Then there are the grains: corn (whole, cracked, meal, and hominy),

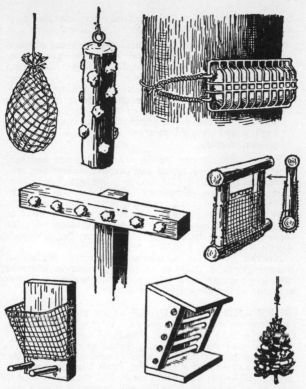

Suet feeders come in many forms—from a crocheted bag and a suet stick to the use of a soap tray and pine cones.

popcorn (popped and ground), whole or rolled oats, barley, wheat. Buckwheat. Kafir corn and other sorghums. Soybeans. Pasture grass seeds.

Tip—Screenings from grain mills and sweepings from haymows are sources of inexpensive seed feed.

To provide for varying tastes, a mixture of seeds is better than a single type. Commercial "chicken feed" is a usable mixture. Better still is the so-called "wild-bird seeds," mixtures which may be bought by the pound in many grocery stores, and through the National Audubon

Society. Most of these wild-bird mixtures contain hemp, millet, Kafir corn, cracked peanuts, sunflower seeds.

> *Tip*—To arrive at the formula for the most effective seed mixture for your local birds, measure out by weight an equal amount of different seeds. Place them in separate containers on your feeding tray. Just before the first container is emptied, remove all containers and find out, by weighing what is left, the amount eaten of each type of seed.
>
> *Tip*—Add 1 ounce fine poultry grit or coarse sand to each pound of seed mixture when snow covers the natural supply.

FRUITS—Simplest to handle are dried fruits and berries: chopped, dried apples and peaches, raisins and currants. Cut up fresh apples, oranges, bananas.

MISCELLANEOUS—Numerous other foods will be taken by birds: leftover bread, crackers, fatty cakes like doughnuts and pastries, crumbs, bakery scraps, dog meal or crushed dog biscuits, cooked spaghetti or macaroni, table scraps, chopped lettuce, egg shells, ants' "eggs," mealworms.

NECTAR—A nectar substitute for summer feeding of hummingbirds is made by dissolving sugar in water—1 tablespoon sugar to 2 tablespoons of water, or larger amounts in the same 1 to 2 proportion.

SUET AND FAT FEEDERS—Your feeders can be as simple or as elaborate as you care to make them, as long as they serve their purpose. Pieces of suet, for example, may be tied directly to tree branches with cords, or served up in a number of ways (illustrations, page 81):

SUET BAG—Make a crocheted mesh bag for the suet, or a small bag from curtain mesh. Fill with suet. Nail to post or tie to branch. The bag will prevent a greedy robber from stealing the whole suet supply in one fell swoop.

SUET STICKS—The suet stick is a popular device: Drill a number of holes, 1 inch in diameter, 1½ inches deep, in a small log, about 2 feet long, 2 to 3 inches in diameter. Leave the bark on. Or use a piece of 2×2 or 2×4 instead of the rustic log. Press suet into the holes.

Suspend stick by a screw eye in one end, in a piece of wire. Or spike it horizontally to a post.

SUET MIXTURES—Mixtures of suet and fats with other foods have a great variety of uses.

Mix melted-down suet and fats with bread crumbs, chopped peanuts, and wild-bird seeds, in the proportion of two parts fat to one part dry ingredients. Pour mixture into holes of suet stick. OR pour into half shells of grapefruit or coconut and hang these up by strings or wire. OR

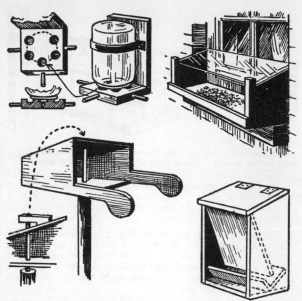

Seed feeders may be made from jars or from pieces of wood.
They can be made to swing with the wind (bottom left).

smear into deep cracks in tree bark. OR pour over
branches of discarded Christmas tree to produce a *bird
Christmas tree*. OR pour into a can from which the mixture can be removed as a *bird cake* when cooled, by dipping for a moment in hot water.

SEED AND FRUIT FEEDERS—Seed feeders are the
most common food dispensers for winter feeding.

FOOD TRAY—A food tray or shelf, a foot square or
larger, made from 1-inch wood, is about the simplest
possible feeding device. Nail a 2-inch rim around the edge
to keep the food from being brushed or blown off.

The food tray may be attached to a pole or a tree in a
sheltered spot, or in front of a window. In the latter case
build it the length of the window and 1 foot wide, and,
if possible, arrange it so that the food may be replenished
from inside the house. Provide it with a glass roof, if
desired.

Tip—Birds may shy away from your window feeder.

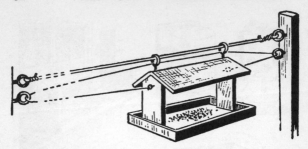

A trolley feeder can be suspended between your window and a post in the garden. It moves in screw eyes along a wire.

To draw them near, make a *trolley feeder*—a roofed tray on a pulley line between the windows and a nearby tree. As the birds get accustomed to coming, draw the feeder closer and closer to the window.

Box FEEDER—For winter feeding, a box feeder is preferable to a tray. In its simplest form, it is a topless wooden box placed on one side so that the opposite side forms a protecting roof over the food. Mount it on a pole or a pivot so that the open front can be turned away from the wind, and rain and snow.

Tip—By attaching one or two vanes to the box, the wind itself will keep the opening turned in the proper direction (see diagram, page 83).

FEED HOPPER—A small hopper will simplify the matter of feeding, by replenishing the food automatically, by

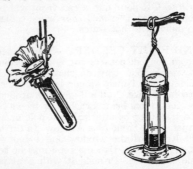

Hummingbird feeder from vial (left); from pill glass with perforated plastic top glued to unbreakable watch crystal (right).

gravity, from a main supply. Commercial hen-house hoppers may be used. You can make your own from wood, alone, or in combination with a glass jar or a lamp chimney (see drawings page 83).

NECTAR FEEDERS—Hummingbirds need a different kind of dispenser for their liquid food.

HUMMINGBIRD VIALS—The sugar "nectar" may be served in tiny vials or small test tubes (size A) hung by "flower wire" among flowers regularly visited.

Tip—For quick attraction, attach a small collar of bright red or blue crepe paper or cloth around the opening of the tube, with scotch tape.

FEEDING GAME BIRDS—The winter feeding of birds may well be extended beyond the garden fence, to game birds in fields and woods—bobwhite and other quails, pheasants, partridge, grouse. The most effective method is by erecting combination shelter-and-feeding stations, of brush or corn stalks, then keeping them dependably stocked.

Tip—It is generally easy to get the whole-hearted cooperation of farmers, sportsmen, Scout Troops, and other interested people of the community to take part in an organized campaign to conserve local game birds.

CORN-SHOCK FEEDERS—In the field, it is easy to turn

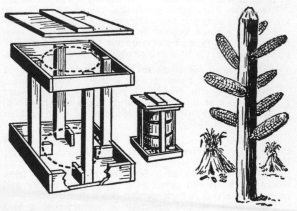

A nail keg can become a grain hopper for feeding game birds (left). Ears of corn may be impaled on nails in a post.

corn shocks into tepee-shaped feeder shelters by opening them up wide on one side. Face the opening south or southeast for maximum protection against winds from north and west. Arrange the shelters within a hundred feet of natural cover of brush or thicket so that the birds can get into hiding quickly in case of sudden danger.

CORNCOB FEEDING—Corncobs may be impaled on short sticks and placed in the ground, or pushed onto nails driven through a board.

GRAIN DISPENSERS—Grain can be fed with least waste by the use of a hopper made from a box, a nail keg or other small barrel (see page 85).

WATER FOR DRINKING AND BATHING

Year round, more individual birds and more species are attracted by water than by food. They all need it for drinking and bathing, and some need it further to produce mud for nest building.

If there is a brook or a lake near your house, the problem is solved. If such is not the case, remedy the situation by making water available—especially during the worst heat of summer and during freezing spells of winter.

The water supply should be at least ½ inch deep, and not more than 2½ to 3 inches. Edge and bottom of container should be rough to provide secure footing. Water should be replenished regularly.

BIRD SAUCER—A flowerpot saucer makes a suitable birdbath. So does a pie tin or any shallow dish. Because of their small size, they need to be filled and cleaned often.

BIRDBATH—Numerous birdbaths, raised on pedestals, are available commercially. They come in numerous styles and prices, with or without fountains and figures. If you hanker for this type of structure for your formal garden, pick one that fits your surroundings and your pocketbook.

Tip—A good substitute may be made from the lid of a garbage can. Paint it with a thin, gravelly cement mixture (1 cup cement, 1 cup fine gravel, 3 cups sand), to give it a rough texture and a masonry look. Mount on a section of concrete sewer pipe, or on three logs sunk in the ground.

BIRD POOL—Not all birds like a raised bath—most of them prefer a water supply at ground level. The best location for a bird pool is a spot that is shaded part of the day. Pick it within a few feet of bushes or trees where the birds can perch after their bath, to dry and preen themselves. A rock garden is a natural.

There is no special difficulty in constructing a bird pool. Scoop out a depression, 3 to 4 feet wide, 5 to 6 feet long, so that the sides slope gently to a depth of 6 inches

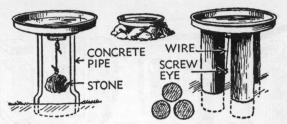

Bird bath from a garbage can cover: placed on rocks (center), on top of a concrete pipe (left), on three posts (right).

in the middle. Line with a piece of chicken wire. Cover the inside with a 2-inch thick layer of a soft cement mixture (one part cement, two parts sand, two parts gravel). Don't smooth it down—keep the surface rough. Allow it to set.

Tip—Moving water has a way of attracting birds' attention. To make your water ripple, attach a ¼-inch copper pipe, with a converter coupling, to the water outlet for your garden hose. Run it to the pool. Bury it 2 inches below the ground. Adjust the pool end of the pipe so that the water falls from a height of a couple of inches, when turned on.

Nesting Helps

One of the most effective ways of increasing the bird population of your garden or orchard is by providing nesting helps—birdhouses for those species that are willing to have nests prepared for them, building materials for the more independent species.

BIRDHOUSES—The construction of birdhouses is a satisfying handicraft, watching them as they become occupied, an absorbing pastime.

TYPES—Different species of birds are attracted to different types of birdhouses:

BOX HOUSES—Among the better-known species that may move into individual, box-shaped houses are: wrens, chickadees, titmice, nuthatches. bluebirds, flycatchers, flickers, woodpeckers, certain owls (barn, saw-whet, screech), sparrow hawk, wood duck, merganser.

APARTMENT HOUSES—A colony of purple martins may take over an apartment-house-type structure.

OPEN SHELVES—A bracketlike "house" consisting of shelf, back, and roof may be occupied by robin, phoebe, or barn swallow.

Log bird houses: hollow log, scraped out; log split in halves and gouged out; log cut in sections and reassembled.

Tip—A birdhouse building contest can be developed into an exciting activity for a school grade, a Scout Troop, or other youth group.

MATERIALS—Scrap wood from packing cases and fruit crates, ½ inch thick and thicker, and slab wood from lumber yards are perfectly suitable for birdhouses.

If you have to buy yard lumber, get so called 1-inch pine, redwood, or cypress (which is really ¾ to ⅞ inch thick finished), in the commercial widths of 6, 8, or 10 inches (5½, 7½, and 9½ inches finished, respectively). Develop your design to make most economical use of your wood.

Tip—Keep your eyes open for hollow limbs and tree trunks. They will need little further inside work, and may be turned into birdhouses by simply cutting to right length, nailing on a top and a bottom, and boring entrance hole.

CONSTRUCTION—As far as design is concerned, you can pretty well follow your own head. You may settle for a square box, with a flat, sloping, or ridged roof. Or you may add to the looks of your birdhouses—although not to their effectiveness—by developing a more complicated pattern.

REFERENCES—*Homes for Birds*. Conservation Bulletin 14, U. S. Department of Interior. 10 cents, from Superintendent of Documents, Washington 25, D. C.

Paul V Champion. *Bird Houses*. Bruce Publ. Co., Milwaukee, Wis.

L. Day Perry and Frank Slepicka. *Bird Houses,* Chas. A. Bennett, Peoria 3, Ill.

Whatever the design, there are a few rules you need to follow:

SIZE—Decide on the bird species you want to attract, then build the houses to the floor dimensions and height of cavity that have proved most acceptable to those species (see chart below).

ENTRANCE HOLE—The diameter of the entrance hole should fit the bird fairly snugly—especially in the case of the smaller birds. It should be large enough to permit the bird to enter easily, but small enough to keep out unwanted birds, such as English sparrows and starlings.

Generally speaking, the entrance hole should be located in the upper third of the front wall, except for martins, which build shallow nests and prefer the entrance not much more than 1 inch above the bottom.

Tip—Use expansive bit for boring entrance hole. Tip it up slightly toward the inside, to keep out the rain.

A perch at the entrance is an unnecessary fixture.

VENTILATION AND DRAINAGE—The entrance hole will usually provide sufficient ventilation. A few holes, ½ inch in diameter, may be bored under the eaves to make the house cooler.

Drill a couple of ¼-inch holes in the bottom for drainage, and for quicker evaporation of moisture

BIRD HOUSE DIMENSIONS		No. 1	No. 2	No. 3	No. 4
Height of Cavity		8"	8"	10"	16"
Diameter of hole		Wren 1" Chickadee 1⅛" Titmouse 1¼"	Bluebird 1½" Tree Swallow 1½" House Finch 2" Martin 2½"	Flycatcher. 2"	Flicker 2½" Screech Owl 3" Sparrow Hawk 3"
Center of Hole to Bottom		5" (Wren 1"-5")	5" (Finch and Martin 1")	7"	12"
Size of Bottom		4" x 4"	5" x 5"	6" x 6".	7" x 7"

CLEANING AND OBSERVATION—The roof or one side should be hinged or otherwise removable for cleaning and observation. At other times, keep it closed with a screen-door hook.

Tip—If you intend to observe from the side, place a removable piece of glass inside the hinged wall to prevent nest or nestlings from falling out when you open up the side.

Tip—Nests are often infested with mites or insects. Clean out litter after each brood, and burn. Dust inside of house with pyrethrum or spray with DDT.

FINISHING—Paint outside with a dull green, brown, or gray oil paint, or stain with oil stain. Leave inside unpainted.

Tip—Put up houses about one month before expected occupancy, for weathering and to remove paint odors. Even better, put up in the fall, but with the entrance hole closed to keep field mice or English sparrows from taking over.

PLACEMENT—The correct location is as important as the right size.

Height above ground—The most effective height above ground varies. It is from 4 to 10 feet for bluebirds and wrens; 5 to 15 feet for tree swallows, chickadees, titmice, and robins; 8 to 20 feet for flickers, woodpeckers, flycatchers, and nuthatches; 15 to 30 feet for owls and sparrow hawks. A house for a wood duck may be put up as high as 20 feet or as low as 4. Mergansers prefer a low location of 3 to 4 feet.

Number of houses—The amount of territory taken over and defended varies with the birds. Put up the houses 30 to 50 feet apart. In most cases, one or two boxes per acre for any one species will prove sufficient. Any more will often remain unoccupied.

CAUTION—Place the birdhouse in partial shade so that it will not be exposed to the broiling sun of midsummer. Protect it from prowling cats by placing a sheet-metal or barbed-wire guard around the post below the house.

NESTING MATERIALS—Birds not attracted by nesting boxes may instead appreciate a ready supply of materials for nest building.

TYPES OF MATERIAL—Get together a handful of 6- to 10-inch pieces of string and yarn, hair (horse hair, or hair from your hairbrush or comb), flax, hemp (from a piece of unraveled rope), excelsior, dry sphagnum moss, tufts of cotton. Place in a tree crotch, tie loosely to a

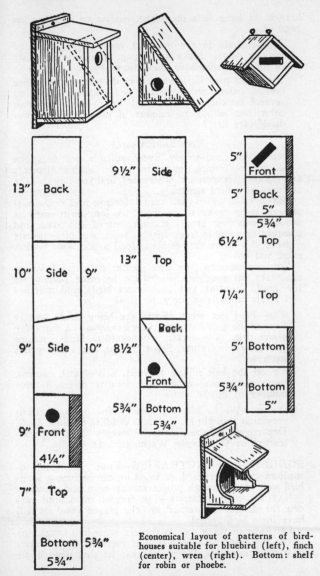

Economical layout of patterns of bird-houses suitable for bluebird (left), finch (center), wren (right). Bottom: shelf for robin or phoebe.

branch, or hang in a mesh bag, similar to suet bag on page 81.

Tip—Include in the material yarns and strings of various colors. Make an attempt to locate the nests of the birds that have made use of them.

Tip—You may be interested in determining whether certain colors are preferred over others. Hang up several bunches of yarn, each bunch of a different color, but with same number of pieces. What color disappears first?

BIRD SANCTUARIES

Dependable food supply, water, suitable nest locations —add one more thing: protective shelter against elements and enemies (human and otherwise), and you have all the features of a bird sanctuary.

But it takes more than casual feeding and occasional protection to make a sanctuary. A long-term view is needed, involving proper management of the area, and planting of suitable trees, shrubs, vines, and other plants —preferably those that combine food production, nesting sites, and cover.

You can develop your own garden or orchard into a sanctuary for songbirds. Fields can be made sanctuaries for quail, pheasant, and other game birds, and marshes and ponds sanctuaries for water fowl.

Tip—Find out what efforts are being made locally toward the establishment of bird sanctuaries, and offer your help. Co-operate with garden clubs, nature groups, service clubs, Scout Troops, and other youth groups.

Or set the ball rolling yourself. Schoolyard, campus, park, camp site—almost any locality offers a wide number of opportunities.

REFERENCE—W. L. McAtee. *Local Bird Refuges*. Conservation Bulletin 17. Fish and Wildlife Service. U. S. Department of the Interior. 10 cents from Superintendent of Documents, Washington, D. C.

SONGBIRD SANCTUARIES—Even a small-to-medium garden, orchard, or wood lot can become a songbird sanctuary through proper management and planting.

NATURAL SURROUNDINGS—The formal, manicured garden, the cleaned-up orchard, and the grazed wood lot will have little bird appeal.

Let some of those garden corners grow into tangles of weeds and briers; let those rambler roses and blackberries turn into unpruned, thorny hedges; let that dead apple tree remain where it stands; let underbrush and wood-edge flora have a freer play—and the birds will move in. In other words, permit part of your garden, orchard or wood lot to get into a semiwild state and keep it there.

PLANTING—Then decide upon plants that will, at one and the same time, appeal to your horticultural taste and your ornithological hopes.

SEED PLANTS—*Flowers*—Aster, cornflower, coreopsis, cosmos, marigold, portulaca, and zinnia are among the usual garden flowers that produce seeds acceptable to birds. The mammoth Russian sunflower beats most of them for bird appeal. See also list of seed plants below, under Game Sanctuaries. *Trees*—Alder, beech, birch, cedar, elm, oak, pines, and other evergreens.

FRUIT PLANTS—*Shrubs*—Bayberry, blackberry, blueberry, elderberry, honeysuckle bush, huckleberry, raspberry, sassafras, shadbush, spicebush, viburnum. *Trees*—Apple and other fruit trees, chokecherry, dogwood, hackberry, holly, mountain ash, mulberry.

NECTAR PLANTS—Hummingbirds are attracted by bee balm, columbine, coral bells, delphinium, and larkspur, flowering tobacco, hollyhock, and trumpet creeper.

INSECT PLANTS—Practically all the plants mentioned above attract insects which, in turn, attract insect-eating birds.

REFERENCES—Roger T. Peterson. *Song-Bird Sanctuaries*. National Audubon Society. 1130 Fifth Avenue, New York 28, N. Y.
Fruits attractive to birds. Fish and Wildlife Service, U. S. Dept. of Interior. Pamphlets: BS 42, Rocky Mountain States; BS 43, Northern Plains States; BS 46. Great Basin States; BS 50, Florida.

GAME BIRD SANCTUARIES—Fields and pastures can be turned into sanctuaries for large populations of game birds at little or no cost, with little or no effort. It is again a matter of management and planting.

COVER AND FOOD—Instead of cultivating clean to the fence rows, leave lanes of cover and food; grow hedgerows, but keep them low by pruning; let some of the brush piles remain unburned, some of the corn shocks unshucked; let tangles form, of cat brier, grape, and honeysuckle; leave patches of grain unmowed; use flushing bars on mowing machines to flush ground birds off their nests, then leave a clump of ground around the nest for protection.

SEED PATCHES—Patches of seed-bearing plants may be sown along fences and hedges, and in corners of fields and pastures. The following have proved of strong appeal, especially in mixture: alfalfa, buckwheat, clover, corn, cowpeas, flax, hemp, lespedeza, millet, oat, rye, sorghum, soybean, Sudan grass, sunflower, wheat.

REFERENCE—*Plants Useful in Upland Wildlife Management.* Conservation Bulletin 7. U. S. Dept. of the Interior, Fish and Wildlife Service, Washington 25, D. C.
Floyd A. Johnson. *Upland Game Management.* Wildlife Management Institute, Investment Building, Washington 5, D. C.

WATERFOWL SANCTUARIES—The establishment of waterfowl sanctuaries starts with a great DO: DO develop ponds and lakes to sustain a waterfowl population (see page 240); and a great DON'T: DON'T drain marshes dry, but retain their water in shallow ditches and ponds.

A waterfowl sanctuary is generally a major undertaking that requires community support. But even a small pond or lake can become a refuge if planted for cover and food.

WATERFOWL PLANTS—Bulrush, wild celery, duckweeds, wild millet, musk grasses, pickerelweed, pondweeds (sago and bushy pondweeds), wild rice, water cress, water lily.

REFERENCES—*Natural Plantings for Attracting Waterfowl.* Wildlife Leaflet 223. Fish and Wildlife Service, U. S. Department of the Interior, Washington 25, D. C.
C. E. Addy and L. G. McNamara. *Waterfowl Management on Small Areas,* Wildlife Management Institute, Investment Bldg., Washington 5, D. C.

Bird Photography

Whether you happen to be a bird student wanting to make your observations permanent by recording them on photographic film, or an amateur photographer with a newly awakened interest in bird life, you will find bird photography an exciting activity. It will put all your patience and inventiveness to the test, but the results will more than offset your efforts.

BOOK OF BIRD PHOTOGRAPHY—J. Warham. *Technique of Bird Photography.* Hastings House.

REFERENCE—*How to Take Bird Pictures.* Free from Sales Service Division, Eastman Kodak Co., Rochester 4, N. Y.

STILLS

EQUIPMENT—CAMERA AND LENSES—Start with whatever camera you have. Learn what it can do, then concentrate on the phases of bird photography that come within the scope of your camera—until you decide to buy a better one.

For close-ups of perching birds and of nests, it must be possible for you to focus your camera at an object three to four feet from the lens—either by the camera's own devices, or by the added help of portrait attachments or extension tubes. With a telephoto lens, this distance may be increased three to four times.

Pictures of birds in flight require a camera with shutter speeds up to 1/1000 second. Using a telephoto lens, you can fill your negative with bird as you follow it in its flight.

OTHER EQUIPMENT—Most bird shots need to be taken with the camera on a *tripod,* and with a *remote shutter release* or from a *blind.*

For extensive bird photography, a *flash gun* is a necessity. When "shooting" birds, you must be prepared for all kinds of light conditions—including the deep shade of hidden nest locations. With the dependable light of a flash bulb, you can get stop-action shots anywhere, any time, with good depth of focus. Electronic flash, at 1/3000 second or less, will even make it possible for you to stop the beat of a hummingbird's wings.

CLOSE-UPS—The simplest way to get a close-up of a bird is to observe it carefully and to locate one of the places to which it returns regularly—its perch, its nest, or its feeding ground.

When you have found such a place, forget about the bird while you set up and focus your camera on the spot where it descends. Then wait for the bird to come back to have its picture taken.

USING A BLIND—There is a great advantage to using a blind (see page 70) in bird photography. From within its hiding walls, you can watch the bird closely through the finder of your camera, get it in knife-sharp focus by focusing on its eyes, and snap the shutter when the bird shows to best advantage. Also, you can change film and reset the shutter for another shot without scaring the bird away.

Tip—When setting up the blind, check the position of the sun. You don't want to shoot into the sun. The best location for the blind is to the south of the perch. Place it here if at all possible.

PHOTOGRAPHING WITHOUT BLIND—If you prefer to photograph without the use of a blind, put up your camera on its tripod a few feet away, focus it, set diaphragm and shutter, arrange a method of releasing the shutter by remote control (page 97), remove yourself an appropriate distance. Snap the bird as it returns.

Sounds simple—but there's a trick to it. The bird will probably resent the presence of your camera so close to its perch and stay away. Therefore, put up your camera first at a distance of thirty to forty feet and let the bird get accustomed to it. Then move it increasingly closer, each time permitting the bird to get so well acquainted with the gadget that it approaches it without fear.

> *Tip*—If you want to save your camera from exposure to sun and weather, use a dummy in the early stages, consisting of a small box on a tripod of sticks. When the proper distance has been reached, replace dummy with the camera.

COMPOSITION AND BACKGROUND—In taking a bird shot, you are not just concerned with getting a sharp picture. You want a pleasing one. Therefore, watch your composition and the background.

It is comparatively easy to get a pleasing picture of a bird perched on a branch, taken from a low angle. Similarly, around a feeding station, you have a chance to arrange your props into an attractive composition.

Your main problem is to prevent the background from interfering with the main action.

Aim for a background of an even tone—either the dark of a solid shadow, or the light of the sky, mellowed with a filter.

If you can't evade a blotchy background of highlights and shadows, soften it by throwing it out of focus. To do this, get your bird into critical focus, then open up the aperture as wide as feasible.

NEST PHOTOGRAPHY—Shots of nests may prove your toughest bird assignment.

A nest is usually located among grass, reeds, or branches that would throw a confused crisscross pattern over your picture. Now, don't immediately pull up the grass or tear off the branches. By doing this you may expose eggs or nestlings to the sun at certain times of day and cause their death. Instead, spread the grass softly apart so that it will have a chance to straighten up again, and tie interfering branches back temporarily while you take your shots.

To look its best, a nest with eggs or young should not be photographed directly from the side or from straight above. A picture taken at an angle of 45 to 60 degrees will give a far better effect. To accomplish this, use a tripod with a tilting top or with a swivel head (ball-and-socket joint).

Tip—In photographing nests high off the ground, lash the tripod to a tree opposite the nest, or use a clamp with toothed jaws, such as a Kodapod, for attaching the camera to a branch.

Tip—When a nestling is at least a week old, try for a feeding shot. Focus the camera on a branch close to the nest. Lift the nestling carefully onto the branch and be ready to shoot when the mother bird comes to the rescue. Snap, then replace the nestling.

The diffused light of a hazy or cloudy day is better for nest photography than direct sunlight. Highlights will be less glaring, shadows less black. On a cloudless day, throw a shadow over the nest and its surroundings. Use a piece of cardboard, cheesecloth or photographers' "scrim" tacked over a wooden frame.

EXPOSURE—Set your shutter speed for the action involved, then open or close your aperture correspondingly.

PERCHING BIRD: 1/30 to 1/100 second. On a calm day, time exposure up to 1/2 second. Slight swaying of branches, 1/25 to 1/50 second.

SETTING BIRD: 1/4 to 1/50 second, depending on the disposition of the bird.

FEEDING: 1/30 to 1/50 second.

Tip—If your lens is not fast enough for the necessary speeds under the subdued light of nest photography, you may solve your problem by using flash equipment. Set your speed at 1/200 and your aperture according to the tables of the flashbulb you are using.

Remember to use daylight flashbulb in color photography with daylight color film.

SNAPPING THE PICTURE—Make all the preparations as quickly as possible during the absence of the bird. This is particularly important in photographing a nest, since

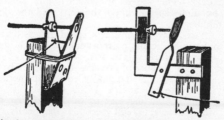

Two simple remote releases for cable release cameras. Attach release to separate support, not to the camera tripod.

otherwise the eggs may cool before the mother bird has a chance to return.

Pick a hiding place from which to have a good view of the spot on which the camera is focused. When the bird reappears, do not snap it the very moment it alights. Wait until it strikes an attractive pose, then click the shutter.

Method of releasing the shutter varies.

If camera has a shutter lever, tie a strong thread to it, lead it down to the ground, through a screw eye attached to a peg driven in the ground, then on to your place of concealment. A gentle pull will do the trick.

For some cameras, wire cable releases up to twenty feet long are available.

A camera that can be operated by cable release can also usually be equipped with electric tripper.

Still other cameras may be fitted with bulb and tubing —tubing may be bought by the foot to any length desired. For cameras with electrically operated, synchronized flash-guns, simply extend the wiring the necessary distance— up to 100 feet or more.

> *Tip*—A simple remote release may be made from a hinge and a few rubber bands, or from a 2½-inch corner iron (see drawing page 97). Place on a separate post so that the camera will remain steady.

FLIGHT PICTURES—Photographs of birds in grace-ful flight have a special appeal. In a way, they are the easiest kind of bird pictures to take. Even if you are a rank amateur with an inexpensive camera you may have luck with a flight shot—provided you take it on a bright day and use a fine-grain film so that the resulting tiny spot on your negative may be enlarged to a fair size.

If you want to be certain of your results, use a high-speed camera, preferably equipped with a telephoto lens, and use a yellow filter to darken the sky background.

EXPOSURES—The speed at which flight photographs should be shot depends upon the bird and the direction of its flight.

SLOW FLYERS (birds flying at a speed of less than thirty miles an hour—pelicans, cormorants, ravens, large gulls, herons, soaring turkey vultures, and hawks): Photo-graphed from a distance of 50 feet—flying directly toward camera, 1/150 second; diagonally toward camera, 1/300 second; crosswise to camera, 1/500 second.

OTHER BIRDS—At a distance of 50 feet—flying directly toward the camera, 1/200 second; diagonally toward camera, 1/500 second; crosswise to camera, 1/1000.

Notice that the speeds are for birds fifty feet away

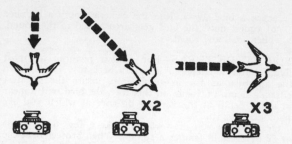

Exposure speed depends on bird's flying direction. Double the speed for diagonal flight, triple it for crosswise flight.

from the camera. For birds at half the distance (25 ft.), you need to shoot at twice the speed; for birds at double the distance (100 ft.), the speed may be cut in half.

Tip—Instead of attempting to focus on an approaching bird, set camera at an arbitrary distance. Snap your shutter when your range finder or ground glass shows the bird in focus.

Tip—After some training, you will be able to take certain flight shots at slower camera speeds, releasing the shutter while moving the camera to follow the bird.

MOVIES

Most of the suggestions for bird stills apply to bird movies as well. A few more may be of help:

CLOSE-UPS—Nests may be photographed in full sunlight, although the result will prove less pleasing than when "scrim" is used to diffuse the light over the nest.

A nest in deep shade may be illuminated with light thrown on it by "silvered" cardboard or metal reflectors out in the sun. If it is not possible to "pep up" the light sufficiently, take the shot at 8 (or even 4) frames a second.

A strong telephoto lens will make it possible for you to obtain certain shots from a distance at which the bird does not mind your presence—either in the open or from the interior of a room or from a parked automobile. Nevertheless, close-ups of adult birds are most effectively taken from a blind, with the camera focused at perch, nest, or feeding ground.

Tip—The sound of the whirring camera motor may

scare a bird away. Run the camera empty a number of times, until the bird gets accustomed to the sound. Then load and shoot.

FLIGHT PICTURES—For motion pictures of most flying birds, a telephoto lens is a necessity. Close down the aperture as far as feasible, to insure the greatest possible depth of focus. In this way, the bird will appear in sharp detail at the varying distance at which you are photographing it.

Occasionally you may want to take a few flight shots at 32 or even 48 frames a second. When projected at the usual home speed of 16 frames a second, the bird will be soaring with a more majestic sweep and will remain for a longer time on the screen.

Bird Collections

It is no longer necessary to kill a bird to identify it—with a modern binocular you can name it on the wing. If it does become important for you to study a bird by actually handling it, you will find almost complete sets of study skins in any large natural history museum or university.

The days of dusty stuffed birds are gone—there are other types of bird collections that are of interest. None of them will deplete our bird population.

Bird Nests

Nests are cradles, not homes. They are seldom used a second time. They may be collected as soon as the fledglings have left, and any time during fall and winter.

COLLECTING—Many nests rest loosely in tree crotches. Lift them out carefully. If you are interested in using the crotch for a display base, cut it off and take it along. In cases where the nest is firmly attached to a branch—vireo, oriole, hummingbird—cut off the branch a few inches toward the tree trunk.

> *Tip*—Carry pruning shears on your bird-nesting expeditions. They will cut the branch in a single snip, and leave the nest intact.

Ground nests are the hardest to collect. They generally come apart when you try to lift them. The only safe way is to slice off the sod on which they are built, and collect sod and nest both.

The simplest way of carrying home a nest is to place it in the middle of a square cloth, bring the corners toward the center and tie them together hobo fashion.

Make immediate notes of each nest you collect—including name of bird, location, how high above ground, date

By mounting bird nests on the branches on which they were found, you can produce an interesting-looking display.

found, and so on. The nest will, of course, have special significance if you have seen it being built and have followed the life of the inhabitants, from eggs to flying fledglings.

PRESERVING—Recently deserted nests are often infested with mites and insects. Before storing them, dust them with pyrethrum or DDT.

To keep the nests fresh looking, give them a thin coating of shellac, sprayed from an atomizer or spray gun. This has the further effect of sticking the ingredients together so that the nest does not come apart so easily as would otherwise be the case.

Nests may be kept in boxes with well-fitting lids. Place a few crystals of paradichlorobenzene or naphthalene with each nest to protect it against insect enemies.

DISPLAYING—You can develop an attractive nest display by fastening the crotches in which the nests were found, or the branches to which they were attached, to wooden bases.

Tip—An interesting study—and display—can be made of the items that constitute the nests of a single species. Pull the nests apart, sort out the ingredients, list them.

Facsimile eggs are cast from plaster of Paris in a form made by pushing a dowel stick into modeling clay.

EGGS

The mania for collecting eggs went out at about the same time that stuffed birds disappeared from the parlor —fortunately. Nevertheless, there's no question that a nest collection looks more intriguing filled than empty. The remedy is to produce a clutch of "reasonable facsimiles" for each nest.

ARTIFICIAL "EGGS"—Find out from a bird book the diameter of the egg at the widest point, and the length of it. Whittle a dowel stick of the same diameter to an approximate egg "point." Push it as deeply into modelling clay (plasticine) as the egg is long. Make as many holes as there are eggs to the clutch of your particular bird.

Fill each hole with a plaster-of-Paris water mixture (see page 101). Let set for an hour or longer. Sandpaper down the blunt end of the plaster "eggs" to proper roundness. Shellac and paint in the natural colors.

EGG PRESERVATION—In your nesting surveys, you may occasionally come upon an egg that didn't hatch, or eggs in a deserted nest. Rather than having them "go to waste," you may want to include them in your collection.

With extreme care, drill a small hole in the *side* of the egg, with a regular egg drill. When the hole is large enough, insert the tip of a blowpipe, or of a thin glass tube drawn to a point. Hold the egg with the hole down and blow air softly into it. The air will drive out the contents.

When emptied, fill your mouth with water and blow this into the egg for rinsing. Rinse several times. Shake out the water. Or get it out by blowing air in. Put the egg aside for a couple of days, hole *up,* to permit the remaining water to evaporate. Don't place it to dry hole *down*—if you do, you risk that the egg will stick to whatever it is placed on.

When completely dry, mark the egg with a number to

To preserve a nonhatched egg, empty it. Drill a hole in the egg, then blow out the contents with a small blow pipe.

 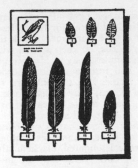

Feathers are mounted to cardboard sheets with pieces of scotch tape. Be on the lookout for the four main types of feathers.

correspond to your notebook description of it. Store it in a box on cotton.

Tip—You may discover when blowing out the egg, that it contains an embryo that cannot be removed through the tiny hole. Blow out the liquid contents, then fill the egg with household ammonia from an eye dropper. Set aside. The ammonia will usually dissolve the embryo in a day or so. If not, repeat process. When dissolved, blow out egg as described above. *Don't get ammonia in your mouth.*

FEATHERS

Feathers are found in greatest numbers during the molting season, from late July to early September. Be on the lookout for the four main types of feathers from each bird: wing flight feathers, tail feathers, coverts, down.

MOUNTING FEATHERS—Attach the feathers to thin cardboard, of a standard size picked by you for your collection. Use household cement or scotch tape.

Several arrangements are possible: by species (all feathers of same species on same cardboard), by types of feathers (flight feathers of different birds in one display, of tail feathers in another, and so on), or by location (all feathers found in one habitat).

PELLETS

The pellets of undigested—and undigestible—food parts regurgitated by owls, hawks, herons, crows, gulls, and some other birds, may be the basis for an interesting collection.

STORING PELLETS—Pellets may be kept and displayed in individual boxes for the different species, or in a larger flat box, with partitions. Mark the boxes to fit your notebook records, or keep a label with each pellet.

The simplest way to identify pellets is by their location: under and near nests and roosts of the respective birds. Their shapes and contents are further clues:

Owl: Oval, gray pellets, looking like matted felt, containing hair, *whole* bones and often fairly well-preserved skulls of mice and shrews.

Hawks: Pear shaped or round, with hair and *crushed* bones of mice, sometimes feathers.

Heron: Elongated, blackish, almost always with twisted point at end. With hair of mice and rats, but seldom bones—bones are digested by the heron's gastric juices.

Crow: Like miniature horse manure, with remains of beetles, pebbles, and always a mixture of plant parts—straw, chaff, or grass seeds.

Gull: Fish bones and remains of various sea animals.

Tip—Pick apart a number of pellets from one species. Attempt to reconstruct skeletons of mice and shrews. Cement to cardboard as display of the food habits of species.

BIRD TRACKS

Along sea shore and lake front you will often come upon the clearly delineated tracks of some of our wading and swimming birds—the astonishing large imprints of the great blue heron, tracks that show the webbed feet of ducks and gulls, the delicate marks of the least sandpiper.

You can't collect the tracks themselves, but you can make plaster casts of them that will retain all the details of the original tracks.

For details of track casting, see page 132.

4. ANIMALS

OF ALL wild creatures, the four-footed, fur-bearing animals—more exactly called mammals—are probably the most secretive. They are all around you as you hike over field and through the woods—but you hardly ever see them. Most of them are asleep in the daytime, in burrows, caves, or dens. Those that are awake hear your approach, they smell you—that dangerous human scent—and disappear hurriedly.

Most people get to see very few animals in the wild—an occasional woodchuck or a gray squirrel in the daytime—a rabbit and deer by twilight—an opossum or skunk in the headlights of an automobile by night. It takes skill and infinite patience to get close enough to animals to see their actions. But you will be well paid for your efforts.

There is an excitement that cannot be described in watching a small herd of antelope come down to a desert water hole to drink, in seeing a mountain goat among its crags and peaks, a grizzly in its wilderness home, a beaver on its dam.

It is less exciting, but more fun—and far easier—to watch pocket mice filling their cheek pouches with food, to follow the antics of chipmunks among rocks and logs, to sit at night listening to the rustling overhead as flying squirrels take off from one branch to land on another—maybe even use your head for a landing field.

Mammals play a great part in nature's scheme. But it is only recently that we have come to recognize this, and it will be many years yet before we will have full knowledge of their relationship to nature's other children, to plants and to man.

Large or small—every mammal has an intriguing appeal

to anyone interested in the out-of-doors. When once you have felt that appeal, you cannot help but follow it in the future.

BOOKS ON ANIMAL LIFE—Victor H. Cahalane. *Mammals of North America.* The Macmillan Company.

E. W. Nelson. *Wild Animals of North America.* National Geographic Society, Washington, D. C.

Ivan Sanderson. *Living Mammals of the World.* Doubleday & Co.

WORKING WITH OTHERS

Most of your animal activities will have to be solitary occupations. It is hard enough for a single person to get close to wild animals. It is almost impossible for a small group, or for even two people, to get near them without being detected.

However, in some of the activities relating to animals, you will be benefited greatly if you can get other people to share your interest and enthusiasm.

If you happen to be in or near a large town that has a zoo or a natural history museum, contact the curators there who specialize in mammals. In a university town, there may be a zoology or biology professor who can guide you and perhaps put you in contact with others who share your interest. And, by all means, get in touch with your home state's game commission, or with one of the game wardens of your county.

Through the American Society of Mammalogists and the Wildlife Society you have the chance to find out what other animal students—beginners or experts—are doing.

In addition to all the above, the Fish and Wildlife Service of the U. S. Department of the Interior will assist you with advice and suggestions.

SOCIETY—American Society of Mammalogists. Hdqrs.: Zoology Department, Oklahoma State University, Stillwater, Okla. Periodical: *Journal of Mammalogy.*

Wildlife Society. Hdqrs.: Remington Farms, Chestertown, Md.

Field Study of Animals

EQUIPMENT FOR ANIMAL STUDY

CLOTHING—If you expect to get close enough to all kinds of animals to study their ways, you must be prepared to cruise through underbrush and hike for miles through the countryside. Most of your roaming will be done in the cool and dew of evening, night, and early morning, when the majority of the animals are active.

Sturdiness, warmth, and water repellency are therefore the main considerations in choosing suitable clothing. The best materials are wool, corduroy, gabardine, with knees and elbows reinforced with patches of soft leather.

Tip—Steer clear of canvas (duck). The drum sound of twigs hitting it as you travel through brush will warn animals of your coming.

To the eyes of most animals, what we see as colors appear as various shades of gray. The color of your clothing, therefore, makes little difference. But the tone does. A great contrast between your clothing and your background—very light against dark shadows, very dark against brilliantly lit sand—attracts attention to your slightest move.

WARNING—Play safe during hunting season by wearing conspicuous red.

Your footwear should suit the territory you intend to cover—hiking shoes, climbing boots, waders for marshland. Many field workers use rubber-footed pacs over woolen socks.

STUDY EQUIPMENT—For seeing more clearly, and for identifying what you see:

FIELD GLASSES—Normally, you have to keep at an appropriate distance from the animal you are watching so as not to scare it away. A good binocular—as described on page 59—will assist you greatly by bringing the animal much closer to you.

A high relative brightness is important since so much of your study will have to be done under poor light conditions. Watch out, therefore, in picking a binocular, that you do not purchase magnification at the expense of relative brightness. You will be better off with a six-times magnification and a relative brightness of 25, than with eight-times magnification and a brightness of only 14 (see page 60).

FLASHLIGHT—A powerful flashlight will make it possible for you to discover and watch certain animals at night—a five-cell flashlight with a focused beam is excellent. A headlight-type flashlight leaves your hands free.

ANIMAL BOOKS—Bring your favorite field book.

BOOKS FOR FIELD IDENTIFICATION—H. E. Anthony. *Field Book of North American Mammals.* G. P. Putnam's Sons.
W. H. Burt and R. P. Grossenheider. *Field Guide to the Mammals.* Houghton Mifflin Company.
E. Lawrence Palmer. *Fieldbook of Mammals.* E. P. Dutton & Company.

Ann Haven Morgan—*Field Book of Animals in Winter*. G. P. Putnam's Sons.

NOTEBOOK—To make complete notes on the animals you see and records of your observations, carry a pocket-size notebook—loose leaf, if you prefer.

ORIENTATION EQUIPMENT—Animal study is field work in the truest sense of the word. The pursuit of an animal may often carry you into unknown territory from which you need to find your way out when you have accomplished your mission.

COMPASS—For extensive field trips, always carry a compass. With a knowledge of its use and a mental picture of the general lay of the land you are traversing—gained through past experiences—you should have no difficulty in getting back to your base.

MAP—If the territory in which you are traveling is new to you, a compass alone will be of little help. In that case, bring along a topographic map, or, if a printed map is not available, a sketch map containing the main features of the landscape—rivers and lakes, hills and ridges, roads and trails.

Tip—For a long wilderness trip carry a canteen with water, a small first-aid kit, emergency ration, and matches in waterproof case.

FINDING ANIMALS

Animals are elusive creatures. The best approach to the problem of finding them is to discover their haunts, then come back at the time most opportune for seeing them.

WHERE?—Comb your territory in search of signs of animals.

ANIMAL HOMES—Be on the lookout for animal homes wherever you go. Check for occupancy around them—fresh tracks, droppings, remains of food, clipped vegetation.

BURROWS in open fields, pasture land, under tree roots, in hillsides, in stream banks will indicate many different animals, depending on size and geographical location: woodchuck, skunk, prairie dog, gopher, fox, coyote, badger, otter, mink, various mice.

MOUNDS and ridges of moles are familiar to everyone. Various mice live in tunnels deserted by moles.

CAVERNS in rocky ledges: porcupine, gray fox, bobcat, bear.

HOLLOW TREES—Raccoons and opossums live in "den trees," flying squirrel and gray squirrel in smaller cavities.

NEST of leaves and twigs: squirrel, wood mouse.

HOUSES—Muskrat in houses of reeds and twigs, beaver in houses of branches and mud.

"FORMS"—Rabbit and hare bed down in depressions in the ground.

"YARDING GROUNDS"—The bedding-down places of deer in dense thickets.

TRACKS AND RUNWAYS—Scattered tracks indicate that the animal is around; runways that it lives near by. Runways vary from the tiny grass tunnels of the meadow mouse, the streamside trails of muskrat, the crossing place of the mountain lion from one side of a mountain to the other, the path of the coyote to the desert waterhole, to the broad lane of deer to the lake shore.

OTHER SIGNS—SCAT (droppings, dung)—The size, color and shape of scat identify many different animals (see page 137). Droppings in an attic, cave, or loft may indicate the presence of bats in cracks and crevices overhead.

FEEDING SIGNS—Cut twigs, gnawed bark, peeled saplings, nut shells, chewed cones, remains of bones and feathers. Stored food.

TORN BARK—from deer rubbing its antlers against the tree to remove the "velvet."

"REST TREES"—where porcupines stop for the day when moving from place to place.

"MEASURING TREES"—Trees with claw marks of bear.

"SCENT POSTS"—Spots where members of the dog family —fox, coyote, wolf—stop to urinate.

"SCRATCH HILLS" Small mounds formed by members of the cat family—bobcat, lynx, mountain lion—covering their urine.

"OTTER SLIDE"—Smooth slide down river bank into the water—playground of otter.

"BEAR WALLOW"—Water hole where bear and other animals roll in the mud.

REFERENCE—George F. Mason. *Animal Homes.* William Morrow and Co.

WHEN?—TIME OF YEAR—Most mammals are active all summer long and, with some exceptions, throughout the winter as well. Many of them slow down when it is cold, spending more of their time sleeping. A few hibernate, going into an almost comalike sleep—mainly bats, woodchuck, eastern chipmunk, ground squirrel, certain mice. The black bear is not a true hibernator, but simply a deep sleeper.

TIME OF DAY—Each animal has its own favorite time for moving about, mostly in search of food.

NIGHT—A large number of species are *nocturnal*. They

sleep during the day and come out in the dark of night. That is when you hear the bark of the fox, the howl of the coyote, the scampering footfalls of skunk and raccoon, the squeal of mice.

DAY—Comparatively few animals are *diurnal*. Gray squirrel, ground squirrel, shrew, woodchuck, chipmunk, prairie dog.

TWILIGHT—Many mammals move about during twilight hours. Some of them are *crepuscular:* you have your best chance to observe them in the evening twilight—muskrat and beaver. Others are *matutinal:* you can study them in the morning twilight, before daybreak—deer, for instance. Some of these animals may be abroad on overcast days.

GETTING CLOSE TO ANIMALS

Each kind of animal must be studied in its own special way. Depending on your skill and resourcefulness, you can get close to animals by attempting to attract them to you or by following their tracks and stalking them to their haunts.

ATTRACTING—You can play on the hunger and curiosity of certain animals to attract them to you.

BAITING—Different varieties of bait may draw some animals to a spot where you can study them closely from a window, a tent door, or a blind.

You are familiar with the garbage-can night marauding of skunks and raccoons. Garbage-can ingredients, with a possible further addition of other vegetable and animal matter, will bring in opossums, martens, weasels as well, and may even appeal to a fox.

Rodents of all descriptions go for cereal grains and nut meats, shrews occasionally for small pieces of meat.

If you live in deer country, you can attract the deer with salt licks—blocks of rock salt that you can purchase at feed stores. The same idea will have the wholehearted approval of porcupines if they happen to be around.

Commercial scent baits are also useful in attracting animals.

WATCHING NOCTURNAL ANIMALS—Most of the animals that you can attract with bait will be the night-roaming kind. You will hear them at the food, but will only see them if you light up the scene. Simply play a flashlight on them. Peculiarly enough, this will disturb few nocturnal animals as long as you do it quietly.

An even better method is to string a wire from the house current and turn on a bulb directly over the feeding spot for illumination. If in camp, use a storage battery or hot-shot battery and an automobile sealed-beam lamp.

Tip—Pettit suggests the insertion of a rheostat in the wiring so that you can increase the illumination slowly, rather than switching it on suddenly, which may scare the more timid animals away.

CALLING—The best-known calling method is possibly the imitation of the bellow of the bull moose in mating season, to draw the cow moose near. Some experts can make this trumpeting sound without apparatus, but most of them use a birch-bark megaphone to increase the volume. Roll up a piece of birch bark, approximately 16 by 20 inches, into a cone, with a front opening about 6 inches in diameter, and a mouthpiece approximately 1 inch wide. While bellowing, point the megaphone up in the air, then toward the ground and up again, to get the proper effect.

You can make a reasonable facsimile of the eerie, bleating call of deer with the help of a wide blade of grass. Hold your thumbs together sideways. Stretch the grass between them so that it forms a free membrane between first and second knuckles. Bring the thumbs up to your mouth and blow between the knuckles to make the grass vibrate and give off a sharp bleat.

Male elks, and moose as well, may be attracted during the fall mating season by the sound of clashing antlers of two rivals fighting. Hitting brush and trees with a stick may do the trick.

In beaver territory, beavers can occasionally be called with an imitation of their own warning signal of slapping the tail against the surface of the water. Use a piece of bark or a canoe paddle, or just your hand.

The squeaking produced by kissing the back of your hand (see page 63) usually works with squirrels. It may

You can imitate the eerie bleat of a deer by blowing over a wide blade of grass stretched tightly between your fingers.

also call fox, muskrat, and weasel from their hideouts.

At night, you may get answering calls to an imitation of the yap of a fox, the howl of a coyote, the screech-owllike whistle of a raccoon. You may draw them nearer, but they will probably keep at a safe distance.

Tip—The OLT's adjustable game and bird call (P. S. Olt, Pekin, Ill.) has proved successful in calling and decoying coyote, deer, bobcat, ground squirrel and chipmunk.

Tip—Squirrels, chipmunks, rabbits, may often be lured close by the sound made by clicking two small stones or two large coins together.

POSTING—Posting is the method of placing yourself in hiding at a strategic spot to which you expect the animal to come, sooner or later. It may be its home, its feeding ground, watering place, or runway. The top requirements for posting are time on your hands and infinite patience.

Be sure that the wind is in your face—and that it blows from the direction from which you think the animal will arrive. Otherwise, you will almost certainly wait in vain.

Sit down, make yourself comfortable. You can't concentrate on watching if you are in a strained position, worrying about keeping your balance or about a foot that is going to sleep.

BLINDS FOR POSTING—A blind is often of great advantage in posting. Construct it in the way you do a bird blind (see page 70). The location of it depends on the animal you are studying. The blind may have to be placed a hundred feet or more away from large, keen-sensed or suspicious animals, thirty feet from dens of medium-sized animals, a few feet only from the small, unsuspecting kinds.

TRACKING—Tracking is especially important for locating the larger animals—deer, elk, moose, bear—although it will often help you to find the homes of others.

TYPES OF TRACKS—Shape and size of tracks will tell you what animals made them; their relative position, at what speed the animals traveled.

For tracking purposes, animals fall into four categories:

LONG LEGGERS—Animals with comparatively long legs of about equal length—members of deer, cat, and dog families, for instance. Tracks are comparatively far apart, generally form a zigzag line. Tracks of hind feet often fall in forefeet tracks.

SHORT-AND-LONG—Rabbits, hares, squirrels, certain mice, with very short forelegs and long hind legs, move

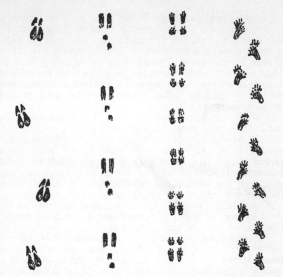

The four main patterns of animal tracks, from left: the long leggers, the short-and-long, the short leggers, the fatties.

in jumps. They usually make paired tracks of hind feet in front of paired tracks of forefeet.

SHORT LEGGERS—Martens, weasels, minks, and otters with long slender bodies and short legs bound along. In walking, tracks of hind feet are made behind tracks of forefeet. In running, hind feet may fall into tracks of forefeet, or even ahead of them.

FATTIES—Animals with thick bodies and comparatively short legs—raccoon, bear, porcupine, beaver, woodchuck, skunk—waddle along, flat footedly. Their tracks usually form two lines, with the imprints close together. When these animals pick up speed, they proceed in short jumps, placing forefeet and hind feet in paired tracks.

Familiarize yourself with the different tracks so that you will know which animals made them, as you find them in soft ground or snow.

BOOKS ON TRACKS—Ellsworth Jaeger. *Tracks and Trailcraft*. The Macmillan Company.

Olaus Murie. *Field Guide to Animal Tracks*. Houghton Mifflin Company, Boston, Mass.

TRACKING TECHNIQUES—Before you start to follow a track for the purpose of getting close to an animal, be sure it is a fresh track. Otherwise you will have no luck. A fresh track has sharp edges, and no debris has fallen or been blown into it. Tracks show up especially well in sandy soil with little vegetation, in moist river banks, and along lake shores. Snow is perfect. It takes a considerable amount of skill to follow tracks on hard bare ground and in dead leaves.

If possible, track against the sun. The shadows in the tracks will make them show up clearly.

Walk at the side of the track you are following, not directly in it. Don't keep your nose in the track. Look up and ahead. It is often easy to see the track for quite a distance. Instead of moving slowly, looking at each imprint, you can move ahead quickly. And, incidentally, you may see the animal you are tracking ahead of you.

If you lose the track, try to imagine yourself in the place of the animal: "Where would I go from here?" Then investigate in that direction.

Move forward fast when the tracks show that the animal has been running. Slow down when the tracks slow down. When a deer starts zigzagging, for instance, it is usually a sign that it is looking for a place to bed down. You may be almost on top of it.

When you think you are close to the animal, stop, look, and listen. Do you see it? Then bring up your field glasses slowly to follow its actions.

STALKING—Tracking may locate an animal for you, but you have to resort to stalking (still-hunting) to get near enough to it for close observation.

Animals depend on their keen senses of smell and hearing to protect themselves. Some have sharp eyesight as well—others are nearsighted: They see movement, mainly, not details.

If an animal gets your scent or hears you, it may take flight immediately. Therefore, approach it carefully with the wind in your face. If you have discovered it from the wind side without disturbing it, make a semicircle around it before you proceed closer.

> *Tip*—To find the wind direction on a still day, wet a finger in your mouth. Hold it up. The side toward the wind will feel cooler. Or toss leaves in the wind and watch their drift.

Watch where you place your feet. The cracking of a dry twig may sound like a pistol shot. Soft ground, wet forest floor, and light snow are excellent for stalking. Dry leaves and crunchy snow make tough stalking.

If the animal detects you, "freeze" on the spot. It may move about to find out what scared it. If you are motionless, it may look directly at you without noticing you, then quiet down again.

Make good use of all available cover—trees that you can hide behind, stumps, rocks, culverts, hillocks, and mounds.

> *Tip*—Here's an old trick for bringing antelopes and some members of the deer family nearer to you. Tie a handkerchief to a stick and wave it slowly back and forth over your hiding place. The animals will approach to find out what is up.

ANIMAL LISTS AND SURVEYS

What animals are there in your territory? As you discover them, start keeping a list of them, adding to this record the observations you may make from time to time.

LIFE LISTS—The simplest way of making a life list is to note down in the margin of your field book—opposite to the name of the animal—the date when you first discovered evidence of its presence and the date when you actually saw it for the first time. There is quite a difference between the two—you will almost certainly find evidence of fox, for example (den, scat, food remains), long before you actually see this elusive critter.

The only way in which you can find out what small animals—mice, shrews, and the like—live in your area will be by trapping them.

SURVEYS—In addition to knowing *what* animals are around, it is important for good wildlife management to find out *how many*. As an individual, you may be able to make a valuable contribution in this respect; but your work can be even more ambitious if you can secure the co-operation of a club or a youth group. Get in touch with your state game department for suggestions, and co-ordinate your efforts with the work already underway in your state.

REFERENCES—Arthur H. Carhart. *Hunting with a Lead Pencil*. Sportsman's Club Bulletin, Sports Afield Magazine, 405 Second Avenue South, Minneapolis 1, Minn.
Reuben Edwin Trippensee. *Wildlife Management*. McGraw-Hill Book Company.

LIVE-TRAP CENSUS—A census by live trapping can be used to find the population in a small area, such as a wood lot, or in a sample section of a larger area, of mice, rats, squirrels, skunks, opossums, raccoons, and a few other animals. You need a great number of live traps to do the job properly—80 or more for the small animals, 40 or more for the larger. For their construction, see pages 118 to 122.

Set out the traps to cover thoroughly the area you are investigating. In some cases, a checkerboard arrangement is preferable—setting out 81 traps, for instance, in 9 rows of 9 each, evenly spaced. Where the territory does not adapt itself to this method, arrange the traps in the way you find most suitable. In any event, the spacing between the traps is important. Some of the medium-sized and small animals range over several hundred yards, others over a few yards only. Find out about the range of the animals you have under study from your own observations and preliminary trappings, or from books on the subject. Then place 3 or 4 traps per range diameter. Mark each trap in such a way that you can easily find it. Number the traps, and make a sketch map of their location.

Check the traps every morning, and mark or tag the animals caught. Make a record of each animal, and note the trap in which it was caught. Then set the animal free.

Note—When setting traps for diurnal animals, make certain that they are shaded. Otherwise, a trapped animal will suffer unnecessarily.

Marking of small animals may be done by toe clipping or ear punching, or by ear tagging with fingerling tags. Develop your own code system, or use one of the Blair codes (W. Frank Blair: "Techniques for the Study of Mammal Populations." *Journal of Mammalogy.* Vol. 22, no. 2, 1941, pp. 148-157).

Larger animals can be ear-tagged with numbered metal tags. Attach them with the special clincher designed for them. Bats may be arm-banded with the type of bands used for birds.

SUPPLIES—Salt Lake Stamp Company, 43 W. Broadway, Salt Lake City 1, Utah.

The first trapping will tell you a bit about the animal population. A second trapping performed shortly afterward will tell you much more. By applying to it the collection ratio formula, you will arrive at a rough animal count: Total animal population is equal to the number of all animals in second trapping, multiplied by number of marked animals in first trapping, divided by number of marked animals retrapped in second trapping.

SURROUNDS—A "surround" or "drive" is just what those words imply. It is a group project for up to a hundred men, or even more, used effectively to determine deer populations.

Lay out the area to be surveyed—a quarter square mile or a full square mile, depending on the terrain and number of men. Arrange the "counters"—the men who will do the counting—along the three sides of the square, close enough together so that each man can see the nearest person on either side of him. Form a line of "drivers" along the fourth side. On a signal, the drivers move forward, driving the deer within the square before them. As the deer break through the line of counters, each counter counts the deer that run to the right of him, between himself and the counter on his right. The combined counts give you the actual deer population in the square surveyed.

If the surveyed area is a truly representative section of a larger area, the population of this area can be estimated by simple arithmetic.

In addition to deer, the surround may be employed to survey fox, coyote or prairie wolf, and cottontail.

FIELD OBSERVATIONS

In spite of all the studying of animals that has gone on over the years, our knowledge of life histories and relationships is still amazingly incomplete. Suggestions for field observations are therefore almost limitless.

HOME RANGE—How far the animals range, as indicated by their homes, runways, scat, feeding marks, and by observation on marked animals.

MATING—How are mates selected? Courtship; fighting among males? How long do mates stay together?

YOUNG—How many litters a year? How many to a litter? How are young cared for? How long do they remain with mother?

DISPOSITION AND BEHAVIOR—Skulking, playful, curious, and so on. Reaction to sounds, odors, movements.

CALLS—What calls have they? Alarm, challenge, courting, and others.

TRACKS—Special study of individual imprints and of imprints in relation to each other. How do distances between imprints change at various speeds? Size of tracks as related to size, sex, age.

Tip—Make sketches of tracks. Simplest way is to place piece of glass or sheet of plastic over track and draw its outline with crayon or marking pencil. Transfer the outline to paper, rub crayon lines off glass and use again.

MIGRATIONS—Any evidence of migration? Where to; where from? Dates of appearance and disappearance.

HIBERNATION AND AESTIVATION—Local animals that hibernate or aestivate. What is the last date of appearance, first date of emerging?

> *Tip*—A simple way of discovering the movement of an animal into and out of its burrow is to place a light crisscross layer of fine sticks over the entrances. Visit the place regularly to see if twigs have been displaced.

EYE REFLECTIONS—The tapetum layer in the retina of the eyes of some animals has the power to reflect the light from a flashlight or headlight, for instance, with a luminous glow. The color of the reflection varies with the animal—red in the case of opossum and bear, orange in deer, green among members of the cat family. What colors are the eye-glow—*chatoyancy*—of other animals?

SPECIAL PROBLEMS—Relationships between animals and their surroundings. Relationships between animals and man—effect of man's activities in lumbering, draining, farming.

REFERENCE—Walter P. Taylor. *Outlines for the Study of Mammalian Ecology and Life Histories.* Wildlife Leaflet 304. Fish and Wildlife Service, U. S. Department of the Interior, Washington, D. C.

Wild Animals in Captivity

The ideal place for studying the activities, behavior, and intelligence of animals is, of course, their natural habitat. But wild animals in the field have a way of non-co-operating. They simply disappear. To find out more about them, it is often necessary to study them in captivity. This is generally a matter of trapping, caging, and keeping your captives healthy as long as the studies last.

In many states, it is unlawful to capture animals outside of the regular hunting season for the different species. Some states require you to take out a special license to hold wild animals captive. So, before you decide what animals to keep, find out what your state laws have to say, then follow them scrupulously.

BOOKS—Clifford E. Moore. *The Book of Wild Pets.* Chas. Branford Co., Newton Centre 59, Mass.

Roy Pinney. *Golden Book of Wild Animal Pets.* Golden Press.

TRAPS

The traps used by fur trappers are of no use to you. They usually kill or maim. Those for your purpose are referred to as live-catch traps. They are available commercially, in many different designs and sizes, at rather reasonable prices. Some of them may be had in two forms—regular and collapsible.

SUPPLIES—National Live Trap Co. Tomahawk, Wisconsin (medium sizes).

Havahart, 1911 Water Street, Ossining, N. Y. (medium sizes).

H. J. Spencer, P. O. Box 131, Gainesville, Fla. (small size).

Instead of buying traps, you can follow in the steps of such pioneers in the development of humane traps as Bailey, Evans, and Hatt, and make up your own.

TRAPS FOR SMALL ANIMALS—Traps for mice, shrews, and other small animals can be made from tin cans, pieces of wire mesh, even from milk bottles.

SNAP TRAP—The snap trap described by Hatt is one of the most effective. It makes use of the traditional mousetrap, a No. 2 tin can, wire, and a piece of ¼-inch wire mesh (hardware cloth).

Somewhere along the top edge of the tin can, make a rectangular cut the size and shape of the trap trigger. Wire the can to the base of the trap with the trigger

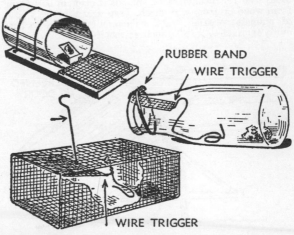

A live trap for a small animal may be produced from a mousetrap and a can, from a milk bottle, or from ¼-inch wire mesh.

fitting into this cut. Wire a piece of wire mesh, cut to size, over the square loop of the spring. Set the trap the way you would the ordinary mousetrap. When sprung, the wire mesh keeps the animal closed up in the can.

MILK BOTTLE TRAP—For this trap, suggested by Bailey, cut a piece of wire mesh to a size of $1 \times 3\frac{1}{2}$ inches. Bend up 1 inch at one end. Bring the straight end into the milk bottle, and fit the bent part over the edge of the bottle. Hold it in position with a couple of rubber bands around the bottle neck. Make a trigger from an 8-inch piece of no. 16 wire. Bend one end of it into a swanlike neck-head-bill, the other into a double loop, ending in a point. Push the wire-mesh door open and insert the wire so that the bottom of the door rests perilously on the "swan's" bill. When touched, the wire falls over, and the trap snaps shut.

CAN TRAP—Almost any size can—square or round—can be turned into a trap. Cut a swing door from a piece of tin, slightly longer, up and down, than the opening of the can. Hang the door at the top with two wire rings in such a way that the bottom of it fits about an inch inside the can. Set the trap by suspending the door on a "swan's-neck" wire tripper as used in the milk bottle trap, or use method suggested for swinging door trap on page 119.

TRAPS FOR MEDIUM-SIZED ANIMALS—The usual trap for medium-sized animals is made in box form, from wood or from wire mesh. Trap sizes vary with sizes of animals: weasels, rats, chipmunk—$6 \times 6 \times 18$ inches; mink, squirrel—$7 \times 7 \times 20$ inches; rabbit—$9 \times 9 \times 24$ inches;

SCREENED DOOR

Tripper of figure-4 trap is put together from three whittled sticks. Box has a screened door for removal of captive.

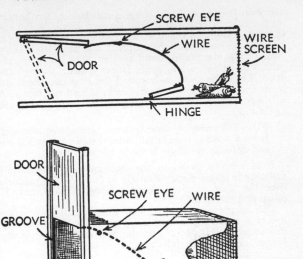

The swinging-door trap (top), and the falling-door trap (bottom) may be made from wood or from coarse wire mesh.

woodchuck, raccoon, skunk, opossum—11×11×36 inches; fox—12×12×48 inches.

FIGURE-4 TRAP—The old-fashioned figure-4 trap is as good as ever. It consists of a box, held up at one edge by three whittled sticks fitted together by their notches. The general design is shown in the diagram on page 120. The length of the sticks depends on the size of the box to be supported. When the bait is touched, the whole structure collapses.

> *Tip*—Place the trap on a board floor so that the animal cannot dig itself out. To prevent the captured animal from moving the trap, place a stone on top of the box, for extra weight.

SWINGING DOOR TRAP—Form a piece of wire mesh into a square tunnel. Close one end with mesh. Fit a piece of tin, as a door, into the opposite end. Cut it slightly larger, up and down, than the tunnel opening. Fasten it at the top with two wire rings. Make a nail hole at the bottom of the door. Attach a stiff wire through this hole and run it through the trap roof. At the roof line, make a double bend in the wire that will prevent the door from being raised from the inside. Bend another wire into a trigger with a short and a long arm. Bring it down through the roof. Twist the short end around the long one. Bend the short end to hold up the door. Bend the long end into such a shape that an animal entering the trap will brush against it.

Tip—The swinging door trap can be made equally well from a wooden box. It will attract more animals if the end opposite the door is made of wire mesh.

FALLING-DOOR TRAP—In the falling-door type of trap, the door is raised perpendicularly in two grooved supports over the door opening. When tripped, it falls straight down and closes the trap.

One of the simplest forms of this type of trap makes use of a treadle (see diagram page 121). When the animal steps on this, the trigger holding up the door is dislodged, and the door falls down.

TRAPS FOR LARGE ANIMALS—Bears are caught in log pens. Deer are taken in specially constructed traps or corrals. Other large animals are captured by highly specialized procedures—ranging from lassoing them to catching them in pit traps. Those are jobs for professionals. Few amateurs will ever have reason or occasion to do them.

TRAPPING

The trap is only part of it. Next come the steps of setting it where the animals are and baiting it with food they like.

PLACING THE TRAP—Investigate your countryside and locate burrows, nests, and runways. Place your traps in strategic positions nearby.

In the field, animals often move along low fences, strips of cover. In the woods, they keep close to fallen logs, trunks of trees. Along waterways are places where animals come down to drink. All are good trap locations.

BAITING—Small animals—rodents especially—are attracted by rolled oats, doughnut crumbs, peanut butter, raisins, small pieces of fried bacon—served separately or mixed together.

Larger vegetarians like bananas, apples, carrots, turnips, corn.

Such delicacies as dead mice, chicken heads, and fish heads may attract skunk and raccoon. Mink and weasel may fall for chunks of meat. Dried salted herring keeps well in traps and often proves an effective bait.

The majority of animals like salty things—potato chips, salted peanuts.

Tip—Throw a few samples of the bait outside the trap entrance as a "come-on."

You can learn only by experience what baits will attract the animals of your locality. Even then, don't be too disappointed if you don't catch the animal your trap is baited for, but possibly an entirely different one. You may have better luck next time.

TRANSFERRING THE CATCH—When an animal is caught, slip a sack over the mouth of the trap. Open the trap inside the sack and shake out the animal. Then transfer it from the sack to its cage.

CAGES AND CAGE HEALTH

In deciding on a cage for your captive, you have three important points to consider: size, comfort, and cleanliness.

The *size* of the cage depends on the size of the animal, its habits, and the study you intend to do. In general, the size should be sufficient to give the animal a chance to get a fair amount of exercise.

Comfort to most animals means protection against drafts and bad weather, and, especially in outdoor cages, provision for a spot to nestle down to sleep, lined with dry grass, strips of paper toweling, cotton, rope fibre.

Cleanliness in small cages may be achieved with a layer of sawdust or sand that can be readily renewed. It simplifies matters to provide such cages with a floor tray of

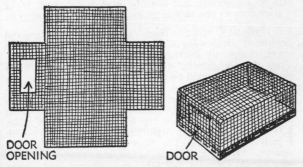

DOOR OPENING

DOOR

Quarter-inch hardware cloth (wire mesh) is a good material for making up simple observation cages for small animals.

sheet metal that can be pulled out for cleaning. In large cages, the floor may consist of a slightly sloping cement surface that can be washed clean with a garden hose.

Tip—Practically all wild animals are infested with fleas and other pests. Dust them as soon after capture as possible with an insect powder.

INDOOR CAGES—Cages for indoor studies are available from biological supply houses and from many pet shops. They range in floor sizes from 8×9 inches to about 2×3 feet.

SUPPLIES—Laboratory cages. Bussey Products Co., 6000 West 51st Street, Chicago 28, Illinois.

SMALL INDOOR CAGES—Cages for mice may be made out of ¼-inch hardware cloth (wire mesh). For a simple cage, cut a piece of hardware cloth into a top with the four sides attached (see page 123). Bend down the sides, and wire the corner edges together. Staple this structure to the sides of a piece of board. Cut a square hole in one end of the cage, large enough for your hand. Cut a piece of wire mesh to fit as a door over this hole. Hinge it in position with wire rings.

Other types of small cages may be made along the lines of the snake cages suggested on page 157. If your captives are rodents, line the inside with hardware cloth to prevent them from gnawing their way out. If you like, you can install a floor tray to be pulled out for cleaning.

LARGE INDOOR CAGES—Make a framework of 1×2-inch or 2×2-inch wood. Cover with ¼-inch hardware cloth or with ½-inch or 1-inch poultry wire, depending on the size of the animal that is to be kept in the cage. Make a wire door in one side large enough for you to reach in.

OUTDOOR CAGES—There is no end to the sizes and designs of outdoor cages. They may take the form of true cages, completely enclosed, or as screened-in enclosures. They may be directly on the ground or raised with a slightly sloping wood or cement floor. If possible, imitate the natural surroundings of your captives.

ENCLOSED CAGES—For squirrels, flying squirrels, raccoons, porcupines, and opossums make a frame from 2×2-inch lumber or rustic poles, at least 4 feet wide, 4 feet long, and 6 feet high. Enclose top and sides with 1 inch chicken wire. The floor can be of wood, mesh, cement, or the ground itself. In the latter case, the chicken wire should extend 1 to 2 feet below ground level. Cover the top with roofing paper. Place some stout branches inside the cage before you close it up. Make a door on

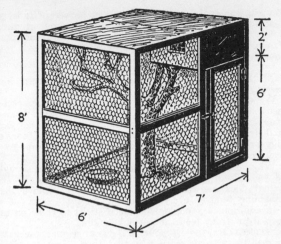

Make an outdoor wire cage to fit your needs. The size above is
suitable for squirrels, raccoons, and opossums.

one side for entrance for cleaning and feeding. Fasten a
nesting box inside at the top.

Cages for foxes, rabbits, minks, and weasels may be
constructed in a similar manner but need not be as high
—4 to 5 feet high for foxes, 2 feet for minks. Fasten
nesting box on the outside, at ground level.

ENCLOSURES—For animals which do not usually attempt
to escape by climbing, a completely enclosed cage is not
necessary. Instead, make a wire enclosure or run.

Chipmunks, ground squirrels, and prairie dogs require
a soil floor for making their burrows. Special precautions
are necessary to keep them from digging themselves out.
Start your construction by digging a hole in the ground
the size of the enclosure, to a depth of 2 to 3 feet. Place
uprights in the corners for the frame, and line the sides
with galvanized chicken wire. Pour in a thin layer of
cement—1 inch or so. Throw the dirt back in, and finish
the above-ground part of the enclosure. No nesting boxes
inside.

For deer, use 8-foot wire fencing, stretched between
strong posts. Erect an open-front shelter within the enclosure, to protect the animals in inclement weather. The
open side should be to the lee side of prevailing winter
winds.

If you have a brook running through your grounds, you

can make an enclosure for muskrats or beavers. Use wire fencing. Put it up so that it extends 4 feet above ground, 2 feet under ground for beavers, 4 feet for muskrats. Provide a large supply of branches, sticks, and reeds for house construction.

FEEDING—Proper feeding is your main concern for keeping your animals healthy.

WHAT TO FEED—Check the food habits of your specimens in Anthony's *Field Book of North American Mammals,* and do your best to provide them the food they eat in their wild state. If that isn't possible, follow Moore's suggestions in *The Book of Wild Pets,* or do some experimenting of your own.

Whatever the feed is, be sure it is fresh. Greens should be young and succulent, meat absolutely fresh. If an animal does not eat all that you give it, remove the remaining food before it spoils.

In addition to food, rodents need sticks to chew on to keep their front teeth at normal length.

FEEDING CHARTS—Do your feedings at regular intervals so that the animals learn to expect them. Some animals are interested in one daily meal only, others require frequent feedings.

Keep track of the feedings on a chart attached to the cage of the animal, or in a record book, with a page for each specimen. The notes should include name of animal, date, time of feeding, kind of food, amount given, amount eaten.

The feeding charts will tell you the foods that appeal to your animals, and the amounts they require. The charts will also quickly show you when an animal is "off its feed" and may require special attention.

WATER—Have water available at all times. Some animals dirty up their water supply very quickly and need to have it replenished frequently.

TAMING ANIMALS

Many of your captives will tame easily and will make interesting pets.

The main tricks for taming are food and your personal touch. Use some appealing tidbits for a bribe to get your captives to come close to you and to get accustomed to your presence. They will soon learn that they have nothing to fear from you and will approach you boldly.

Small rodents will quickly get enough confidence to climb right into your hand for a treat of nut meats. Chipmunks, squirrels, minks, will take the food from your fingers.

Some of the medium-sized animals may eventually let

themselves be picked up and will clamber all over you. This is especially the case if you get them young. Young raccoons, opossums, and skunks make good pets—skunks only, though, if you have no dogs around. These pets often become tame enough to be given the run of the house. When they grow older, they can not always be depended on. They may become destructive, snappy. That is the time to return them to their cages, or better, to let them loose.

Tip—Skunks may be "de-natured" by having their two scent glands removed. It is a simple process—especially if done while the animal is only a month or two months old. The operation may be undertaken by a local veterinarian. This operation does not seem to affect a skunk's health, but, of course, deprives it forever of its natural weapon.

Animal Photography

Photographing wild mammals is probably the toughest assignment you can have in the whole field of nature photography. To get close enough to a wild animal in the daytime to "shoot" it, you need all the skills of an expert stalker. To take the shot at night, you need the qualifications of an amateur engineer for rigging up a suitable flash arrangement. To add the larger animals to your collection you will have to be an inveterate traveler and frequent visitor to national parks and game preserves.

There are certain shortcuts and tricks that may simplify the job for you. Nevertheless, if you succeed in getting a number of good animal shots, you have every reason to be proud of your accomplishments.

STILLS

EQUIPMENT—American mammals range in size from the 3-inch-long little shrew to the moose with a shoulder height of six feet or more. Some of them approach your camera fearlessly, others must be pursued into the highest, wildest type of mountain territory. It is evident that you must either limit your photographing to animals that fit the scope of your camera—or get equipment that will suit all types.

CAMERA AND LENSES—If yours is an ordinary snapshot camera, you may be able to get successful shots of our larger animals, and with portrait attachment and flash gun some of our medium-sized night prowlers.

For more extensive photography you require a better camera—whether miniature, view, or reflex—with shutter speeds from time to 1/500 of a second. You also need a fast lens because much of your work will have to be done under poor light conditions. A telephoto lens will be a great advantage—not just for that antelope at 200 yards, but also for the white-footed mouse that scampers along almost underfoot.

OTHER EQUIPMENT—For remote control and nighttime flash-gun photography a *tripod* is indispensable. It is of little use for daylight open-range photography. You must be able to move your camera freely and quickly in order to follow the actions of your subject—by the time you have a tripod set up and the camera focused, the animal will be out of range. Instead, learn to take a firm stance with your elbows against your chest when standing, arms as steady supports when lying prone. By attaching your camera to a *gunstock base,* it will be possible for you to handle and aim it as a gun. Such a gunstock base is particularly desirable when you use a telephoto lens.

For photographing at night, you have the choice between a separate *flash gun,* for open-flash shots, and a gun synchronized with your camera.

You may need to buy or rig up a *remote-control release* or a trip release—depending upon the kind of photography you intend to do.

FILMS AND EXPOSURES—For photographing animals grazing peacefully out in the open sun, you can use slow films—black and white or color—and slow exposures— 1/20 to 1/60 of a second. Animals on the run may have to be shot at 1/500 to stop their action.

Most animals keep in hiding during the day. They prefer twilight and cover. To take them under those conditions, you will need a supersensitive film and often a wide-open lens.

For flash-gun night shots, you can again make use of a wide range of black-and-white and color films.

BOOK ON ANIMAL PHOTOGRAPHY—Sam Dunton. *Guide to Photographing Animals.* Chilton Company, Philadelphia 29, Penn.

DAYTIME PHOTOGRAPHY—The most important features in animal photography are knowing where the animals are, and the skill to get close to them. All the tricks you learned while studying animals in the field will come into play (pages 110 to 115).

Many small animals can be brought close to the camera by *attracting.* Pocket gophers, chipmunks, squirrels can be led right up to the camera by a trail of bread crumbs or peanuts. Focus on the feeding place.

If you have discovered the runways or the den of an animal, you can get its picture by *posting.* Place yourself in a strategic position from which you can watch the approach of the animal. Or put up a blind, as for bird

A gunstock base is better than a tripod in "shooting" animals. It keeps the camera steady, yet permits great ease of movement.

photography and hide in it. Focus on a likely spot. When the animal gets within range, press the shutter release.

You may have even better success if you place the camera itself in position on a tripod close to where the animal will be. Focus it, and attach to its shutter a remote-control release—tube and bulb, electrical or home-made gadget (see pages 97 and 130). Retire to a hidden location as far away as the release permits. Then wait.

For the larger animals you may have to resort to *stalking*. This is particularly the case if you have no telephoto lens—you have to get very close to get a satisfactory picture. With a telephoto lens you can often get good results shooting from a distance of 100 feet or more.

> *Tip*—It takes no stalking skill to photograph animals from an automobile. Nevertheless, you may sometimes succeed in getting within shooting range. Use the opportunity.

In ordinary stalking the main precaution is to approach the animal against the wind. The same holds true, of course, in photographic stalking, but in addition, you have to watch the light. The sun should be at your back or to one side—back-lighted models are poor subjects.

> *Tip*—Just before shooting, make a squeak with your lips, similar to the sound used for attracting birds (see page 63). The squeak will startle the animal and make it look your way, may even stop its flight for a moment.

NIGHT PHOTOGRAPHY—Successful night photography depends on reliable flash-gun equipment. Use tri-

pods for setting up camera and flash gun in a likely spot
—a runway or a feeding place.

Tip—Flash gun should be to the side and slightly
above camera, to give good modeling of the animal.
Flash guns attached to the camera will give poor results—an animal looking into the flash when it goes
off will seem to have blind eyes because of the eyes'
"cat's-eye" reflection.

You can set off the flash yourself by remote control.
Or you can have the animal do it by touching a bait or
trip string.

AUTOMATIC TRIPPER—An ordinary 5-cent mousetrap can
be the main item in an electrical tripping gadget—for setting off cameras with electrically operated synchroniza-
tion, for activating a solenoid coil for pushing the shutter
release of a camera with synchronized flash gun, or for
setting off the flash gun in open flash photography. Attach the mousetrap to a small post. Point the post to
make it easy to drive it into the ground. Connect one wire
from flash gun or solenoid to the spring of the trap, the
other wire to a brass plate or brass screw fastened to
the trap's baseboard at such a location that it will be hit
by the spring loop (see diagram below). Set up your
camera, then, working *without bulb in the flash gun,* tie
a small loop (slipknot or bowline) in the end of a string
and slip the loop loosely over the release of the unset trap.
Lead the string through a screw eye on the trap, and on
through screw eyes in pegs placed in the ground, either
to the feeding place, tying the end of the string to a piece
of bait here, or across the runway, tying it to a firm support on the other side. Go back over the layout, set the
trap, place a bulb in the flash gun, open the camera if you
are using open flash, and retire to wait for the flash to be
set off. When flash has occurred, go back to the camera
to reset it, or close it.

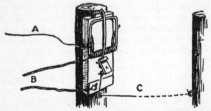

Two uses of a mousetrap for automatic tripping: A. String tied
to shutter lever. B. Electrical wiring; top wire from spring, bottom wire from brass plate that will be hit when trap is sprung.
(C is thread leading across runway or to bait).

Tip—If you have no flash gun, you can still take your flash shot, by wiring a regular lamp base to two flashlight batteries and to the mousetrap trigger described above.

SHOTS OF CAPTIVE ANIMALS—It is exceedingly difficult to get good shots in the wild of our smallest animals—mice, shrews, and the like. You will have better luck if you capture them first, then photograph them in a glass-surrounded enclosure, against a naturally arranged background, either in the open or indoors, in sunlight or under artificial light. Take these pictures at as fast a speed as lens and film allow. Use of flash will permit shorter exposure with smaller diaphragm, thus giving more depth of focus.

TRACK PHOTOGRAPHS—Photographs of animal tracks in mud or snow can be developed into a unique feature.

Take the shots from an angle of 45 degrees, with a fairly low forenoon or afternoon sun hitting them from top left, if at all possible. By a queer fluke of the human eye—or mind—tracks lighted in other ways seem to pop up instead of appearing depressed.

Tip—For tracks in snow, take light-meter reading directly on the snow, then double the indicated exposure for details in the shadows.

MOVIES

The usual run of animal movies falls into three types: 1. semitame animals in our national parks—bears in Yellowstone, antelopes and elk in Jackson Hole, buffaloes in various game refuges, and so on; 2. more or less tame animal pets—raccoons, skunks, opossums; 3. captive animals photographed in their cages. The technique for taking such movies is the usual one of long shots, medium shots and close-ups.

For really wild animals, the suggestions for daylight stills apply. You will need a telephoto lens, a firm support—preferably a gunstock base—ample tracking skill, and a goodly amount of patience.

Some animals may be photographed around their dens or feeding places by setting up the standard-lensed camera and releasing the shutter by remote control—by a string run from the release lever through screw eyes attached to small posts in the ground to your hiding place, for instance.

The difficulty with nearby movie taking—as against telephoto shooting—is that the sound of the motor almost invariably scares the animal away. The only way to overcome this is to get it accustomed to the sound. To do this, run the camera a number of times without film. When the sound no longer bothers the animal, put the film in the camera and take your scene.

Animal Collections

The notion that a naturalist's home should look like a museum, with stuffed animals on shelves and pedestals, has long been outdated. Although you may eventually want to try your hand at preparing a hunting trophy or mounting a medium-sized animal according to the best traditions of taxidermy, there are many other types of collecting that will help you to increase your knowledge of animals and their ways.

Track Casts

Track casting is one of the best and easiest means of keeping track—literally—of the animals in a certain territory. For this you use the track itself as a mold, filling it with a liquid that hardens as it sets or cools.

To be a true picture of a track, the final cast should be a *positive*—it should show the track as it actually is, a depression. You can't make such a cast directly. You have to go through the step of making a *negative* first—showing the track as a raised hump. This negative can then be used to make the positive.

Negatives are made in the field, positives usually at home.

If you are satisfied to do what most track collectors do —to stick to negatives—your best material is a good grade of plaster of Paris. On the other hand, if you have your mind set on positive casts, you will be better off using paraffin or some other meltable material. The reason is that a number of the tracks you find, especially in soft ground, will be so deeply undercut that you will not be able to separate plaster negative from plaster positive without damaging both. A paraffin negative can be melted out of the plaster positive made in it, in a warm oven.

TRACK CASTING—THE NEGATIVE—Start off by finding a good track. Don't be satisfied with the first track you see. Mark it with a stick, then look around—there may be a much better track near by. If there isn't you can always return to the first one.

You will, of course, take your tracks where you find them. But it pays to search for them in soil that takes impressions especially well—in clayish soil after rain or thaw, in the silt along the lake shore. Tracks of small animals are often found in profusion in dried-up drainage ditches.

Dry leaves, weed seeds, and the like may have fallen into the track after the animal made it. Prepare the track for casting by picking up such debris carefully with your fingers or with forceps, or blow them out with your mouth or with a rubber bulb.

During the winter, you may come on especially clear tracks in hard-packed snow. You may have fair success in preparing such a track for casting—provided you are out in subfreezing weather. Using an atomizer, spray a film of ice-cold water in the track and permit it to freeze. Build up a thin ice shell in this manner to take the cast material.

PLASTER OF PARIS CASTS—For plaster casts, you need a couple of pounds of plain plaster of Paris—patching plaster sets too slowly—a container for water, a cup or tin can for mixing, a stick for stirring, cardboard strips, 1 inch wide, 15 to 18 inches long.

Make a cardboard collar of one of the strips to fit around the track. Hold the two ends of the strip together, with a pin or clip. Or make a halfway-down tear in one end, about ½ inch from the end, a halfway-up tear in the other, and lock the two tears together. Press the collar firmly into the ground, around the track.

Make a rough estimate of the amount of the plaster mixture you will need. Pour about one third of this amount of water into the mixing cup. Sprinkle plaster into the water *without stirring*—let's repeat—*without stirring*—until small "islands" start to form above the surface of the water—the proportion will be approximately 7 plaster to 4 water. Now stir the mixture gently with a stick—it is called "to spatulate"—until it is smooth and even. It should have the consistency of melted ice cream, pancake batter, light molasses—take your pick. If too thin, add a little more plaster. Bang your mixing cup

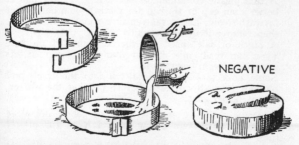

NEGATIVE

In making a negative plaster cast of an animal track, turn strip of cardboard into a collar by notching its ends together.

against the ground a few times to get air bubbles to rise and break. Or hit the side of the cup with the mixing stick for the same purpose.

Note—Usual mistake is to make the plaster mixture too thick. It should *flow,* not *drop!*

Pour the plaster mixture slowly into the track, and continue pouring until it fills the cardboard collar to about ¼ inch from the top. Smooth the surface with the stick or with your finger. Then let it set. While you wait, wash out your mixing cup before the remaining plaster hardens.

When the track cast has hardened somewhat, you can insert a wire loop in it for hanging, if you like. Also scratch on the back of it the name of the animal, date, and place, with a pencil point or sharpened stick. Add a number, and write in your notebook under that number other pertinent information: whether track is of front or hind leg, whether animal was walking or running, kind of soil, and so on.

Leave the cast to set for 20 to 30 minutes—go hunting for other tracks in the meantime and set a cast line the way a trapper sets a trap line. When the plaster has hardened loosen the earth around it with a stick, and lift up the cast with whatever dirt clings to it. Wrap in newspaper and bring home.

When completely dry, brush off the dirt with an old toothbrush. Or wash it under a faucet, then dry the cast again.

Tips—Instead of using cardboard collars, some collectors prefer collars cut from the sides of tin cans—round or bent square. Give the inside a coating of vaseline before using so that the cast will slip easily afterwards.

A thin plastic container or half a large rubber ball is better than cup or tin can for mixing. You don't need to wash it out. Leave the remaining plaster to harden, then remove it by squeezing.

A pinch of salt speeds up the hardening of the cast (you can ready-mix it into your dry plaster in advance)—vinegar retards it.

Some collectors sprinkle talcum into the track and blow it into all crevices, before pouring the plaster, for a cleaner cast.

PARAFFIN CASTS—Clear the track of debris and place a cardboard or tin-can collar around it as for plaster casting.

Melt paraffin (household wax) in a can over an open fire, or, simpler, on a gasoline, or "Heatab" stove. Don't overheat. Pour slowly into the track. The paraffin cools and hardens quickly. The cast can be removed within a few minutes. Undermine the track, and dig up the cast with adhering dirt. Wrap in newspaper. Keep cool in hot weather. Clean it when you get home.

Tip—In a pinch, you can use a candle stub instead of paraffin in a small track. Light the candle. Hold it horizontally and drip the hot candle grease into the track. Reinforce with twigs.

MOULAGE CASTS—Moulage is a composition with a low melting point, used by artists for making hand and face molds. You can get it through art supply stores.

Moulage casts are made in the same manner as paraffin casts.

Tip—You can make your own moulage by melting together while stirring two parts of rosin and one part of paraffin.

SULPHUR CASTS—Sulphur—flowers or lumps of sulphur roll—melts into a thin liquid at a temperature slightly above the boiling point for water and cools into a hard, but rather brittle, cast.

Melt and use as in paraffin casting.

Tip—Melted sulphur may be used in casting tracks in snow. Build up a small incline next to the track. Make a groove leading directly into the track. As soon as the sulphur has melted, take it off the heat. Cool until crystals start to form on the surface, then pour the sulphur into the groove from which it will flow into the track and set almost immediately.

TRACK CASTING—THE POSITIVE—To make a positive, use either a negative plaster cast *without undercuts,* or a negative of meltable material.

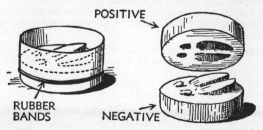

POSITIVE

RUBBER BANDS

NEGATIVE

To product a positive cast from a negative, fasten a high collar around the greased negative, then pour in the plaster.

MAKING THE CAST—If your plaster negative is suitable, prepare it for positive casting by brushing it with a thin layer of vaseline, linseed oil, soft soap, or melted paraffin. A paraffin or moulage negative needs no such preparation.

Cut a 3-inch strip of cardboard. Wrap this as a collar around the negative. Hold it in place with rubber bands.

Mix a batch of plaster-of-Paris batter. Pour it into the collar to a height of at least ½ inch above the highest hump of the negative. Put aside to set completely, for half an hour or more.

Separate the positive from the negative, if necessary by inserting a knife blade between them. If an undercut paraffin negative was used, remove as much of the paraffin as you can, and melt out the rest by placing the cast on a pan in a warm oven.

Leave the track surface intact. Trim down sides and back smoothly with an old knife, then sandpaper. Protect the cast by a thin coat of varnish or shellac. For a more naturalistic effect you can brush the track surface with diluted glue and sprinkle it with sand or dirt. Or you can paint it in an appropriate soil color, using a slightly darker shade in the track indentation.

ANIMAL TRACES

In addition to footprints, animals leave various traces as evidence of their presence. Some of these traces may be incorporated in your collection.

ANIMAL-MARKED TREES—In beaver territory, you can find beaver-cut branches of varying thicknesses, showing the marks of strong front teeth. Woodchucks cut off small seedlings by a clear pruning; browsing deer, elk, moose with fuzzy, uneven cuts. Small gnaw marks running at all angles indicate various mice—pine mouse if below the root collar. Complete girdling with well-defined tooth marks show the porcupine as the culprit.

Other types of markings are the claw scratches of bear, bark fibres torn loose by rubbing deer antlers.

All such animal-marked tree parts may be trimmed to convenient length and wired to plywood panels for display.

REFERENCE—John Pearce. *Identifying Injury by Wildlife to Trees and Shrubs in Northeastern Forests.* U. S. Department of Interior, Fish and Wildlife Service, Research Report 13, 15 cents. Superintendent of Documents, Washington 25, D. C.

GNAWED NUTS AND CONES—If you come upon a heap of nut shells on an old stump, you can be pretty certain that you are in a squirrel "dining room." If the shells are broken in pieces, the evidence is conclusive.

Two or three holes in a nut indicate a mouse. Look at the teeth marks. After gnawing a small opening, some mice gnaw from the inside out with their lower teeth, keeping the upper teeth steady against the outside of the nut; others gnaw from the outside in with their snouts in the hole. Which do what?

Pine and fir cones with scales torn off carelessly suggest squirrel; chewed off smoothly, mouse.

SCAT—Scat or droppings may seem peculiar items for collecting. Nevertheless, they often provide the only readily found evidence of the presence of animals, especially in rocky territory where tracks are not easily seen.

The droppings of *wild vegetarians* are generally found as piles of "beans." The beans of rabbit are coffee-bean size, oval, dark brown; those of hares almost globular. Deer beans are black-glazed, long-oval, uneven, hazel-nut size, sometimes flattened at one end and usually pointed at the other.

The scat of *meat eaters* and *omnivores* are dropped in more coherent form. Droppings of mice are tiny, black, spindle shaped. Scat of weasel, mink, and marten are cylindrical, black, containing feathers, hair, and bone splinters. Otter scat is tarlike, with fish bones and crayfish remains. Fox droppings are finger thick, cylindrical, usually pointed at both ends. They contain a mixture of feathers, hair, bones, beetle wings, and fruit seeds.

If you specialize in "scatology," bear in mind that scat are subject to insect attack. Keep in closed containers, with a few crystals of paradichlorobenzene.

REFERENCE—Olaus Murie's *Field Guide to Animal Tracks* (see page 113) contains excellent drawings of scat, claw marks and gnaw marks and other animal traces, as well as illustrations of animal homes.

ANIMAL SPECIMENS

Large animals can usually be identified in the field. But it is different with the small animals. We have more than a hundred different species and subspecies of pocket gopher, for instance, many of which can only be told apart by close comparison. Similarly, we have more than seventy different meadow mice, more than sixty shrews, around fifty white-footed mice. Some of these species are confined to certain clearly defined geographical locations, but there may be several kinds in your neighborhood, though in different habitats. The way to ascertain which they are is to trap them, measure them, study their colorings, check their skull shape and teeth arrangement. The skins should then be treated and kept for future reference and study.

STUDY SKINS—A study skin is prepared by removing the skin carefully, impregnating it with a chemical that will protect it against deterioration and insect attacks, stuffing it with cotton and drying it.

REFERENCES—*Field Collector's Manual.* Smithsonian Institution, Washington, D. C.

Morris Miller Wells. *Collection and Preservation of Animal Forms.* General Biological Supply House.

R. M. Anderson. *Methods of Collecting and Preserving Vertebrate Animals.* Bulletin No. 69, National Museum of Canada, Ottawa, Canada.

TAKING NOTES—Before skinning, make up two labels, one for the skin, the other for the skull, with notes on the animal: where found, date, finder. Include the main measurements. Stretch out the animal and take its length from snout to tail tip, take the length of the tail from base to tip, and of the hind foot from heel to point of longest toenail.

Also place the animal on a piece of white paper and draw an outline of the body, not the fur. This sketch will help you later.

SKINNING—Place the animal on its back. Make a slit in the skin from a point just ahead of the vent to the breastbone. Be careful not to puncture the belly cavity. With the fingers, free the skin from the flesh the whole way around the body. Use a knife or scalpel only if the flesh sticks. Have on hand a package of oatmeal. Use the meal generously to absorb blood and other body liquids.

Loosen the skin from one of the hind legs. Pull the leg up, sever at the knee joint, and scrape the bone between knee and heel clean of flesh. Treat the other hind leg in the same manner.

Cut carefully around the vent, then loosen the skin around the base of the tail. Pull out the tail bones with the fingers of one hand while holding on to the tail skin at its base with the other.

Grasp the hind legs with one hand and with the other pull the skin carefully off the body, turning it inside out, until you reach the forelegs. Treat them the way you did the hind legs.

The skin usually pulls readily over the neck. Your next trouble spot is at the ears. Cut close to the skull with scalpel or scissors. Do the same when you reach the eye sockets. Be particularly careful here so that you keep the eyelids intact. Cut around the lips, and finally release the skin completely by snipping through the cartilage of the nose.

Keep the skull—or possibly the whole carcass—for further treatment (see page 141).

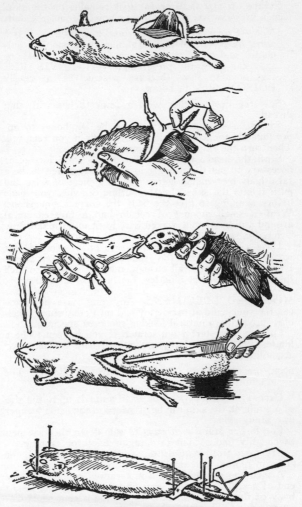

Five steps in preparing a study skin (based on suggestions of members of the staff of the Smithsonian Institution). Stuff the prepared skin with cotton. Pin down the stuffed animal to dry in recommended fashion for study skins.

Scrape off any flesh or fat that remains on the skin. Rub a preservative, such as borax powder, into the skin.

Note—Professionals usually use a mixture of two parts of powdered alum (aluminum ammonium sulphate) and one part of arsenic (arsenic trioxide), or arsenical paste for preserving. NOT ADVISABLE for amateur uses because arsenic is a deadly POISON. Stick to borax.

Sew the lips together with a few stitches with thin thread.

STUFFING—Wrap cotton around the leg bones to approximately the same thickness as the flesh you removed. Then turn the skin right side out.

Stuff the head and body with cotton, using forceps if necessary to put the padding in place. Or, better, make a false body by winding cotton around a piece of wire and push it into the skin. Use the outline drawing you made before skinning to give the body the correct dimensions. Wrap a small amount of cotton into a tapered spiral around a piece of thin, waxed wire to fit into the tail skin.

Finally, sew up the slit to enclose the filling.

DRYING—Place the completed skin on a piece of soft wood, belly down. Pin the front legs straight out to the front, hind legs and tail straight out to the back. Attach the label to the right hind leg. Leave the skin to dry.

MOUNTED SPECIMENS—Any time you like, you can try your hand at taxidermy and turn your study specimen into a more natural-looking mounted specimen.

Or you may start from scratch if you happen to be a hunter yourself or have a hunter friend among your acquaintances.

BOOK ON TAXIDERMY—Leon L. Pray. *Taxidermy*. The Macmillan Company.

PREPARING THE SKIN—For small animals up to the size of a squirrel, the skin can be prepared in the same manner as a study skin.

For larger animals, it pays to salt down the raw pelt thoroughly and send it to a taxidermist for tanning.

STEPS IN MOUNTING SMALL ANIMALS—In general, the steps in mounting a small animal are the following:

Attach the cleaned skull (or a carved replica) to one end of a stiff "backbone" wire about twice as long as the body of the animal. Make a loop in the wire a short distance behind the place where wires from the front legs will meet it, and a double-loop at the hip joint.

If the skin is dried up, relax it by moistening the inside with borax solution, then by working it in your hands.

Push a wire through each paw, tie it to the leg bone with thread or flower wire. Bring the leg wires through the appropriate loops of the "backbone" wire, then wind them firmly on to this wire. Leave a couple of inches of leg wire below each paw.

Stuff the animal with excelsior (wood wool). Where you can't push it in with your fingers, use forceps. As you go along, squeeze the parts you have stuffed into their natural shape. When the stuffing is completed, sew up the slit in the skin. Set up the animal by pushing the leg wires through holes bored in a wooden base and bending them under.

MOUNTING LARGE ANIMALS—There are many short cuts in the mounting of larger animals. Taxidermists' supply houses furnish head forms or real skulls, excelsior bodies of many sizes and shapes, ear linings, artificial noses and eyes, and stands and bases. Before proceeding, contact one of these supply houses and get their recommendation.

TAXIDERMISTS' SUPPLIES—M. J. Hoffmann Company, 993 Gates Avenue, Brooklyn 21, N. Y.
U. W. Elwood Supply Company, 1202 Harney Street, Omaha 2, Neb.
Penn Taxidermy Studios, Hazleton, Penn.
D. M. Wooster Studios, Academy Street, Whitney Point, N. Y.

SKULLS AND SKELETONS

SKULLS—Thousands of wild animals are run over and killed yearly on our highways. Many, of course, have their heads smashed, but some haven't. By being on the lookout, you may secure skulls of squirrel, skunk, opossum, porcupine, raccoon, even coyote and other large animals.

Mice and similar small mammals you can take in traps You can usually make a deal with local hunters or trappers for other animals that will give you a send-off into the science of *osteology*—from Greek *osteon,* bone.

SMALL SKULLS—The most effective way of preparing small skulls, and the way least likely to damage them, is to let the larvae of a dermestid beetle—*Dermestes maculatus,* hide beetle—do the job for you. These larvae will eat off every scrap of flesh, leaving the bones in perfect condition.

It is a simple matter to start a dermestid colony. Just expose a piece of old hide, a dry carcass, or cheese, outdoors in warm weather. The beetles will soon make their appearance. Catch a number of them and keep them in a cage made of window screening, or in a large can or jar covered with screening.

Place the dry skulls to be cleaned in the cage, and let the beetles and their offspring take over.

LARGE SKULLS—Large skulls can also be cleaned by dermestid larvae. But you will probably not have the patience to wait for this long-drawn-out process, and will decide to do it yourself.

Skin the head first. Be careful, and watch particularly around eye sockets and snout. Bring a wire with a flattened, crooked end, or a brain hook, through the hole at the back of the skull, and break up the brain. Flush out the brain matter and rinse well under a faucet. Then scrape and cut off as much flesh as can be done easily with a knife or scalpel, and curved scissors. This is a roughing-out job. The complete fleshing comes later.

Place the skull in a glass or earthenware jar in ammonia water—1 cup household ammonia to 1 gallon of water. Set aside for two to four days.

Make up another batch of ammonia water. Heat, place the skull in it and simmer until the remaining flesh particles slip the bone readily—15 minutes or more. Cool slowly by pouring cold water into the pot. If cooled quickly, the tooth enamel may crack.

Go over the skull for a final cleaning with a scraper and a long-handled brush-plater's brush. Wash thoroughly. Drain and dry in the shade.

If the skull appears greasy on drying, it needs degreasing. Place it overnight in carbon tetrachloride, or some other grease-dissolving cleaning fluid—Renuzit, for instance. Then take it out and dry it again in a drafty place.

SKELETONS—A collection of identified skeleton parts will prove of great value to you. It will permit you to recognize the remains of animals found dead in the field, predator kills, materials in scat and in owl pellets.

SMALL SKELETONS—For small animal carcasses, make use of the dermestid colony you may have established for cleaning skulls. The result will be complete skeletons, with all bones intact and still fastened together.

LARGE SKELETONS—Skeleton parts of a large animal can be prepared in the simple manner described for large skulls. The preparation of a complete skeleton, on the other hand, is a complicated job.

If you should ever want to undertake the preparation of a large skeleton, it will pay you to seek advice and help from a local expert.

REFERENCES—William A. Kruse. *How to Make Skeletons.* Ward's Service Bulletin No. 1. Free. Ward's Natural Science Establishment, Rochester 9, N. Y.
How to Make Skeletons. Turtox Service Leaflet No. 9. Free. General Biological Supply House, Chicago 37, Ill.

5. SNAKES, LIZARDS, AND TURTLES

MANY people have a morbid fear of snakes. Some get hysterical at the sight of a perfectly harmless garter snake slithering away among the rocks. Others become heroic and go on a St. George rampage to kill the "poisonous critter."

The trouble is that there is possibly more superstition and plain ignorance connected with snakes than with anything else in nature. Rather a pity that false teachings should have created the unreasonable and unreasoned fear of these animals! Anyone willing to cut through the myths and approach the subject rationally, will find snakes highly interesting creatures.

There's no excuse today for people being ignorant of the facts about snakes. On the other hand, you can't really blame our forefathers for their attitude. From early biblical days, the snake had stood as the symbol of all evil. From time immemorial, snakes had been known to have caused the death of people—so why not make it the better part of valor to consider all snakes poisonous and fear all of them? And then there were the folk tales of snakes that bit onto their tails and hoop-rolled downhill after their enemies . . . of snakes that hypnotized their prey with their glassy stare . . . of still others that crept into barns and sucked the cows dry.

The list of snake "facts" that "ain't so" is long. And the list of facts connected with lizards is almost as long —for, after all, isn't the lizard the direct descendant of the fire-spewing dragon of old? The turtle seems to be the only reptile that has come down through the ages with a decent reputation—much of it attributable to Aesop and his fables rather than to scientific investigation.

With all the superstitions regarding reptiles, it is only

comparatively recently that we have begun to learn the facts—and we are still far from knowing them all.

BOOKS ON REPTILE LIFE—Clifford H. Pope. *Snakes Alive and How They Live.* Viking Press.
Raymond L. Ditmars. *The Reptiles of North America.* Doubleday & Company.

WORKING WITH OTHERS

You will have many interesting hours before you investigating the life and habits of our native reptiles.

Much of this work you can do alone. But you will have more fun and pick up more knowledge if you can work with other people interested in the same hobby.

To get in touch with such people contact your local school biology teachers or look up names and addresses in *The Naturalists' Directory* (see page 31). If there is a natural-history museum within a reasonable distance you will find, there, people specializing in *herpetology*.

Finally, as your interest mounts, you may want to join a national society and, in this way, keep in contact with the latest developments within the field of snake study.

SOCIETIES—American Society of Ichthyologists and Herpetologists. Hdqrs.: Philadelphia Zoological Garden, Philadelphia, Penn. Periodical: *Copeia.*
Herpetologists League. Hdqrs.: Chapman Grant, Escondido, Calif. Periodical: *Herpetologica.*

Field Study of Reptiles

IDENTIFICATION

In most other phases of nature, the ability to identify a specimen should come as a result of study in the field. In reptile study, it is important to begin with a determined effort to learn to recognize the poisonous snakes of your locality—either for the purpose of avoiding them as you go about studying the harmless snakes or for the purpose of finding them if you intend to concentrate on their study. But don't think of the latter until you have become an experienced herpetologist.

You can pick up some of the skill to identify poisonous snakes through study of pictures and descriptions in field books. A better method is the observation of preserved specimens, and, even better, live specimens in captivity. The most effective method is to take your early field trips under the guidance of an experienced snake student.

BOOKS FOR FIELD IDENTIFICATION—Karl P. Schmidt and D. Dwight Davis. *Field Book of Snakes of the United States and Canada.* G. P. Putnam's Sons.

Roger Conant. *Field Guide to Amphibians and Reptiles*. Houghton Mifflin Company, Boston, Mass.

OTHER BOOKS—Clifford H. Pope. *Turtles of the United States and Canada*. Alfred A. Knopf.

Hobart M. Smith. *Handbook of Lizards*. Comstock Publishing Company, Ithaca, N. Y.

Gayle Pickwell. *Amphibians and Reptiles of the Pacific States*. Stanford University Press, Stanford, Calif.

EQUIPMENT

For general field study of reptiles very little in the way of equipment is needed—unless you get into territory infested with poisonous snakes. Here you will need certain precautionary equipment and specialized tools.

PRECAUTIONARY EQUIPMENT—With reasonable precaution, the likelihood of being bitten by a poisonous snake is remote. The best precaution is vigilance. Look where you are stepping, notice where you put your hands.

The statistics in regard to snake bites are exceedingly sketchy. Estimates range from one hundred to two thousand bites each year in the United States. Of the bites reported, it has again been loosely estimated that about 70 per cent are on feet or legs (bare feet, low shoes), 25 per cent on hands and arms (not watching where hands are placed in climbing rocky ledges; incorrect handling of captured specimens), and 5 per cent head and body (drinking from spring or stream incautiously). The mortality seems to be approximately 15 per cent where no proper treatment is given, 2 per cent where quick, energetic treatment is applied, according to Conant.

Those figures show the advisability of protecting legs and hands, and of carrying a suitable first aid kit.

When hunting snakes, therefore, in territory where poisonous species are present, wear *high-top boots,* or *leather puttees,* or heavy canvas leggings over regular shoes. When climbing, wear heavy *gauntlet-type leather gloves,* with cuffs long enough to protect the wrists.

In rocky country, don't move loose rocks with your hands. Use instead a *potato rake* or a *baling hook* such as is used by truckers.

For further protection, bring a *snake-bite kit.* Small pocket types are available. Each of them consists of a thin rubber hose for tying around the limb to stop the flow of the venom toward the heart, antiseptic, razor blade for opening up the bite, and a rubber suction cup for sucking out the poison-mixed blood. Learn the function of the kit before the need arises to use it. The method is described in the leaflet that comes with the kit, in the *Field Book of Snakes,* and in the *Red Cross Manual.*

SNAKE BITE KITS—Asepto Snake Bite Outfit No. 2006. Beckton, Dickinson & Company, Rutherford, N. J. Compac Snake Bite Kit. Cutler Laboratories, Berkeley, Calif.

Where your explorations through snake-infested territory take you far away from human habitation, it is also advisable to carry *Antivenin,* a polyvalent serum that, when injected into the blood stream, counteracts the poisons of rattlesnake, copperhead, and water moccasin. If at all possible, secure the services of a physician for the injection.

ANTIVENIN—Antivenin Combination Kit. Wyeth, Inc., Philadelphia 3, Penn. or through your local drug store.

STUDY EQUIPMENT—Depending on the subject you are working on, you may need some, or all, of the following.

NOTEBOOK—A pocket-size book for note taking—possibly a loose-leaf binder with record cards with columns for the information you are seeking.

MARKING AND MEASURING EQUIPMENT—*Manicure scissors* for tagging snakes, or *file* for marking turtles. *Balance* for weighing. The simplest type for field work is a spring balance, with a hook on which you can hang the bag that holds your captured specimen. *Rule* for measuring—a short pocket rule for small reptiles, a carpenter's rule or metal tape for large snakes.

FLASHLIGHT—When looking for reptiles at night, a flashlight strapped to the forehead is superior to the usual hand type.

CATCHING EQUIPMENT—see page 152.

FINDING REPTILES

SNAKES

Snakes are elusive creatures. Finding them is mostly a matter of luck—especially as it applies to the larger species. Yet, by knowing WHEN and WHERE to look for them, each of your field trips should make it possible for you to chalk up a further score of specimens observed.

WHEN?—TIME OF YEAR—Snakes are active in warm weather. Cool temperatures slow them down since their body heat depends on their surroundings. They get sluggish when the temperature drops much below 60 degrees. With the exception of some Southern species, most snakes in the United States go into hibernation when freezing weather approaches—often in balls of intertwining bodies, from a few to a hundred or more. They emerge again in the spring when the surroundings warm up, to scatter far and wide over the countryside.

Obviously, then, the best times of the year for finding snakes are fall when they move toward their hibernation points and spring when they leave them. Of those two seasons, spring is the better. At that time, the snakes are less wary. Also, spring vegetation provides less concealment than the lush growth of late summer.

TIME OF DAY—WEATHER—On days that are cloudy and cold, you will have little luck. On cool, sunshiny days from spring to fall, snakes may be found sunning themselves on rocks and on branches. During hot weather, many of them seek cool shade or hunt among rocks near a brook or river.

A number of species, particularly in desert territories, become nocturnal during the hottest season of the year, sleeping in hiding during the day and hunting in the comparative cool of night. They may be jack-lighted. Or look for them crossing roads, by the light of an automobile cruising at slow speed.

WHERE?—The most successful places for finding snakes in large numbers are near their denning areas during the spring awakening. Copperheads and timber rattlers hibernate in crevices among rocks. Ask old villagers. They may be able to tell you of places where these snakes have been known to hibernate year after year. Other snakes hibernate in deserted burrows of woodchucks, prairie dogs, gophers, gopher tortoises, muskrats, rats.

When snakes have left their hibernation places, you will have to hunt farther afield. Keep in mind then, that all snakes seek a certain amount of coolness and moisture and therefore, generally, go into concealment except when hunting their food. Look for them in appropriate hiding places, or chase them to such places where you may have a chance to trap them. In approaching them, remember that snakes are sensitive to vibrations, but not to sounds. You can talk or even shout without disturbing them, but you have to step lightly.

Look for *small snakes* under loose rocks and fallen branches, under bark of decaying trees and in hollow logs.

> *Tip*—Hunt the *small snakes* with a buddy. Even the tiniest snakes can squirm away with incredible speed. Have your buddy lift the stone while you do the grabbing.

For *larger snakes,* investigate piles of dead leaves, heaps of bark slabs around old sawmills, corn or grain shucks left in the field, rock crevices along a creek. Look under pieces of tar paper, tin, and similar debris.

Tip—If you live near a farmyard, vacant lot, camp grounds, you may have fair success in attracting certain snakes. Scatter a number of one-foot squares of tar paper, linoleum, cardboard (waterproofed with paint or shellac), in such a way that they are suspended slightly above the ground, by grass, pebbles or the like. Visit your "traps" several times a day and investigate which snakes may have been attracted to them.

For *snakes that take to water,* wade carefully upstream looking for them sunning themselves on rocks along the stream's edge, or, in the case of certain species, on branches overhanging the stream.

LIZARDS

Lizards are creatures of the sun. For the largest variety of lizards, go south, or better, southwest. You will find a number in other sections of the country, but none in northern New England.

WHEN?—A bright, sunny summer day is the best time to look for lizards. When the days turn cloudy and cool, they go into hiding. Winter finds them in hibernation.

WHERE?—Lizards are usually found in abundance in deserts. You may see them rushing over the surface, popping in and out of rock piles and debris of yucca or Joshua trees.

Fields and woodlands hold other lizards, perpetually on the go on warm days hunting for insects and worms. Investigate stone fences, rotting stumps, decaying logs. Strip off the loose bark of southern dead pines and you will almost certainly come upon lizards. And look up from time to time—a lizard may be scurrying up the tree right in front of you.

TURTLES

Sandy deserts hold some of our native turtles, but the majority of them have aquatic habits.

WHEN?—Turtles, like other reptiles, spend their winters in hibernation. They appear on the scene again when spring and warm weather set in. The best time of the year to look for them is during their nesting season—May and June.

WHERE?—While you will come on a few of the turtles in woods and fields—mostly wood and box turtles—you will find far more in and around lakes and streams. On a warm day, you may see turtles sunning themselves on every log and rock protruding from the water. Approach them carefully—they have a way of sliding into the water the moment they realize that an enemy is around.

FINDING REPTILE EGGS

Some snakes bear living young—or rather, bring them forth in thin membrane sacs that are ruptured shortly after birth by the snakelet. Other snakes lay elongated, creamy-white eggs. Eggs are generally laid in June and July, rarely the first couple of weeks of August. The young emerge from a week to three months later, depending on species and outside conditions influencing incubation.

Snake eggs may sometimes be located through a search of manure piles, heaps of rotting sawdust, decaying wood pulp in old stumps and logs, occasionally in stone piles. Make careful notes of places where eggs were found, type of soil in which laid, depth below surface, number, arrangement, whether separate or adhering to each other. Measure length and thickness with calipers, if possible, for exact dimensions.

Turtle eggs are globular or slightly elongate, with hard or pliable, creamy-white shells. You may be lucky enough to locate a nest of them in sand or soft soil near lake or stream.

It takes an expert to tell what species laid a particular clutch of eggs. And even experts aren't always certain. The only way you can be sure is to take a few home and hatch them (see page 160).

REPTILE LISTS AND SURVEYS

LIFE LISTS—Keep careful records in your notebook of the reptiles you come across—including name, habitat, weather conditions. Your notes may help to add to our knowledge of reptiles and their habits.

SURVEYS—A thorough reptile survey requires the work of a number of people. It may prove an intriguing activity for a nature club or a youth group.

If you can mobilize enough manpower to surround the area to be investigated, do so and have the group work toward the center, carefully checking every possible reptile hideout. If your group is small, have it make as wide a swath as possible along one edge of the area, then another and still another until the area has been covered.

SNAKE MARKING—Growth studies of snakes call for measuring and weighing of a large number of specimens, and of recapturing them from time to time. To recognize the individuals, make use of the tagging method suggested by Blanchard and Finster. This consists of snipping off scales from the underside of the tail, with a pair of manicure scissors—or still smaller scissors for the diminutive species. The snake seems to feel little or no pain in the process. When most of a scale has been removed down to the muscle layer, a scar forms which is usually recognizable even after several years.

Develop a simple code system, snipping one or two scales off the left side, one or two off the right, up to and including the ninth. In such a system, two scales removed from one side are indicated as 24, if the second and fourth are snipped off. If only one scale is removed, a zero is added, as for example, 40, if the fourth scale alone is removed. The system makes possible the following table for each side (the first scale after the anal plate is seldom touched since in some species it is not clearly defined).

20	30	40	50	60	70	80	90
23	—	—	—	—	—	—	—
24	34	—	—	—	—	—	—
25	35	45	—	—	—	—	—
26	36	46	56	—	—	—	—
27	37	47	57	67	—	—	—
28	38	48	58	68	78	—	—
29	39	49	59	69	79	89	—

In tagging, hold the snake, underside up, with tail away from you. Locate the anal plate. Count from here, along the left row of scales, toward the tail tip, the desired number of scales, say to number 3. Snip this scale off. Now count along the right row of scales, from the anal plate. Snip off scales 6 and 8. Your snake is now tagged 30-68.

TURTLE MARKING—The construction of the shells of all hard-shelled turtles make turtle marking easy. You simply notch the small plates, marginals, along the edge.

Hold the turtle in front of you, head up. Starting from the small plate directly behind the turtle's head, the nuchal, but not counting it, count along the plates, and mark certain of them by nicking them along both edges with a triangular file. Use the same code system as suggested for snakes.

Note: Never mark a turtle shell with paint. The shell consists of living tissue. Paint or enamel prevents its proper growth, deforming the turtle.

FIELD OBSERVATIONS

Discovering reptiles in the field and watching their

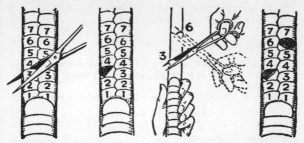

By snipping off a few scales according to a code system, it is possible to identify individual snakes when they are recaptured.

activities can provide you with a lot of interesting experiences. But reptile hunting becomes even more fascinating when you are out to find the solution to a problem you have decided to investigate.

NUMBER OF SNAKES—Common or uncommon in your vicinity? Fluctuation in numbers from year to year.

GROWTH—By months, by years. When large numbers of snakes are captured, it will be found that they fall into size groups, according to age. But tables of "average lengths" are still far from complete.

WEIGHT—Before and after hibernation. What is the weight loss?

FEEDING—The stomach contents of a snake that has recently taken a meal can be pushed out without injury to the snake, by kneading the snake's body gently below the food "bulge" and slowly pressing the food forward until it is disgorged.

LOCOMOTION—Speed, method of movement. What is hunting range of the species you are investigating?

HOMING INSTINCTS—Will a snake or lizard or turtle return if removed a couple of miles from its home ground?

INTELLIGENCE, SENSES—A great number of methods may be invented for testing the intelligence and senses of various reptiles.

In addition to the investigations that you may deliberately plan, good luck or keen observation may give you a chance to contribute to our knowledge of reptiles through chance occurrences. On your hunts, you may happen to come upon some of the life functions that have rarely been observed. It is then a matter of knowing what to look for, how to make complete observation notes, how to sketch or photograph the occasion.

Among such observations may be the following:

SKIN SHEDDING OF SNAKES—Note what movements are made to facilitate the shedding, the length of time it takes.

COURTSHIP AND MATING—Complete description of the actions of male and female.

EGG LAYING—Nest making of egg-laying species. The actual process of egg laying, how many eggs, length of time required.

BIRTH OF SNAKELETS—In snakes bearing living young.

Reptiles in Captivity

CATCHING REPTILES

The best "instrument" for catching harmless snakes is the hand. A quick reach and a firm hold behind the snake's head will do the trick. The snake may thrash around and let off excrement or a musky-smelling secretion from its anal glands, but if you then support its body with your other hand, it will soon quiet down.

The hand is also the best tool for catching turtles and lizards. In the case of lizards, your hand needs to be extra fast—even at that, you may often wind up with a squirming tail in your hand while the animal itself disappears.

SNAKE STICKS—If catching snakes with the bare hands does not appeal to you, use a *snake stick* or tongs.

> *Note*—A snake stick should ALWAYS be used for poisonous snakes.

The snake stick, in its simplest form, is a branch 4 to 5 feet long with an L-crotch in the end. Whittle down the side branch that forms the bottom of the L to approximately 2 inches. Pin down the snake by placing this end of the stick over its neck. You can then readily pick up the snake with thumb and forefinger.

A snake stick may also be made by screwing a 2-inch-long, ½-inch-wide angle iron (inside corner plate) to the end of a ¾-inch-square stick, OR by hammering a ¼-inch-thick piece of iron rod, bent at a right angle, into a hole bored in a 1-inch dowel. With this type, you can lift up a snake by bringing the hook of the stick in under the snake's midsection.

> *Tip*—You can file down an old golf iron putter or a discarded garden hoe into an efficient snake stick. The "shelf reacher" used in grocery stores for taking down boxes from high shelves makes another type of snake stick, especially suited for catching snakes in water. Some snake experts use a regular butterfly net for catching snakes.

When handling poisonous snakes, use a *strap stick*. This is a square stick with a leather strap that runs in guides fastened to the stick. The loop is laid over the snake's head, around the neck, whereupon it is tightened, holding the snake by the neck in a firm grip.

LIZARD CATCHER—You can turn a stick or old fishing rod into a lizard catcher by providing it with a small horsehair slip noose. In using the catcher, slowly slip the noose over the lizard's head. A quick jerk, and the noose closes around the lizard's neck.

"NOODLING" ROD—Snapping turtles can be caught during hibernation by "noodling" for them with a piece of ¼-inch iron rod, 3 to 4 feet long, with a pointed hook at one end. With the straight end, probe along lake banks, under stumps, in old muskrat holes, until you get the "feel" of a turtle. Turn the rod, and pull out the turtle with the hook in the other end and with your hands.

TURTLE TRAPS—Aquatic turtles are often caught in traps. Use 2-inch mesh poultry netting for such a trap. Roll an 8-foot-long piece of 5-foot netting into a cylinder, approximately 30 inches in diameter. Provide each end with an inward-pointing funnel of netting, with a flattened opening, 1 inch high, 20 inches wide, through which a turtle can just squeeze itself. Cut a door in the top. Bait the trap with fish heads, poultry "innards," or other juicy tidbits, and anchor it in shallow water, with the top above water.

> *Tip*—By wrapping the bait in wire screening so that it won't be eaten by the first snapper to enter, the same bait may lure a number of turtles into the trap.

REFERENCE—*Turtle Trapping*. Fishery Leaflet 190. Fish and Wildlife Service, U. S. Department of the Interior.

TRANSPORTING YOUR CATCH—Have available a number of *cloth bags* in various sizes for transporting your cap-

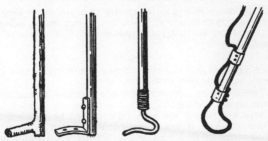

Snake sticks, using L-crotch, angle iron, ¼-inch iron rod. Strap stick (right) has leather strap running in metal guides.

Make a number of cloth bags for transporting your reptile specimens. Do not depend on a draw-string, use a piece of tape.

tives. Unbleached muslin is excellent for making these bags. Flour bags and sugar sacks are satisfactory, with a gunny sack thrown in for large snappers.

Don't depend on a draw string for a snake bag; instead, sew a piece of tape to the outside of the bag, about 1 inch from the top. Fold down the top of the bag, after the snake or lizard has been thrown in, then tie it.

Small reptiles may be transported in *screw-top jars*. Make perforations in the cover to let in air. Make the holes from the inside, so that there will be no sharp points to injure your specimen.

> WARNING—Leaving specimens exposed to the sun, even for a few minutes only, in hot weather, may be fatal to them. Keep the bag in the shade. If the snakes have to be carried any distance, put some damp moss or wet leaves with them.

Reptile Cages and Cage Health

Reptiles get along satisfactorily in captivity as long as the temperature is right, the ventilation good without drafts, food adequate, and water and hiding places on hand.

snakes

SNAKE CAGES—In constructing snake cages, you can pretty well suit your own ideas.

TYPES—Many different types are possible—among them those shown on page 157.

wire lid cage—The wire lid cage can be knocked together quickly. It has a glass front held in position by wood strips or moldings, and a "lid" of wood strips with wire screening tacked to it. The lid fits the outside measurements of the top of the cage and lifts off for feeding and cleaning. Further ventilation is provided through screened holes in ends of cage.

BATTERY CAGE—The battery cage is made with a solid wooden top. Several cages of this type may be stacked on top of each other, battery style. The top part of the back contains screening for ventilation. It is hinged to swing down. The glass front is held in place by moldings, or set in grooves about ¼ inch deep, ¼ inch from the front edges of top and bottom.

SLANTING FRONT CAGE—A cage with a slanting glass front has the best possible arrangement for observation. The glass is held in position by pieces of angle irons, such as linoleum moldings.

MATERIALS—Scrap wood is suitable for snake cages. A discarded apple box may give you all the wood you need. Or use pieces of commercial 1-inch pine boards.

Regular window wire screening will take care of the ventilation. Use brass, copper, or aluminum screening rather than iron screening; it doesn't rust. Some snakes pick up a habit of rubbing their noses against the screening, causing abrasions and infection—therefore keep the size of the screening at an absolute minimum.

Use a piece of glass for front or top to make observation easy.

SIZE—As a general rule of thumb, the cage should be one snake long, half a snake wide, and half a snake high. This rule applies specifically for the smaller species, such as DeKay and ring-necked snakes for which 12×6×6 inches are suitable. For the larger snakes, 2 feet and over, the proportionate dimensions can be somewhat smaller about two thirds of a snake long, one third wide, one third high—16×8×8 inches for 24-inch garter snakes, for instance.

Cages of these sizes will accommodate two to four snakes, if necessary. If you have room for several cages, it is better to have only one snake in each cage. This makes study of individual snakes simpler.

FINISHING—Fill cracks and inside corners with patching plaster, plastic wood, regular putty, or a putty made from plaster of Paris and shellac. Finish with varnish. It is especially important that the bottom of the cage be waterproof so that it will not absorb moisture from excrements.

Two coats of paint are better than varnish. And why not make your cages colorful? Finish them in a color that suits your taste or use one that will contrast with the color of the snake.

FURNISHINGS—Snakes need to have water available at all times for drinking and bathing. Place the water dish —butter dish or the like—in the middle of the floor.

Snakes have a habit of crawling along the sides of their cages and may turn over a dish placed too close to the side. Pick a dish large enough for the snake to coil up in.

A snake also needs a hiding place in its cage. This may be a small board raised on cleats, a piece of bark, a flat stone on top of a few pebbles.

SNAKE PITS—During the warm part of the year, snakes may be kept in an outdoor snake pit. In its simplest form, this is a small piece of ground surrounded by a low wall.

Pick a spot that has both sunlight and shade, at least 6 feet square. Dig a narrow ditch around it, about 8 inches wide, 12 inches deep. Fill with a mixture of cement and crushed rock or small stones. On top of this foundation, build a 3-foot wall of field stones, brick, or cement blocks, provided with an overhang toward the pit, of 3 to 6 inches. Coat the inside of the wall with a smooth finish of cement (illustration, page 159).

Build up the ground in the middle of the pit into a mound sloping toward the south. Pile up a couple of stone slabs in such a way that they form a hiding place. Put in pieces of logs for decorative effect.

Sink a water basin into the ground, or make a cement pool, a couple of feet in diameter, one foot deep. A water moat along the inside base of the wall is even better than a pool, and makes it more difficult for the snakes to escape.

> *Tip*—A dozen or more snakes may be kept in a snake pit. But be sure that they are of fairly even size. Do not place king snakes, milk snakes, indigo snakes, and other snake-eating species in the same pit with other snakes.

SNAKE HEALTH—An important condition for keeping your snakes healthy is to pick them healthy in the first place. It doesn't pay to hold on to snakes that are damaged or sick, or off their feed.

Snakes newly caught are often infested with tiny mites. Place infested snakes in jars filled with lukewarm water. By morning, all mites will have drowned except possibly a few around the eyes. Touch them with a drop of olive oil.

Cuts or abrasions on the body may be brushed with an aqueous antiseptic, such as mercurochrome. Treat infected eyes with boric-acid solution.

Snakes thrive best at a temperature ranging between 65° and 80° Fahrenheit. They suffer if the temperatures vary too greatly.

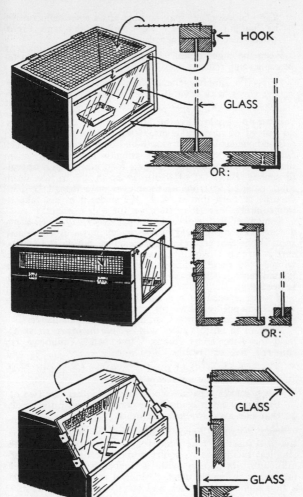

HOOK

GLASS

OR:

OR:

GLASS

GLASS

Reptile cages can be made to many patterns: wire lid cage (top),
battery case (center), slanting front cage (bottom).

Tip—Snake cages may be kept at an even temperature by hanging an electric light bulb in the cage. Light when more heat is needed.

Keep the cages clean. Clean out excrements as soon as possible, and remove food that has not been eaten.

Tip—To simplify the cleaning, cover the bottom of the cages with several layers of newspapers that can be thrown out regularly, or use white pebbles.

FEEDING—Snakes live on animal matter only. There is no record of any snake practicing vegetarianism.

The bone structure of mouth and body makes it possible for snakes to swallow whole animals that are larger in diameter than themselves. Living food has greatest appeal to snakes. But most of them can be taught to take dead food, dangled in front of their eyes on a thread, held in forceps or on a thin stick. If the snake does not take it immediately, leave it in its cage for a few hours.

Remember that snakes do not eat every day. Feed them a fair-sized meal every week or ten days. A fair-sized meal is one that creates a definite bulge, but doesn't necessarily stretch the skin between the scales. During the winter—the regular hibernation season—a meal a month is sufficient. If the snake is in true hibernation, no food is needed.

If your specimens are small, feed them small earthworms, chopped earthworms, chopped meat or fish, larvae and grubs, tiny minnows, small tadpoles, salamanders.

Medium to large snakes will eat earthworms, strips of meat or fish, frogs, toads, "live bait" (minnows or shiners), live or freshly killed mice.

Tip—Check in *Field Book of Snakes* for list of food usually taken by your captive species.

Keep snakes separate when feeding. Otherwise two of them may catch hold of the same food, with the result that one may swallow the other.

FORCE FEEDING—Force feeding may be necessary if the snake refuses to take food for a couple of weeks. The simplest method is to squirt a mixture of raw egg and milk into its mouth with a rubber syringe. Another method is to impale meat, a skinned mouse or a frog on a thin blunt-pointed stick and push it down the throat.

Force feeding is seldom successful. Instead of trying to keep a native species alive, better turn it loose and find another.

LIZARDS

LIZARD CAGES—Lizards may be kept in cages like .

snakes, but they get along better in a terrarium—a desert terrarium for desert species, a woodland terrarium for the rest (see page 267). Include a couple of hiding places in the furnishings—rocks or strips of bark—and a couple of sticks for climbing.

FEEDING—As far as possible, feed live food: live insects, such as flies, roaches, grasshoppers; mealworms; Enchytra worms, small earthworms. After having kept lizards in captivity for a while, you may succeed in having them take chopped meat, if you dangle it in front of them.

Water is necessary. Some lizards drink from a dish, but others need to have it sprayed on the plants of the terrarium so that they can sip the drops.

TURTLES

TURTLE CAGES AND PENS—Land turtles will get along well in a snake cage or snake pit, as long as the temperature and food are to their liking. Box turtles may be given the run of the house; they may even hang around in the back yard for years if you let them loose.

TURTLE AQUARIUM—Aquatic turtles need an imitation of their natural habitat. Small specimens may be kept in an aquarium that has a sandy beach or a rock they can climb up on (see page 236).

TURTLE PEN—Larger aquatic specimens are best kept in an outdoor turtle pen. You can build it the same way you make a snake pit, surrounding a small pool with a low wall. Or, instead of going in for masonry, put up a simple enclosure of poultry netting. Drive a number of 3-foot-long pieces of 1-inch pipe into the ground along the outline of the enclosure, slanting them toward the

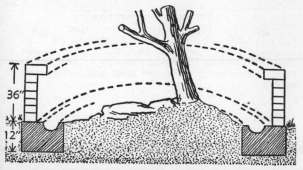

A professional-looking outdoor pit for snakes, lizards and turtles, with a 36-inch wall resting on a concrete foundation.

middle. Wire 3-foot poultry netting to the posts, digging it a few inches below the ground.

FEEDING—Turtles need only be fed a couple of times a week. They take earthworms, slugs, insects, and occasionally lettuce, apples, bananas. Add fish and tadpoles to the diet of aquatic turtles. Some of your captives may learn to take raw hamburger from your fingers.

HATCHING REPTILE EGGS

If you have had the luck to find a clutch of snake or turtle eggs, by all means, try hatching them.

Moisten a paper towel, then wring it out. Place it in a double layer on bottom of a glass jar. Place the eggs on the paper in a single layer. If they adhere, leave them sticking together or separate them, as you prefer. Cover the eggs with a piece of moistened paper toweling. Place a piece of glass over the container. Keep the "incubator" at room temperature—about 70 degrees.

Be sure that the contents are kept moist but not wet by sprinkling the surface occasionally with water. If the eggs get moldy, take off the glass cover for a while; if they shrink, more moisture is indicated.

Examine the eggs from time to time—say, once a week. When the eggs seem to look swollen and bulgy in spots, examine them more often—hatching is close at hand, and you may have the chance to see snakelets open up their prisons with their "egg teeth." You may even be able to record the event photographically. There will usually be plenty of time to set up a camera—it may take the snakelets several hours to free themselves completely.

Set most of your hatchings free in their natural habitat. Keep a few only for observation in captivity. You will have your hands full feeding them.

Photographing Reptiles

The peculiar shape that snakes have makes it a tough job to photograph them. The only way to get a good composition is to get them to coil up or to assume a zigzaggy position. Lizards are easier—if you can keep them still. Turtles make the most satisfactory reptile models.

STILLS

INDOORS—The simplest method of photographing a reptile is to snap it in a glass-front cage. Arrange a few props for a pleasing background. Put a single floodlight to give the effect of sunshine. Fill in the shadows with reflected light from the light-colored wall of the cage, or prop up a piece of white cardboard opposite to the floodlight. Focus the camera. Watch out for light reflections on the glass of the cage. Finally arrange the snake and snap the picture.

OUTDOORS—An outdoor shot, in natural surroundings and with the sun as the light source, will give you a better picture than is possible in a studio. Focus your camera on a suitable spot. Place your snake gently in position, and cover it immediately with a black cloth. When your model is quiet, pull the cloth away with one hand, as you snap the shutter with the other. Snakes have a way of disappearing unless you act fast.

Tip—If you have a helper, have him cup his hands over the snake until it quiets down. Be ready to shoot the moment he takes his hands away.

MOVIES

A turtle makes a good movie—if you have the necessary patience. A snake, on the other hand, is a poor actor. It usually slithers off the screen before you have a chance to catch a glimpse of it.

If you do want to shoot movies of a snake in action, take advantage of the fact that reptiles slow down and get sluggish when the temperature drops below 60 degrees. Place the snake in the refrigerator, in a bag, for about half an hour, while you set up your equipment. If the actions are still too fast after this cooling-off process, take the movies at 32 frames a second. When projected at the regular 16-frame home-movie speed, the snake's movements will become more deliberate, and it will remain on the screen twice as long.

Reptile Collections

A collection of well-preserved reptiles makes an attractive museum display. The work connected with it is relatively simple, the materials inexpensive.

PRESERVATION OF REPTILES—KILLING REPTILES —Reptiles may be killed by injecting a few cubic centimeters of ether or chloroform in or near the heart, with a hypodermic needle. Or wrap them up fairly tightly in a bag and submerge in the liquid you intend to use for the preserving—formalin or alcohol.

Tip—". . . snakes are quite promptly killed if placed in a tight jar with a layer of common moth repellent 'di-chloricide' on the bottom. . . ." according to Schmidt and Davis.

PRESERVING—Reptiles may be preserved in 10-per-cent formalin (one part commercial formalin to three parts

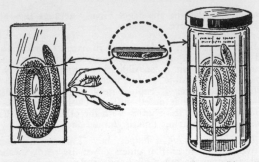

For a neat display, tie the snake to a piece of glass. Place glass upright in a standard biological display jar.

water) or in 70-per-cent alcohol (rubbing alcohol). Formalin will make them rigid and destroy the color, while alcohol will keep them soft.

Tip—To conserve some of the color, try adding 10-per-cent cane sugar to the formalin.

Before submerging in the preservative, cut a number of ½-inch slits at intervals of a couple of inches, in the stomach wall and in the underside of the tail. This will permit the preserving liquid to penetrate. Or inject the liquid in the body cavity with a hypodermic needle—this is particularly important for turtles. If the extended belly of a snake shows that it is full of food, slit it carefully and remove the food.

A snake should be arranged for preservation underside up, in a flat coil in a glass jar or earthenware container of suitable size. Cover it with preservative for a couple of inches. Put a cover over the container. For the next few days, press it gently each day with a blunt stick until all air bubbles have been removed.

If a snake is especially large, it may not be feasible to preserve it in its entirety. In that case, slit the underside from chin to vent and remove the body, cutting it off an inch or so from the neck and close to the vent, leaving head and tail attached to the skin. Roll up loosely and place in the preservative.

MOUNTING—When the snake is partly preserved, it may be coiled up, tail down, in a screw-top glass jar—a domestic jar, such as a mayonnaise or pickle jar, or a standard biological display jar.

A neater display is made by tying the snake, in a flat coil, to a piece of regular, opal, or opaque black glass. This should have been cut to such size that it will go through the opening of the jar and stand upright in it. Use a strong linen thread and a heavy needle. Bring the thread through the snake, tie on the back of the glass plate.

When the snake is properly arranged, pour the final preservative (formalin or alcohol) over it and screw the top on.

LABELING—A label glued to the outside of the jar will fall off sooner or later. Instead, write out a waterproof tag with India ink or crayon and place this inside the jar on the glass plate. The tag should contain name of specimen, where found, when, by whom, length and weight, and other pertinent information.

EQUIPMENT—Waterproof Museum Tags. Turtox or Dennison Manufacturing Company.
   Higgins' Waterproof Black Drawing Ink—any artists' or stationery store.

CURING SNAKE SKINS

CURING SNAKE SKINS—Snake skins may be cured by a simple salt-and-alum process: Remove the head (preserve it in formalin, if desired). Slit the skin along a line running through the middle of the underside, from neck to tip of tail. Remove the body carefully without tearing the skin. If your specimen is a rattlesnake, leave the rattles in place. Spread out the skin, scaly side down, on a smooth board, and "flesh" the inside with a dull knife until all fat and muscle fibres have been removed.

Dissolve ½ pound salt and ¼ pound alum (ammonium aluminum sulphate) in 1 quart hot water. Cool. Submerge the skin in the solution and leave it in it for five days to a week.

Take out the skin, rinse it in water and blot partly dry in a cloth or between paper towels. Tack the skin along the edges to a board for drying, flesh side up. When almost dry, rub in saddle soap to keep the skin soft. Then dry thoroughly. A small amount of neat's foot oil applied to the flesh side after drying will help to keep the skin pliable.

A mold for making a cast of a snake can be built up by brushing on layers of ground-hide mold glue or a rubber-mold mixture.

SNAKE CASTS—For museum displays, wax or plaster casts are often used instead of the real things.

To make a snake cast you need a mold. A plaster mold has to be made in several pieces, otherwise it is impossible to remove the cast. It is easier to make the mold of some flexible material—molding glue or rubber —that can be pulled off the snake.

GLUE MOLD CASTING—Buy ground-hide mold glue from a biological supply house, or make your own molding glue by following the American Museum of Natural History formula: Soak 2 ounces agar in warm water, add 1 pound glycerine, and cook in double boiler until the water has evaporated. Cool. Cut the resulting rubbery mass into cubes and keep ready for use.

Arrange the snake to be cast on the bottom of a shallow glass dish so that the underside of its body is flattened against the dish. Liquefy a sufficient amount of the agar-glycerine by heating. Pour over the snake enough to cover it completely. When cooled and set, remove the snake carefully. Harden the inner surface of the mold with alum water.

Make your plaster-of-Paris mixture as explained on page 133. Mix slowly with a stick. Pour into the mold. Let set for an hour or longer. Take out the cast and let it dry thoroughly, then shellac it and paint it in appropriate colors.

RUBBER MOLD CASTING—There are several rubber mixtures on the market with which suitable rubber molds may be made.

Plastex and Elastex mixed together cold may be poured over the snake in the same way as the molding glue mentioned above. When set, the result is a solid, but very flexible, mold that is good for numerous castings.

Pro-Mold consists of two formulas and is used in a different manner: Formula A is brushed over the original, then dried for about half an hour. Formula B is applied on top of Formula A with a spatula, in sufficient thickness to give body to the mold. It sets in twenty-four to forty-eight hours. The mold is stripped off the snake, and the plaster cast made in the usual manner.

MATERIALS—*Plastex* and *Elastex*. Plasticast Company, 5961 Madison Street, Chicago, Ill.

Pro-Mold Bing Products, Inc., 88 Broad Street, Boston 10, Mass.

SNAKE SKELETONS—The delicate structure of a snake skeleton makes it difficult to prepare it by hand. However, a dermestid colony (see page 141) will make an excellent job out of cleaning a small, dried snake.

6. INSECTS

THERE'S no doubt about it: You have had more intimate contact with insects than with any other members of the animal kingdom—with the exception possibly of the species *Homo sapiens*. Think of the mosquitoes you've squashed, the flies you've swatted, the bugs you've sprayed in your garden, the ants in your picnic food, the moths in your clothes closet, the bees whose honey you've eaten, the butterflies you've admired in their fluttery flight.

Without "good" insects—good to *us*, that is—there would be no human life as we know it. There would be little to eat, no vegetable or animal fibres for clothing, no forests and fields for recreation. On the other hand, if "bad" insects were destroyed, we would be rid of insect-borne diseases, and would save ourselves the billion dollar losses caused annually by hungry insect enemies.

We are stuck with insects by the trillions—"for better or for worse." Fortunately, nature herself is keeping the good and the bad in a fairly even balance. As long as she does, we puny humans are safe. If the balance should ever be upset so that the bad win out, the human race would be destroyed more effectively than a million atom bombs could do it.

There's fascination to insects—not just because of their importance, their colors, their structure. But even more because of some of the wonders of the insect world: the social life of ants and bees, the migration of the monarch butterflies, the carpentry, pottery, paper-making skills of some of the wasps and hornets, and numerous other peculiar feats.

Much is known about insects, but there's still much more to learn. The great advantage of insect study is that you can go about it in your own way—learning by

165

staying quietly at home, if that's your inclination, like a French Fabre or an American Teale, or by traveling to the ends of the world, like a British Joicey, if you have ambitions in that direction.

BOOKS ON INSECT LIFE—*The Insect World of J. Henri Fabre*. Comments by Edwin Way Teale. Dodd, Mead & Company.
Edwin Way Teale. *Grassroot Jungles*. Also *Near Horizons* and *The Golden Throng*. Dodd, Mead & Company.

WORKING WITH OTHERS

It would be possible for you to go on for years, occupying yourself with whatever phase of insect life has caught your fancy, inventing your own approach and methods for arriving at conclusions. But you can, almost certainly, save yourself a great deal of effort by finding out from others what methods they have used in similar work. Also, sooner or later, you will want to share your findings with others. You can kill both of these "birds" with one stone by joining a local or national entomological society and taking part in its deliberations.

SOCIETIES—Entomological Society of America. Hdqrs.: 1530 P Street, N. W., Washington 5, D. C. Periodical: *Annals of the Entomological Society of America*.
American Entomological Society. Hdqrs.: 1900 Race Street, Philadelphia 3, Penn. Periodicals: *Entomological News*.

Very probably, there are insect students right in your own vicinity with whom you can exchange views. A local biology teacher or museum director may put you in contact with them, or you may be able to locate them through the pages of *The Naturalists' Directory* (see page 31). In this directory you will also find the names of collectors who are interested in exchanging specimens.

In addition to study and collecting helps, you may need aid in identifying some of your species. When local experts give up, send your specimen to the entomology department of a nearby museum or university, your state entomologist, or to the Bureau of Entomology and Plant Quarantine of the U. S. Department of Agriculture, Washington, D. C.

Note—Be sure that your specimen is *dead* before sending it for identification. It is against Federal Law to send live specimens of insects through the mails. However, certain specified live insects may be sent, but only by permit obtained from the Bureau of Entomology and Plant Quarantine.

There may be money in your insect hobby if you have the time and the interest for collecting specimens for the larger biological supply houses (for addresses, see page 28). Drop a line to them for their "lists of desiderata" and instructions for sending the insects.

Insects in the Field

EQUIPMENT FOR INSECT STUDY

Lutz, in his *Field Book of Insects,* gives the requisites of a successful insect enthusiast: "eyes, fingers and an inquiring mind. . . ." With those three things a firm foundation can be laid for getting close to the life of the six leggers.

STUDY EQUIPMENT—MAGNIFIERS—When it comes to studying minute insects and to distinguishing between tiny species, the naked eye is not sufficient. A magnifying glass is needed. The simplest kind for field work is one of the folding-type pocket magnifiers.

The most popular pocket magnifiers are made with one, two, or three lenses in individual mountings. The two-lens magnifier makes it possible for you to choose between three magnifications—such as 5×, 7×, or 10×—depending on whether you use one lens, the other or both together. The three-lens magnifier, similarly, gives you seven choices—usually from 5× to 20×.

Another pocket magnifier is the Coddington type. This consists of a single lens of special construction. Four models are available with magnifications of 7×, 10×, 14×, and 20×.

The most efficient—and most expensive—is the Hastings triplet. It is made up of a combination of highly corrected

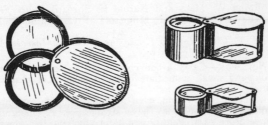

Three types of magnifiers: pocket magnifier (left), Coddington magnifier (top right), Hastings triplet (bottom right).

lenses, and has a wide angle of view. Here, also, you can take your choice between models of four magnifications.

KNIFE—You will need a knife to dig out the insects that live in bark and dead wood, or in the ground. A Scout sheath knife or hunting knife will be your best bet.

Tip—Or why not try this stunt: File down one side and the tip of a small, narrow garden trowel into a cutting edge. In this way you have a combination cutting and digging tool.

INSECT BOOKS—To the average person an ant is an ant, a bee a bee, a butterfly a butterfly. But the moment you start watching insects, you immediately discover that there are many kinds of ants, numerous different bees, hundreds of varieties of butterflies.

You will need a good field book to find your way in the insect world. When you know that more than 650,000 species have been described, and that new ones are still being found and added to the list, you will realize that it takes an outstanding expert to make a positive identification of anything but fairly common species.

But don't let that scare you away from identification. The field of insect study is wide open for people who have the patience and necessary power of observation to become experts in any of its multitudinous branches.

BOOKS FOR FIELD IDENTIFICATION—F. E. Lutz. *Field Book of Insects*. G. P. Putnam's Sons.

Alexander B. Klots. *Field Guide to the Butterflies*. Houghton Mifflin Company, Boston, Mass.

Ralph B. Swain. *The Insect Guide* (Orders and major families). Doubleday and Co.

OTHER BOOKS—J. H. Comstock. *An Introduction to Entomology*. Comstock Publishing Co., Ithaca, N. Y.

H. E. Jaques. *How to Know the Insects* (Illustrated key to common families). William C. Brown Co., Dubuque, Iowa.

Ralph W. Macy and Harold H. Shepard. *Butterflies*. The University of Minnesota Press, Minneapolis, Minn.

H. F. Chu. *How to Know the Immature Insects*. W. C. Brown, Dubuque, Iowa.

NOTEBOOK—Carry a conveniently sized loose-leaf notebook, and make immediate notes of your field observations.

In insect observation, even seemingly unimportant happenings or actions may have significance. A change in temperature as a cloud passes before the sun, the appearance of another insect on the scene, a suddenly encountered obstacle across the insect's path—these may each give an insight into the insect's reactions. Most of such observations will be lost unless they are recorded on the spot.

COLLECTING EQUIPMENT—See section starting on page 173.

FINDING INSECTS

Generally speaking, the answer to Where? and When? to find insects is "Anywhere—anytime." Wherever you are, you will always be able to find *some* insects. But when it comes to locating *certain* insects, you need to know their feeding habits, their way of propagating, their life cycles.

WHERE?—With eyes trained to see, you will notice insects in almost any outdoor locality you visit—and many indoor places as well.

GRASSES AND WEEDS harbor numerous crawling and jumping insects. Even in midwinter, colonies of insects may be found in grass tufts and in weed rosettes.

TREES AND SHRUBS—Look for insects feeding on leaves or hiding in bark furrows.

FLOWERS attract the large airborne insects—butterflies, moths, bees, flies—as well as numerous minute species.

SHALLOW MUD PUDDLES also draw butterflies, bees, and a number of other insects.

STREAMS AND LAKES contain hundreds of species—some of them scurrying over the surface, some swimming, others crawling on the bottom or burrowing in the mud, hiding under stones. The debris that has floated up on the windward shore of a lake may prove a regular treasure trove.

Numerous species—especially beetles—may be found by turning over ROCKS, DEBRIS, LEAF PILES, LOOSE BARK, COW DUNG AND OTHER MANURE, DEAD ANIMALS AND BIRDS.

Still others must be dug out of the GROUND, or cut out of ROTTING WOOD, FUNGI, GALLS, PLANT STEMS, FRUITS.

And then there are the HOUSEHOLD PESTS—the insects you find in woodwork and in food, in wool and in books, in warm attic and moist cellar.

Anywhere is right!

WHEN?—TIME OF YEAR—A great number of insects go through the complete metamorphosis of egg-larva-pupa-adult. Others have incomplete metamorphosis of egg-nymph-adult. The time when the insect changes from one form to the next varies with the species, but you can be sure to find one, two, or all of these forms the year round.

Eggs are most readily located from fall to spring, larvae and nymphs from spring to late summer, pupae from fall to spring, and adults in spring and summer. Some insects winter over in the larval stage. A number hibernate as adults, but the majority of adult insects die as soon as eggs have been laid to insure a new brood.

TIME OF DAY—WEATHER—Insects that move about by day are most active in warm, sunny weather. They are sluggish in the cool of morning, get more active in the middle of the day, slow down again as night falls.

Warm, sultry, overcast nights are the best for discovering the insects that travel by night. You will see very few when the night is cool. Similarly, you will have little success on clear nights—especially nights with a brilliant moon—no matter whether they are warm or not.

ATTRACTING INSECTS

Instead of going hunting far and wide for insects, you may prefer to take it easy and persuade the insects to come to you—and, by so doing, possibly even pick up species that you wouldn't come upon in your hunts.

You have your choice among several methods of attracting. Each of them is effective in its own way, bringing in insects that may not be attracted by any of the other means.

SUGARING—Sugaring is especially good for drawing moths and other nocturnal insects. It attracts them with a bait consisting mainly of slightly fermented fruit pulp and various kinds of sugars.

MAKING THE SUGARING BAIT—The three requirements for a successful mixture are these: it must *smell* sweetish; it must *taste* sweet; it must *paint well* without running too much. Here are several suggestions that may help you develop your own patent formula:

Rub pitted peaches, plums, or apricots (fresh, canned, or stewed dried) through a sieve. Let the pulp stand a day or so to ferment, then add white or brown sugar. OR mash overripe bananas; mix with sugar; stand in warm place to ferment. OR stir teaspoon of rum or rum flavoring into heavy molasses or honey. OR dissolve brown sugar in stale beer.

METHOD OF SUGARING—Set out just before dark on a sultry evening or even on a night with a warm drizzle— with can of bait, paint brush, and flashlight.

Choose a territory with trees or posts, preferably on the outskirts of woods or orchards. Select a circular route of about half a mile—one you can cover in fifteen minutes or so.

Paint a palm-sized dab of your sugaring bait on the lee

side of some of the tree trunks, at shoulder height. Use trees that stand about fifty feet apart—more or less.

When you have finished the painting, start from the beginning with your flashlight and take your pick from the moths and other insects that have arrived. Make your rounds several times during the night, each time adding to your collection.

Some of the insects will let themselves fall into your collecting jar, if you hold the jar directly under them. Others may need a slight poke with the edge of the jar before they let go and drop in.

> *Tip*—Go back over your "trap line" during daylight the following day. Your bait may prove equally irresistible to a number of butterflies, wasps, bees, and other day-roaming insects.

LIGHTS—Most of the night fliers are subject to *phototaxis*—or, in simpler language, are attracted by light. You remember having seen moths by the hundreds—and gnats by the thousands—fluttering around a street lamp or a porch light, mostly on warm humid nights.

You can make use of this phenomenon in several ways.

DISHPAN METHOD—Place a large dishpan on the ground. Pour in 1 inch of water. Put three small stones on the bottom of the pan in a triangle, and place a lighted kerosene or gasoline lantern on the stones, thus keeping it raised above the water surface. Wait for the insects to fly around until they drop into the water exhausted.

SHEET METHOD—Hang up a sheet or other white cloth between two trees or posts, with 1 foot of the lower edge flat on the ground. Or, if in camp, simply use a white tent. Suspend a kerosene or gasoline lantern three to four feet in front of it. Or even better, run a wire from the house, if possible, and use an electric bulb.

A light trap may be made from wood or from a large can, with a front of two pieces of glass with an opening between them.

Tip—Experiment with different-colored light bulbs. Blue light may prove most effective.

Place a reflector (a piece of tin can) behind the light source, so that the light falls on the sheet.

Tip—Your car gives you a quick light source. Drive it up in front of the sheet, and train the headlights full on it.

Some insects will finally come to rest on the sheet, others will drop to the ground in front of it—hence the turned lower edge.

LIGHT TRAPS—The best method for a number of insects is to use a light trap that will attract them and keep them imprisoned so that you can watch their reaction, or until you are ready to take them out.

Such a trap may consist of a box made from plywood or from a five-gallon can, with a front of two pieces of glass arranged with an opening between them, and at such an angle that the insects can get in but can not find their way out (see drawings on page 171).

The light source may be an ordinary electric bulb wired to the house circuit, or a flashlight bulb powered by two or three flashlight batteries.

GROUND TRAPS—Many insects—particularly roaches, crickets, and beetles—may be caught in baited ground traps.

MOLASSES TRAPS—Sink pint jars or tin cans into the ground with their tops level with the surface. Pour in about 1 inch of a mixture of two parts molasses and one part water, or one of the concoctions suggested for sugaring.

The insects are attracted by the sweetness, drop in, and drown. Lift them out with a tea strainer, and wash them free of molasses.

Tip—You can establish a trap line by placing a number of these traps, 20 to 30 feet apart, in a circular course. Mark the locations clearly with sticks. Make your rounds once a day.

CARRION TRAPS—Certain burying and scavenging beetles are attracted to decaying meat and fish.

Place a dead mouse, or other dead animal, a slice of meat, a pat of hamburger, or a piece of fried fish on the ground. Cover it loosely with a board to prevent carrion-eating birds from stealing it. Inspect it a day later and take your pick from the insect assortment that has congregated.

PLANTING FOR INSECTS—You may increase the insect population of your garden by planting trees, flowers, and vegetables that attract the species in which you are particularly interested. Some of these plants may provide food for larvae, others nectar for the adult insects. Some will do both. Most of them will add beauty to your garden, or will be among your usual vegetables.

TREES AND SHRUBS—Fruit trees, especially apple. Most shade trees: maple, oak, hickory, elm. Linden, willow. Wild cherry. Sassafras. Spicebush. Lilac. Buttonbush. Barberry. Butterfly bush.

FLOWERS—Hollyhock, bee balm, milkweed, butterfly weed, verbena, marigold, zinnia. And such night-scented flowers as flowering tobacco, garden heliotrope, honeysuckle.

VEGETABLES—Carrot, cabbage, bean, cucumber, pea, squash, potato, tomato. Remember that plants raised to attract insects may not yield much for the household table. Insects and insecticides don't mix.

Tip—Lutz's *Field Book of Insects* lists the food plants of all the important species of insects.

CATCHING INSECTS
The method for catching insects depends on the life

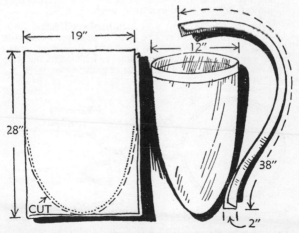

Fold the material for the sweeping net in half before cutting. Re-enforce edge with strip of material, 4 inches wide.

habits of the species you are after. The necessary equipment may be bought through a biological supply house (page 28). In most instances, you can make it yourself.

SWEEPING—Sweeping usually produces quicker results than any other method for catching insects. It consists of swinging a net back and forth, like a sweeping broom, over and through grasses and other vegetation to scoop up the insects.

SWEEPING NET—The net used for sweeping is literally meant to "take a beating." It must therefore be made of sturdy material: lightweight canvas, unbleached muslin, or better still, airplane cloth. The diameter of the net is about 12 inches, its depth approximately 28 inches, with a 2-inch pocket-hem along the top. Thirty inches of material in the commercial width of 38 inches will suffice. Cut it to pattern and sew as shown on page 173.

> *Tip*—If you want to be able to see your catch, make the bottom-quarter of the bag of voile or marquisette.

The frame consists of a piece of spring steel wire, 8 or 10 gauge, 45 inches long. Bend approximately 38 inches of it into a circle, 12 inches in diameter, leaving the ends of the wire straight—one for 3 inches, the other for 4 inches. Bend ½ inch of each tip at a 90-degree angle.

> *Tip*—Many entomologists swear by the angler's "landing net," using its collapsible frame with insect netting instead of the regular cotton mesh.

Make the handle from a ¾-inch hardwood dowel stick, or an old broom handle. The usually preferred length is 18 to 24 inches, although you may find some other length more suitable for your sweeping style. Gouge out two grooves at one end of handle, on opposite sides, to fit the

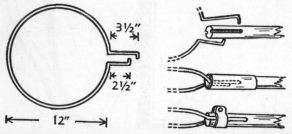

The frame for the sweeping net is a wire ring. Hold it in position with ferrule (right center) or hose clamp (right bottom).

Sweeping consists in moving the net vigorously from side to side
with the net always open in the direction of the stroke.

straight ends of the frame wire. The bent tips of the wire
lock into holes bored in the handle. Wrap thin wire
around the frame ends and handle, or hold in position
with electrician's tape or adhesive tape. Even better, keep
it in place with a hose clamp, or place a brass ferrule
around the handle. Clamp or ferrule makes it possible to
remove the frame from the handle.

SWEEPING TECHNIQUE—Make a few practice sweeps.
Grasp the end of the handle. Sweep the net from right
to left, with the frame opening toward the left, using a
forehand stroke. At the end of the sweep, twist the wrist
so that the frame opening now is toward the right, and
make a left-to-right sweep, using a backward stroke.
Continue sweeping back and forth in this manner, in an
uninterrupted, smooth movement.

Stop with the handle in horizontal position, twisting it
quickly, so that the frame opening is toward the ground.
This causes the lower part of the net bag to fall over
the rim of the frame, with the result that everything
swept into the bag is now "locked" in. Get into the habit
of doing this final twist automatically whenever you stop

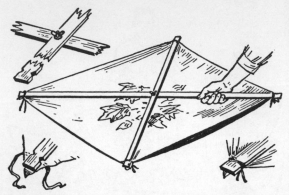

The beating cloth is a yard square. Tie it to rustic sticks or to two pieces of lath, held together with bolt and wing nut.

sweeping. It is one of the marks of the expert collector.

After a small amount of practice, you are ready for the "real thing": In your first strokes, sweep through tops of weeds and grasses. In subsequent strokes, sweep closer to the ground. After a few sweeps, stop and investigate.

BEATING—Some insects stick so closely to tree branches and brushes that sweeping doesn't loosen them. Beating the branches may dislodge them.

BEATING EQUIPMENT—The necessary equipment consists of a club and a beating cloth—or an old umbrella.

The club is a stout stick, about 1½ inches thick, 2½ to 3 feet long. Cut it in the field, or bring it from home.

The *beating cloth* is made from a piece of unbleached muslin or sheeting, a yard square. Hem the edges. Sew a 6-inch piece of tape in each corner. Make the frame from two sticks 4½ feet long. Tie them together in the middle to form a cross. Stretch the cloth *under* the frame by tying the four tapes to the four stick ends.

Tip—Instead of rustic sticks, you may prefer to use two pieces of lath, ½ inch thick, 1½ inches wide, 4½ feet long. Drill a small hole in the middle of each. Fasten them together, crosswise, with a small bolt and wing nut. When not in use, loosen the bolt, fold frame together and roll it in the beating cloth.

BEATING METHOD—Beat the branches with the club in one hand. With the other hand, hold the beating cloth horizontally below the branches, to catch the insects as they fall.

> *Tip*—To keep the more vigorous insects from jumping out of the beating cloth, place some dead leaves and other debris in the cloth for them to hide under.

AIR NETTING—The main use of this method is for catching butterflies and moths in flight. While sweeping is an indiscriminate process, air netting is a highly selective one, with more of the thrill of real hunting.

AERIAL NET—The aerial net can be made to the same simple pattern and in the same manner as the sweeping net (see page 174). A better net results when you sew together four pieces, following the pattern suggested below. To cut down air resistance, use a medium-mesh netting—bobbinet, marquisette, brussel, or silk bolting cloth.

Reinforce the pocket-hem with muslin or airplane cloth: Sew a 4-inch-wide strip of this material along the top.

Make the handle of a length to suit yourself—2½, 3 feet or longer.

> *Tip*—An emergency aerial net may be improvised by pinning a piece of mosquito netting or cheesecloth

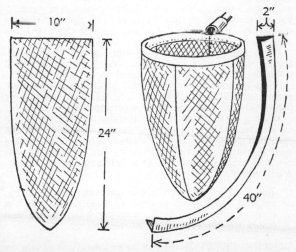

A strong aerial net results when you sew it together from four pieces of material, of the dimensions shown above.

into a bag, and attaching it with more pins to a ring made from a wire clothes hanger.

METHOD OF NETTING—In hunting for butterflies and moths, it is of great help to you to know botany. By locating the right plants at the right season, you are certain to have a successful hunt of flower-visiting insects.

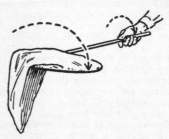

After sweeping, lock in your catch by twisting the handle so that the bottom of the net falls over the frame.

Wait for the insect to settle on the food plant. Then swing the net in an easy, forehand stroke sideways toward the flower, with the net frame vertical, the opening toward the insect. Scoop the insect into the net, reverse the stroke, stop, twist the handle so that the bag locks over the rim.

If you miss, don't go on a wild chase after your intended victim. Stay where you are. The butterfly will probably return—only to be picked up the next time.

Some butterflies have the habit of dropping when disturbed, others fly straight up. You will soon learn their habits, so that you will know where to aim.

With a little practice, it is possible to "draw a bead" on an insect. Hold on to the bottom of the net with one hand, sling-shot fashion, while straining handle and frame with the other. By suddenly letting the net hand go, the net will pick up the insect in a lightning swoop—if correctly aimed.

Tip—On an automobile trip through new territory, suspend a net from a window, frame opening to the front. Cruise at about 30 miles per hour, or less, and empty the net every five minutes or so.

WATER NETTING—Most water insects are caught by netting, although a number of them may be picked up with the fingers.

AQUATIC NET—The aquatic net is constructed in the same way as the aerial and sweeping nets, but it need not be as deep, since the insects that are caught do not have to be "locked in." A depth of 18 inches is sufficient for a bag 12 inches in diameter.

The material used should be extra sturdy—heavy scrim, for instance.

The wire for the frame should be of ¼-inch thickness, preferably of coppered steel so that it will not rust.

Tip—The frame may be kept circular, but becomes more efficient when bent into D-shape, with the flattened side opposite to the handle.

Tip—A simple seine may be improvised from a piece of ⅛-inch window screening, 2 feet long, 1 foot wide. Tack each narrow side to a 2-foot stick.

USING THE NET—Use the aquatic net in a manner similar to the sweeping net, moving it from side to side in the water, with a hand twist at the end of each stroke.

Begin at the surface—or even above it if plants grow out of the water—then sweep deeper and deeper, finally into the mud of the bottom.

In a fast moving stream, wind up by placing the net firmly on the bottom, with the frame opening upstream. Have a companion move rocks and stones, or dig into the bottom above the net. The insects will be swept into the net by the flowing water.

Tip—A couple of pie plates, painted white, makes it easy for you to examine your catch.

DIGGING AND TURNING—Great numbers of species of small insects live in the ground, in decaying wood, in moss and dead leaves, under stones and logs. You can locate them only by digging or turning.

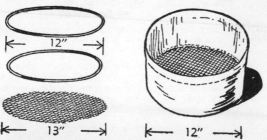

A collapsible sieve is made from two wire rings, a piece of ¼-inch wire mesh, and a cylinder sown from a strip of cloth.

EQUIPMENT—Carry a strong trowel or sheath knife, or the combination digging-cutting tool described on page 168.

To separate insects from dirt and debris, use an *insect sieve* made from ¼-inch galvanized wire mesh. Cut the mesh into a circle, 13 inches in diameter. Make two rings, 12 inches in diameter, of ¼-inch steel wire. Bend the edges of the mesh circle around one ring, solder into position. Sew a piece of heavy muslin, 38 inches long, 10 inches wide, into a cylinder. Sew one edge of this cloth cylinder around the mesh-covered wire ring, the other to the free ring.

Tip—A wire basket used for popping corn may be used for sifting small quantities.

SIFTING—Throw a thin layer of dug-up dirt or dead leaves into the sieve. Sift a small amount of it on to a piece of white cloth. Study the siftings carefully, pick out the insects, throw the debris away, then sift more.

Tip—Some of the insects may be so tiny that they can not be picked up with the fingers or forceps. Use a *suction bottle* or *"aspirator."* This consists of a glass vial, closed with a cork through which two metal tubes lead. One short tube ends just below the cork, the other, longer tube, goes almost to the bottom of the

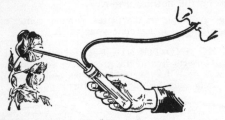

Tiny insects may have to be picked up with a suction bottle or "aspirator." Air current sweeps them into the vial.

vial. By placing the opening of the longer tube near the insect, and drawing in the air sharply through a rubber tube attached to the short metal tube, by mouth or rubber bulb, the air current sweeps the insect into the vial.

INSECT LISTS AND SURVEYS

To the amateur entomologist, the taking of an insect survey can be an exciting adventure.

It is far more than that to the professional entomologists—such as the members of the Bureau of Entomology and Plant Quarantine, of the Department of Agriculture. A correct egg-bed count for grasshopper eggs, a square-infestation check for cotton-boll weevils, a hessian-fly survey is the means of determining whether there's danger ahead, and of deciding what control methods need to be taken. Acting upon an insect survey may mean life or death to fields, gardens, and orchards, prosperity or poverty to the farmer, low or high prices for Mr. Average Citizen.

Surveys involve listing the species that inhabit a given area, and learning, by sampling, the abundance of them.

INSECT LISTING—The moment you start making notes of the insects you see and catch, you have taken your first step toward making your insect survey.

REGIONAL LISTS—Make a determined effort, through your own investigation, and with the help of other insect enthusiasts, to discover and catch confirmatory specimens of the insects that inhabit a certain region—not in terms of square miles, but of a specific locality, such as a garden plot, an orchard, a camp site. Don't bite off more than you can chew. Dr. Frank E. Lutz found 1402 different species in his 75-foot by 200 foot suburban home-lot.

REFERENCE—Frank E. Lutz. *A Lot of Insects.* G. P. Putnam's Sons.

A thorough-going listing of the insects of your locality and recording of unusual species found may be of great interest to the department of agriculture or of conservation of your state. You may have found species not previously recorded. Such a discovery has occasionally meant the stamping out of a newly introduced insect pest before it had a chance to become established.

LIFE LISTS—For your own satisfaction, list all the insects you encounter in your entomological pursuits. Use your *Field Book of Insects* for this record. Write date and place where an insect is seen in the margin of the page that carries the description of it.

SAMPLING—It is obviously impossible to determine the complete insect population of a locality. The nearest you can come to it is to sample a small part of the area, and then multiply to get an estimate.

SAMPLING SURFACE INSECTS—In field and garden, the insects above ground may be sampled by enclosing a certain small area and quickly killing off the trapped insects.

The usual size area surveyed is ½ square foot—72

square inches. Multiply by 87,120 to find number of insects per acre of similar vegetation.

An easy "trap" can be made from a piece of sheet iron, about 12 inches wide, 35 inches long. Bend it into a square box, without top or bottom, with 8½-inch sides. This leaves 1 inch for overlap to be soldered in place. The 8½ ×8½ square inches it encloses is within ¼ square inch of the ½ square foot—exact enough for your purpose.

Cover the inside with a film of kerosene, place it over the area to be surveyed. Spray the interior thoroughly with a contact insecticide. Some of the insects will jump about and get stuck to the side of the trap. The rest may be combed out with your fingers.

Tip—An even simpler sampling trap is produced by knocking the bottom off an ordinary 16 quart galvanized pail with a bottom diameter of 9½ inches. It will enclose approximately 71 square inches. To be exact, the diameter should be 9.56 inches.

SAMPLING GROUND INSECTS—After having removed the top vegetation, dig out the soil enclosed by the sampling trap, to a depth of 6 inches. Find out by sifting (see page 180) the insect count in this ¼ cubic foot of soil.

FIELD OBSERVATION

The books by famous Fabre, Maeterlinck, Teale, and many others suggest the discoveries that the insect world may reveal to you, if you have the necessary patience and keenness of observation. Those books will also suggest methods to employ in the field study of insects. You will find ideas for further study on almost every page of Lutz's *Field Book of Insects,* and in the same author's *A Lot of Insects.*

The number of opportunities for special field observations is so immense that any list of suggestions can only scratch the surface. Nevertheless, here goes:

LIFE CYCLES—The life cycles and life span are known for comparatively few insects. This field is wide open for investigation.

"SOCIAL LIFE"—While the lives of ants and bees have been thoroughly investigated, little has been done with other gregarious insects.

FEEDING HABITS—Larvae of a certain species generally feed on a specific feed plant. Can feeding habits be changed artificially—from cultured plants to weeds, for instance?

LOCOMOTION—Influence of light and shade, temperature, moisture, etc., on speed of crawling and running insects. Flight patterns of winged forms, influence of wind.

Tip—Tiny dabs of different-colored enamel or finger nail polish may be placed on back or "thigh" of hind legs to identify certain insects for the purpose of determining whether they return repeatedly to the same locality.

INSECT HOMES—Kinds of insect homes found locally—nests, tubes, etc. Galls as insect homes; types of abnormal plant growth associated with various insects (see Lutz's *Field Book of Insects*).

"MUSIC"—Influence of temperature, moisture, and so on, on rate of chirps of "music-making" insects—such as grasshoppers, crickets, katydids, and other Orthopterae. Does formula worked out for snowy tree cricket work with others ($T = 50 + \dfrac{N - 40}{4}$; T: temperature in degrees Fahrenheit, N: number of chirps per minute)?

RECORDINGS—*The Songs of Insects.* Cornell University Records, Ithaca, N. Y.

LIGHT OF FIRE-FLIES and other light-bearers. Purpose. Effect of temperature on number of flashes. And the tremendous accomplishment awaiting achievement: producing the same kind of "cold" light synthetically—but that's chemistry, not entomology.

MIGRATION of the monarch and other migrating butterflies. Finding local gathering spots—"butterfly trees." Develop marking method for following their flight in co-operation with entomologists throughout the country.

Tip—Lutz has suggested spraying massed monarchs with a watery solution of an aniline dye—a distinctive color for identification of a specific flock. Add detergent in order to wet down the wing scales to make the color stick.

INSECTICIDES—Effectiveness on different species.

OTHER STUDIES—Protective coloration. Mimicry. Intelligence and senses.

Rearing Insects

One of the most intriguing features of insect study is the fact that you are able to follow and watch the life cycle of many of them—from egg to adult insect. It is difficult to do this out-of-doors—in many cases impossible. The solution is to rear the insects in which you are interested, in captivity.

Some species are suitable for study in this way, others are not. It is exceedingly interesting to watch the social life of ants and bees, for instance. But you would hardly have the patience to follow the cicada eating its way through a seventeen-year diet of roots, nor might you care to introduce a colony of termites into your house.

With hundreds of thousands of species to choose from, it is obviously impossible to suggest methods for raising them all. We have to concentrate on a few of the more important orders.

ROACHES, GRASSHOPPERS, ETC.—The most accomplished insect musicians belong in this group. You may want to raise these hardy creatures for the sake of listening to their sweet (?) music, in addition to watching them go through their incomplete metamorphosis, from eggs, through nymphs to the adult stage.

ROACHES AND CRICKETS—These insects may be reared in almost any kind of a glass container, from a 1-quart mason jar, to a 1-gallon mayonnaise jar, battery jar, or aquarium tank. Spread about 2 inches of soil on the bottom, and place a watch glass on top of this for a water trough. Cover with a lid of screen wire.

Feed bread soaked in water, corn mush, mashed potatoes, bits of lettuce, and occasionally a delicacy such as peanut butter or library paste. Keep watch glass filled with water.

Tip—The lantern globe cage described on page 186 is also suitable for crickets and roaches.

GRASSHOPPERS AND WALKING STICKS—Use the same kind of containers as for crickets, but instead of putting in plain soil, cut a sod of grass, about 2 inches thick, and line the bottom with this. Water the grass from time to time. The grass provides food, the soil a place for the female to deposit her eggs.

PRAYING MANTIS—In fall or winter, you may find a mantis egg case containing hundreds of eggs. Bring it indoors and place it in a container similar to that used for crickets.

The young mantises (mantes, or mantids—whichever plural you prefer) emerge after a few weeks. They are carnivorous, feeding on live insects. Give them aphids for their "baby" diet, later on house flies, bees, roaches. If you don't feed them enough, they turn cannibal and eat each other.

Tip—If you can't manage to provide live insects, try feeding tiny pieces of liver or chopped meat. Serve on the tip of a toothpick, or hold loosely between two fingers.

BUTTERFLIES AND MOTHS—Butterflies and moths may be reared from larvae or pupae. You can also rear

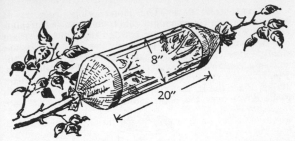

A transparent rearing cage, surrounding caterpillars on their feed plant, makes an interesting display on the nature trail.

them from eggs, laid by captive females, or found in the fields.

CATERPILLARS—The important secret for raising butterflies and moths from caterpillars is to keep them supplied with their food plant. The adult female lays her eggs on a specific plant, peculiar to her species, and the emerging larvae seldom touch any other plant, but rather die from starvation. Therefore, in collecting larvae for rearing it is very important to identify the feed plant, bring home some leaves, and know where to find more to satisfy the larvae's voracious appetites.

Tip—Lutz's *Field Book of Insects* lists the food plants of most common caterpillars.

The food plant must be kept fresh—either by keeping it growing where it is, by potting it, or by placing cut stalks in water. The more airtight the container is in which plant and larvae are kept, the longer the leaves remain fresh and palatable. Have no fear of suffocating the larvae. They need very little air to exist.

OUTDOOR CAGES—The larvae may be left on their feed plant and prevented from straying by enclosing the plant in a piece of cheesecloth or tobacco cloth, tying it up top and bottom.

If you want to observe your captives, make a transparent cage from a piece of cellulose acetate, 20×25 inches (one-half sheet, commercial size). Roll it into a 20-inch-long cylinder. Overlap the two edges about ¾ inch, and glue them together with fast drying acetate cement. Glue (or sew) a 12-inch-wide sleeve of muslin or netting to each end of the cylinder. Slip the cage over the feed plant, and tie the two sleeve ends around the plant.

LANTERN-GLOBE CAGE—The lantern-globe cage is of appropriate size for rearing a couple of larvae of a single species. Fill a flower pot or coffee can with soil. Plant one or more of the feed plants in the soil, if they are small. Otherwise, sink a small mayonnaise jar into the soil as a container for water and for stalks of the plant. Punch holes in the cover in which to place the plant stalks. Place the larvae on the feed plant. Bring a lantern globe down over the plant, pushing its lower edge into

A lantern globe is the main part of a quickly made rearing cage. Place it in a container of sand, around feed plant and larvae.

the soil. Cover the top with a lid of fine wire mesh or screening.

AQUARIUM CAGE—An old aquarium tank is excellent for raising a large number of larvae. Cover the bottom with a couple of inches of moist soil. Plant feed plants in this, or place jars with stalks in water in the cage. Put in the larvae. Cover with a glass plate.

WOODEN REARING CAGE—You can make a very satisfactory cage from an orange crate. Remove the bottom. Cut three ¼-inch-wide slots in the partition board—the middle slot one-third, the other two two-thirds, of the way down. Place the crate on end, paint it white, inside and out. Get two pieces of glass to fit front and back of "upstairs compartment." Pot up three to five feed plants. Slide the stalks into the slots in such a way that the feed is "upstairs," the pots themselves "downstairs." Prop up the flower pots to keep them in position. Place a layer of soil on the partition board. Put the larvae on the feed plant. Fasten the two glass plates in position with L-screws.

Tip—An even simpler cage may be made from any wooden box or crate. Knock off the bottom. Stand the box on one end. Place potted feed plants with the larvae on them in box. Cover front and back with window screening.

PUPATION—The larvae will pass through several moltings, and will finally reach the pupation stage. They will be "off their feed" figuratively, and may possibly literally be off their food plant, if they are the kind that go underground to pupate (hence the dirt on the bottom of the rearing chamber). Leave them alone, but study their activities carefully. Make notes, or take photographs. Keep the pupae for the adult insect to emerge.

Note—You will sometimes discover that instead of raising larva to pupa, you are raising a brood of ichneumon wasps or tachinid flies. Most of these parasitic wasps and flies lay their eggs in caterpillars. The parasitic larvae feed on the flesh of their live host, finally pupate as the host dies. The wasp pupae often look like eggs attached to the outside of the caterpillar.

PUPAE—In addition to pupae that you may have "grown" yourself, it should not be hard for you to locate a few in the open. While chrysalids are generally rather hard to find, the cocoons of the larger species of moths make easy hunting—if you know what to look for and where.

FINDING COCOONS—The cocoons of the polyphemus moth usually fall to the ground under the fruit or willow tree on which the larvae fed. Similarly, luna-moth cocoons may be found beneath hickory and walnut trees. Cynthia and promethea cocoons dangle by one end, while cecropia cocoons are firmly attached at their full length to the branches of host trees.

REARING PUPAE—Almost any container will do for storage and emerging case—a 1-gallon jar, an old aquarium tank, a wooden box, even a large tin can—so long as it has room for a couple of branches onto which the emerged adult can crawl to dry and spread its wings.

Place a 1-inch layer of dirt or sphagnum moss on the bottom of the container. Lay the pupae on it. Plant a few short sticks. Cover with a piece of window screening. Sprinkle pupae and dirt with water regularly—once a week or so—to keep them from drying out. The air in the container should be humid, but not so moist that the contents get moldy.

Tip—Instead of placing the pupae on the ground, many entomologists prefer to glue the pupae to the sticks, with a couple of drops of glue, to keep them from actually touching the dirt.

CONTROLLING THE EMERGENCE—Regulate the temperature so that the adults will emerge at a time to suit your purposes.

In a warm room, the adults will usually emerge in two months' time—or a little more. Pupae found in late fall will provide butterflies or moths, as the case may be, in midwinter. See *Tip* on checking emergence on page 197.

If you aim to secure eggs and to raise larvae, the emergence should be delayed until the normal time when the natural food plants are available. This may be done by keeping your container between a regular window and the storm window on the north side of the house, in a glass container placed on the ground in the garden, or even by storing your pupae in the humidifier compartment of your refrigerator. In the latter case, bring them out as late winter turns into spring. To secure fertile eggs, you need, of course, to have both sexes emerge from your collection of pupae.

Tip—A newly emerged female moth has a magnetic attraction for the males. Put it in a cheesecloth-covered glass jar. Place this outdoors in the evening and wait for the males to come around.

BEETLES—It is comparatively easy to study the life cycle of almost any beetle. Simply keep the specimens confined in a glass container with a fairly high humidity, and provide them with their favorite food.

As an example, you may want to follow the cycle of the tenebrio beetle—the mealworm beetle—and, while studying insect metamorphosis, at the same time produce the favorite food of aquarium fish, pet birds, and small reptiles.

MEALWORM CULTURE—Fill a mason jar or battery jar half full of ordinary breakfast bran, or a mixture of bran and breadcrumbs. Lay a piece of crumpled newspaper or paper towling on top of it, and on this place a thick slice of apple, a scraped carrot, or half a potato—partly for food, mostly for moisture.

The tenebrio is an insect pest often found in granaries, or even in home-stored cereals, where you may be able to find specimens to start a culture. Otherwise, purchase a culture from a biological supply house (addresses, see page 28). This will consist of bran containing adults, eggs, pupae, and larvae of all sizes.

Dump the culture in your container, cover with cheesecloth or wire screening, place in a warm location—and let nature take its course. Replenish the apple slice, or whatever you are using, when it dries up.

DERMESTID BEETLE CULTURE—The raising of a culture

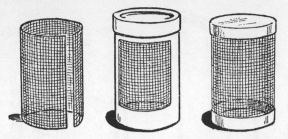

Wire mesh can be used for rearing cages, with an ice cream container, as suggested by Pickwell, or with tin can lids.

of dermestid beetles is another double feature. You can follow the life circle of a beetle, and in feeding it its favorite food, you can use it for cleaning up skulls and small skeletons for a mammal collection (see instructions on page 141).

ANTS, BEES, AND WASPS—The social life of ants and bees probably provides the greatest amount of entertainment and the best possible opportunities for learning to make careful and detailed observation.

ANTS—Two types of ant house—or *formicarium*, if you want to be technical—are popular: the dirt-filled anthill house that gives you a chance to follow the ants' tunnel-digging prowess, and the dirt-free house that gives you an unobstructed view of the ants' comings and goings.

ANTHILL HOUSE—In its simplest form, the anthill house consists of two pieces of window glass of commercial size—10×14 inches or 12×18 inches—attached to the two sides of a wooden frame made up of strips of wood, ¾ inch square. The top side of the frame is removable and provided with three holes—each closed with a small piece of tin or strip of wood, turning on a nail. The whole "house" may be put together with adhesive tape. It rests, on one edge, on a couple of wooden blocks, in slits cut to fit (see drawings, page 190). Cover both panes of glass with pieces of cardboard to keep the interior dark. Remove the cardboard during observation.

FILLING THE ANTHILL HOUSE—Locate an anthill in the field. Dig into the side of it with a trowel or with rubber-gloved hands. Scoop out a couple of handfuls of ant-dirt mixture, and place them in a screw-top glass jar. Include eggs, larvae, pupae ("ants' eggs"), and if possible, a queen—you will know her by her larger size.

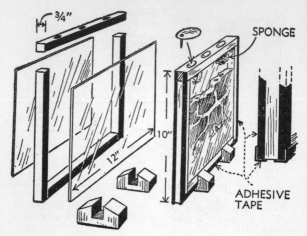

Two sheets of glass, a few strips of wood and a bit of adhesive tape are the ingredients for making an anthill house.

At home, pour the ant mixture into the house through the open top. Before replacing top, hang a small sponge under two of the openings.

Ants need moisture and food. Provide the first by keeping one sponge moist with water, the latter by placing drops of honey and water (half and half) on the other sponge. From time to time throw in a few flies or other insects.

DIRT-FREE ANT HOUSE—The best known dirt-free ant house is the Fielde design. This consists of a flat, glass-covered tray, usually approximately 12 inches long, 8 inches wide, 1 inch deep. Half of it is the living compartment. The remaining space is divided into two smaller rooms—one a moisture room that contains a damp sponge, the other the feeding room.

Such ant houses are commercially available. You can readily make your own.

Use six strips of ½×1-inch wood—two 12-inch pieces, three 7-inch pieces, one 5-inch piece. Tack four strips into a frame, then partition it off as shown on working drawing on page 191. Gouge ½-inch doorways to connect main room and two small rooms. Bore two holes through the outside wall into each small room—of such size that ordinary eyedroppers will fit snugly in them. Tack frame to piece of plywood, 12×18 inches, with the "doorways" down. Varnish or shellac inside and outside. Put eyedroppers into position, one with water, the other with feeding mixture (page 190). Place a small piece of sponge at tip of water dropper. Cover the whole thing with a piece of glass, and lay a sheet of cardboard over this to darken the interior.

Tip—Instead of cardboard, use pieces of red glass, cut to fit over each room. You can easily follow the activities of the ants under the red glass. They behave under this glass as if they were in the darkness they desire. Removing the red glass from any one of the rooms will cause the ants to move into the other two.

INTRODUCING THE ANTS—Purchase an ant colony of half a hundred ants with a queen, or collect the ants as suggested on page 189—dirt and all. The trick now is to get the ants into the house, leaving the dirt outside. To do this, spread a newspaper on a table. Place the house on the middle of it. Place a piece of cardboard over the house to darken the interior. Remove both eyedroppers after having moistened the sponge in the "moisture room." Along the edge of the newspaper, make a smooth, 1-inch-high ridge of dry plaster-of-paris powder, creating a so-called "Forel arena." Then dump your ant-dirt mixture in the arena and watch the proceedings. As the dirt dries out, the ants try to get away. They soon give up their attempts to climb the plaster wall, and seek shelter in the house where moisture and darkness await them. When they are in, put the eyedropper "door" back in, place ant house in its permanent locátion, carefully, without jarring, and remove the newspaper and plaster.

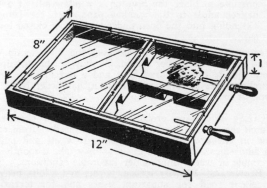

Dirt-free ant house is a wooden frame covered with a sheet of glass. The ants are watered and fed from eye droppers.

REFERENCE—*Studying Ants in Observation Nests.* Turtox
Service Leaflet No. 35. Free. General Biological Supply House, Chicago 37, Illinois.

BEES—The observation beehive—or *apiary*—like the
ant house, will provide endless opportunities for observations. It may be purchased from a biological supply
house, bees and all.

SUPPLIES—Biological supply houses. Addresses on page 28.
A. I. Root Co., Medina, Ohio.

MAKING AN OBSERVATION HIVE—If you desire to construct your own, make the acquaintance of a local bee
fancier. Get his help and his suggestions. And persuade
him to let you buy a few of his beekeeper's supplies. He
gets his brood frames and supers by the dozen or by the
hundred and buys beeswax brood foundations and super
foundations by the pound—where you only need a couple.
The construction of the hive depends on the supplies
you succeed in getting. In main, the hive consists of a
lower compartment with one or two brood frames with
brood foundations attached where the young are raised,
and an upper story with two supers provided with foundations for storing surplus honey. Build an outside frame
to enclose the parts, with runway and entrance hole at
the bottom and with glass front and back. Cover the
glass with cardboard when the bees are not under observation.

> *Tip*—Construct the hive with the entrance runway at
> one side, rather than front or back. This makes it
> possible to place the hive on a window sill, at a 90-
> degree angle to the window pane, with the runway
> extending into the open under the almost closed lower
> sash.

STOCKING THE HIVE—In stocking the hive, again depend on your beekeeper friend. He may be able to supply
you with a few hundred bees and a queen. Otherwise,
purchase bees by the pound from a mail-order house or
from a biological supply house.

FLIES—You have probably already had a chance to
watch the life cycle of the ordinary housefly—from eggs
laid in garbage, through wriggling maggots and pupae,
to adult flies. The whole business may take a month—or
a couple of weeks only, under favorable conditions.
BLOWFLIES—Blowfly larvae, pupae, and adults provide
excellent food for aquarium fishes and for terrarium
frogs and lizards. They are quickly and easily raised in
quantity by placing a strip of meat on which eggs have

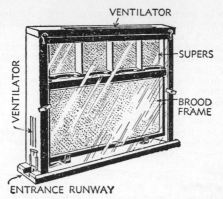

VENTILATOR

SUPERS

VENTILATOR

BROOD FRAME

ENTRANCE RUNWAY

Secure the supers and the brood frame for a bee observation hive from a biological supply house or from a local bee keeper.

been laid in a jar, on top of a few inches of moist sand. Cover the jar with a piece of cheesecloth. As the larvae emerge, they feed on the meat, finally bury themselves in the sand to pupate. The adults appear about a week later.

DROSOPHILA FLIES—The raising of the tiny vinegar flies, *Drosophila melanogaster,* has become an important means of studying heredity and demonstrating the Mendelian ratio.

SIMPLE REARING—Starting a culture is easy enough. All you have to do is to mash a piece of ripe banana and leave it in the open. In a short while vinegar flies appear and deposit their eggs. The larvae emerge in a couple of days and feed on the banana for about a week. They then pupate, to emerge as adults after another five days.

CONTROLLED REARING—For the study of genetics, such a crude method for raising your laboratory "animals" is not adequate. Instead, you need to develop your culture in sterile bottles, on a medium not readily subject to molds—such as Bridges' agar-corn-meal formula (10 gr. agar, 50 gr. corn meal, 35 cc. molasses, and 500 cc. water, boiled together).

Pour approximately 1 inch of this medium into pint jars or half-pint milk bottles, or ½ inch into 4-ounce, wide-mouth bottles. Insert a strip of paper toweling in each bottle in such a way that a couple of inches of it is above the medium—for the larvae to pupate on. The jars are closed with wads of cotton and sterilized in pressure cooker or autoclave.

After cooling, drop one drop of a yeast and water

mixture on the medium, and place a number of drosophila flies in the bottle. The mated females lay their eggs in the medium, and your culture is under way.

The new adults, emerging ten days to two weeks later, are anesthetized with ether. A male and a female with decisive characteristics—red eyes and white eyes, for instance—are then picked out and placed in a bottle with the medium, for your first controlled mating, as soon as they revive.

REFERENCE—*The Culture of Drosophila Flies and Their Use in Demonstrating Mendel's Law of Heredity.* Turtox Service Leaflet No. 15. Free. General Biological Supply House, Chicago 37, Illinois.

AQUATIC INSECTS—A number of insects spend their lives as larvae or nymphs in water. Some of them become airborne when they reach adulthood, others remain in the water. To do a successful rearing job, the condition under which you keep these insects in captivity should imitate their natural surroundings as closely as possible.

BOOK—Ann Haven Morgan. *Field Book of Ponds and Streams.* G. P. Putnam's Sons.

INSECT AQUARIUM—Insects from quiet waters—ponds and lakes—may be raised in an aquarium. See page 235.

INSECT WATER CAGES—Insects from swiftly moving streams do not rear too successfully in an aquarium. They are more easily raised directly in their home stream.

The simplest way of keeping them captive is in a *pillow cage,* as suggested by Needham. This cage is made from a piece of wire window screening, 18 inches square. Bring two opposite edges together and fold them into a tight hem. Flatten one end of the cylinder thus formed, and close it by folding over the edges. Put the insects

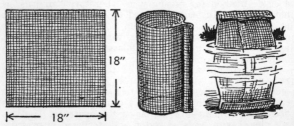

Insects from quickly moving streams do not survive in an aquarium. Rear them instead in a Needham pillow cage.

into the cage with some of their natural foods, and close the top by folding.

Anchor the cage in the stream with a string, leaving a couple of inches of it above water. Visit it every couple of days to check the progress of your captives.

Insect Photography

Insect photography is one of the most rewarding of all the many kinds of nature photography. Your results will amaze other people—and may even astonish yourself.

With a camera, you can catch and keep the grace of a dragonfly and the beauty of a moth. You will discover details in the structure of the tiniest insect which would evade you otherwise, even under the magnifying glass. And you can create the exciting effect of gigantic, pre-historic monsters by blowing up heads of insects into 8×10-inch enlargements, or by filling a motion-picture screen with them.

REFERENCES—Edwin Way Teale. *Grassroot Jungles.* Chapter on insect photography. Dodd, Mead & Company.

Willard D. Morgan and Henry M. Lester. *The Leica Manual.* Chapter 20: Miniature Monsters. Morgan and Lester, N. Y.

STILLS

EQUIPMENT—CAMERA—The first advice in regard to insect photography is a Don't: *Don't* attempt it with the usual snapshot camera. Your results will be poor—or nonexistent.

You need a camera that permits you to shoot at a distance of a couple of inches or less, with a device for critical focusing, a diaphragm that can be closed down to almost pinhole size, and with shutter speeds from fractions of a second to time.

If you have a bellows camera with double bellows extension, you should be able to get close enough to an insect to get a full-size image on your negative. But that, usually, is not enough in insect photography. You may further have to resort to a supplementary slip-on lens, or to an extension tube placed between camera and lens. If you possess a telephoto lens, your main problem is solved—but the expense runs high. For miniature cameras, extension tubes are a necessity.

Tip—If you have available a movie-camera lens of short focal length—one inch—you may follow the lead of Teale and use this in a special mount, instead of your regular lens, to get greater magnification.

Focusing—In close-up work, your camera's view finder becomes useless. The only way in which you will know the field the lens is covering, is by focusing on ground glass or, in case of miniature cameras, by using a sliding focusing attachment or other focusing device.

Because of the extreme close-up, the depth of focus will be exceedingly shallow. It is imperative, therefore, to make your focusing as exact as possible. Then, to add to the depth, close down the diaphragm as far as it will go.

This kind of focusing requires a *tripod*—preferably tilting or with a ball-jointed head.

Exposures—The smaller the diaphragm opening, the longer the exposure. This doesn't make much difference if you are photographing dead specimens, but live insects may not co-operate by holding their pose as long as you would like them to.

The two ways of shortening the exposure is to use a fast supersensitive film—panchromatic for best color definition—and to light up the subject as brilliantly as possible, using sunlight or photofloods or flash, and metallic reflectors of postcard size or smaller.

> *Tip*—In taking a light-meter reading, remember that the insect is so small that it will be the background that will register. Take your reading by substitution, against a piece of gray cardboard.

OUTDOOR PHOTOGRAPHY—You will have no trouble outdoor photographing the more or less stationary insects—caterpillars, aphids, and other leaf-eating or sap-sucking insects. Simply set up your camera on its tripod, focus, and shoot.

For the insects that move about—butterflies, bees, and so on—focus on a flower that the insect is likely to visit, wait for it to come, then shoot.

To be positive that you will get what you want, it often pays to catch the insect first. Anesthetize it by keeping it for a few minutes in a jar containing a wad of cotton with a few drops of ether, carbontetrachloride, or ammonia. In the meantime, focus on a suitable plant part. When the insect has become stupefied enough, arrange it on the plant, and let it cling. Recheck the focus. Snap the shutter.

> *Tip*—Teale suggests photographing certain insects during their quiet "off" hours: butterflies at twilight, moths in the middle of the day.

INDOOR PHOTOGRAPHY—Generally speaking, you will have much better success photographing your insects indoors rather than outdoors. You have a far better con-

trol over the situation—including background, and the
most attractive angle for composition.

Set up your props as for tabletop photography: plants
in a vase or pot, a sod of grass, a piece of bark on the
table. Put up a sheet of gray cardboard for a background,
or a piece of black velvet, if you prefer a dead black
background.

Arrange a single floodlight or flash to imitate sunlight.
Light up shadows with metal reflectors.

Tip—A shaving mirror makes a good reflector for
small subjects.

When everything is in order, bring out your anesthetized insect model, pose it, and shoot.

Tip—Move fast after the insect is out of the jar. The
heat from the floodlights will quickly revive it.

Why not take your shots of dead collection specimens
that will stay quiet? O.K.—for detail shots, such as of
head, mouth parts, antennae. Otherwise, NO—partly because it is almost impossible to arrange them in a lifelike
pose, partly—well, to real nature photographers, it just
isn't cricket.

WHAT TO PHOTOGRAPH—Insect subjects suitable
for photographs are legion. Most photographers have
concentrated on the more spectacular or better known
subjects. So the field is wide open.

The most valuable photographs are *series* showing the
life cycle of the insect, from egg to adult, and *sequences*
—such as of a caterpillar turning into a chrysalis, a moth
emerging from its cocoon.

Tip—For a life cycle or a sequence, don't depend on
a single caterpillar or pupa. It may die before your
series is complete. Be certain to have several stand-
ins on hand.

Tip—You can make a moth announce its emergence
by wiring up the cocoon to a dry-cell, electric buzzer.
Remove button; arrange wire ends so that emerging
moth pushes one wire against the other.

MOVIES

Insect movies are considerably tougher to make than
insect stills. They require infinite patience and a great
amount of inventiveness.

EQUIPMENT—CAMERA—A camera that can be focused
is an absolute necessity. You will also need supplementary
slip-on lenses, telephoto lens, or extension tubes—depending on how ambitious you are!

Tip—You can get a certain amount of magnification by placing a washer, or "shim" between lens and camera body, as you screw on the lens. Get two— one 1/16 inch thick, the other 1/8 inch thick.

If you have a movie titler, make use of it. It simplifies the making of certain shots by being a combination supplementary lens and focuser. Simply place the subject you intend to photograph within the titler's guide frame and shoot. The main drawback to using the titler is that all shots will be of the same magnification, and, in most cases, the enlargement will be insufficient.

MOVIE TECHNIQUES—Generally speaking, the suggestions for taking stills apply equally well for movie making—with the one exception that shots are more easily taken outdoors by sunlight than indoors under artificial light.

The usual method in movie making of taking "long shot, medium shot, close-up" needs to be modified when insects are the actors to "close-up, close-close-up, ultra-close-up." The effect will be striking.

To get the most lifelike action—or any action at all— out of your actors, you will have to vary the camera speed to fit the insect. Some insects are fast moving: butterflies, grasshoppers, bees. Slow down their action to keep them on the screen by shooting them at 32 frames a second. Other insects are slow moving: praying mantises, locusts, katydids. Speed up their action. by taking them at 8 frames a second.

The pupation of a caterpillar or the emergence of a butterfly needs to be taken by time lapse, single-frame exposures, to cover the action within the limits of the usual movie footage (see page 272).

Insect Collections

One of the most absorbing hobbies in the nature field is the creation of a permanent insect collection. Many youngsters begin collecting for the fun of it. As they grow older, their insect hobby becomes an engrossing activity that brings them out into the open, and often puts them in contact with other people who have the same interest.

You can, of course, start a collection by pinning insects in cardboard boxes with ordinary pins. But don't! It takes no more effort and costs little more to do the job right—using correct methods and good equipment, most of which you can make yourself.

The important steps in making an insect collection consist of catching the insects by one of the methods described previously (pages 173-180), killing them without damaging them, preparing them correctly, mounting them properly, displaying them attractively.

REFERENCES—Harold Oldroyd. *Collecting, Preserving, and Studying Insects.* The Macmillan Company.

U. S. Department of Agriculture. Miscellaneous Publication No. 601. *Collection and Preservation of Insects.* For sale by Superintendent of Documents, Washington 25, D. C. Price 15 cents.

KILLING JARS

Insects for collections are killed by exposing them to fumes of various chemicals in tightly closed "killing jars." Some of these chemicals are nonpoisonous for human beings, others are dangerous poisons. Obviously, the nonpoisonous killing jar is recommended for young insect hunters. The poisonous jar is more effective, therefore preferred by advanced entomologists.

NONPOISONOUS KILLING JAR—Place a layer of cotton batting on the bottom of a screw-top pint jar. Pour carbontetrachloride ("Carbona" cleaning fluid) on the cotton, making it moist, but not dripping wet. Cover with a couple of thicknesses of heavy blotting paper or cardboard cut to fit snugly over the cotton.

Cotton needs to be "recharged" with carbontetrachloride before each field trip.

POISON JAR—The killing agent in the poison jar is sodium or potassium cyanide—an extremely potent poison in two ways: by itself and by its fumes.

It frankly doesn't pay to make your own poison jars. Instead, purchase them, ready made, from a biological

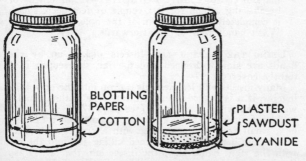

BLOTTING PAPER
COTTON
PLASTER
SAWDUST
CYANIDE

Two types of insect killing jars: nonpoisonous (left), making use of carbontetrachloride; poisonous cyanide jar (right).

supply house (see page 28)—one or more pint-size killing jars for larger insects, and an unbreakable killing tube for small species.

Tip—Most killing jars have screw-top covers. Many insect collectors prefer corks instead. With a little practice, it is possible to hold the jar and remove the cover using one hand only.

MAKING YOUR OWN—If you insist on messing around with cyanide (the purchase of which, in most states, requires that you sign a poison register), here's the way to make the jar:

Place a ¼-inch layer of granulated cyanide in the bottom of a pint screw-top jar. Cover with disk of blotting paper. Add ½ inch of sawdust or dry plaster of Paris. Over this pour a ¼ layer of plaster-of-Paris batter (see page 133). Let set for a couple of hours with cover off, to dry thoroughly.

Tip—A pinch of calcium oxalate or powdered citric acid mixed in with the cyanide before sealing will cause the poison gas to be released more quickly, hence will make a more potent jar—although also a more short-lived one.

Place a couple of thicknesses of blotting paper over the plaster. Put strips of blotting paper or paper toweling, in the jar to absorb moisture and to keep the specimens from shaking around—except in a jar meant for butterflies or moths.

Tip—For added safety, wrap strips of 1-inch adhesive tape around the jar to reduce the chance of breakage.

Note—Keep the poison jar away from children and mark it conspicuously: POISON!!! If jar cracks or breaks, dig a hole for it a couple of feet deep, smash it completely at the bottom of the hole, then bury it. Wash hands thoroughly afterwards.

USING THE KILLING JAR—Insects picked up by the hands are simply dropped into the jar, whereupon it is tightly covered.

Many insects will let themselves drop into the open killing jar, if it is pushed in under them. This method usually works well when "sugaring" (see page 170).

To get an insect from a net into a jar, hold the insect in a small fold of the netting with a couple of fingers of the left hand. Slip the opened killing jar into the net with the right hand. Drop the insect into the jar. Grasp the jar through the netting with the left hand. Bring the cork or cover into the net and place it on the jar.

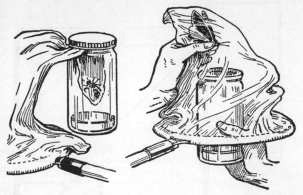

Stinging insects may be subdued by placing net corner in killing jar. Paralyze butterflies by squeezing the thorax.

Tip—If the insect is a wasp or other stinging insect, push the corner of the net in which it is imprisoned into the jar and put on the cover. In a few moments the insect will be overcome by the fumes and can be taken out without fear of stinging.

Tip—To stop a butterfly or moth from beating its wings to bits before it succumbs in the killing jar, pinch the sides of its body under the wings (the thorax) between two fingers. This paralyzes it and quickly stops its movements.

ALCOHOL VIALS—Insects that shrivel up when dried— stone flies, May flies, and the like—and insects in immature stages are dropped directly into vials containing 80- to 90-per-cent ethyl alcohol.

Tip—If ethyl alcohol is not available, use 70-per-cent rubbing alcohol.

TEMPORARY STORAGE

The hydrocyanic acid fumes from the cyanide in the killing jar discolors insect specimens exposed to them too long. The insects should be removed from the jar as soon as they are dead—half an hour to one hour—and transferred to another container.

Tip—Never take insects out of jar with your fingers. Use instead a pair of forceps, 4 to 5 inches long. Some insect collectors prefer forceps with thin, curved tips; others like the broad-tipped variety—take your choice.

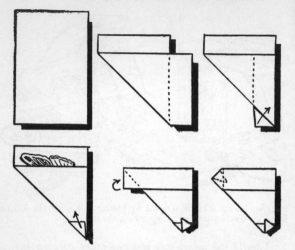

Butterflies, moths and dragonflies are "papered" in individual containers, folded, as shown, from rectangular pieces of paper.

STORAGE BOXES—Beetles, grasshoppers, and similar "hard-shelled" insects may be stored temporarily in small cardboard or tin boxes, or in match boxes—in the unlined boxes—or between layers of glazed cotton batting (jewelers' cotton) or cellulose cotton.

PAPERING—Butterflies, moths, and dragonflies are "papered" in individual paper containers. The traditional container is a triangular envelope formed by folding a rectangular piece of smooth paper, in the manner shown in drawing above. The proportion between the width and length of the paper used is as two to three. Medium-sized butterflies take papers 4×6 inches. Make a supply of triangles for varying sizes of specimens.

Tip—Glazed paper envelopes and envelopes of cellophane are on the market. They will save you the trouble of making triangles—but cost between half a cent to one cent apiece.

PREPARING INSECT SPECIMENS

It pays to go about the job of preparing the insect specimens with great care. The result will be an attractive and workmanlike exhibit.

RELAXING—If at all possible, the insects should be prepared the same day they are collected, before they dry up and become brittle. You won't often accomplish this. Your harvest is too large, or the hour too late.

The alternative is to store the insects, then relax them before working with them, by placing them in a damp container, until they become soft again.

RELAXING BOXES—Relaxing boxes are available through biological supply houses, but almost any covered glass or metal container can be used. A refrigerator dish with glass lid or an empty coffee can will do the trick.

Place a ½-inch layer of sawdust, sand, cotton, or blotting paper on the bottom of the container. Moisten it with water. Cover with a couple of layers of paper toweling. Place the insects in the box and close it.

Small butterflies usually relax overnight, larger insects in a day.

> *Tip*—To prevent mold from forming, use a 1-per-cent phenol (carbolic acid) solution instead of plain water for moistening. OR place a layer of paradichlorobenzene or naphthalene flakes on bottom of relaxing box.

PINNING—The most common method for displaying insect specimens is on pins.

PINS—Never use regular pins for your insects—even if you happen to be the rankest beginner. They are too coarse and bend and rust too easily. From the very start, use *insect pins*. These are slender pins, made of stiff steel wire, japanned to be practically rustless. They come in a standard length of 37 mm. (almost 1½ inches), numbered according to thickness, from 000 to 7.

> *Tip*—Keep several sizes of insect pins on hand: no. 2 for small to medium-sized butterflies, wasps, and insects of similar size, no. 3 for large grasshoppers and butterflies.

PIN LOCATIONS—Insect pins are not pushed indiscriminately through any part of the insect body. They are systematically placed—partly to insure a uniform appearance, partly to leave certain identifying marks undisturbed.

The place at which pins are inserted varies with the insect orders:

> *Butterflies, moths, dragonflies*—through center of thorax, the body part to which wings and legs are attached.
> *Bees, flies*—through thorax, slightly to right of center.
> *Grasshoppers, crickets*—through back section of thorax, slightly to right of center line.
> *True bugs*—through the triangular shield, the scutellum, slightly to right of center.

Beetles—through right wing cover, near front edge and close to inside edge.

PLACING THE PIN—Place the tip of the pin on the back of the insect, at the correct spot for the order to which it belongs. Then thrust the pin through the body in such a way that the insect is at right angles to the pin—crosswise as well as lengthwise.

Finally, adjust the insect on the pin, so that ½ inch of the top of the pin protrudes from the insect's back. This is usually done by bringing the insect up near the pin head, then pushing it down to the correct height. You will soon learn to judge the distance by eye.

Tip—Or use a "setter" for adjusting the height. This is simply a thin piece of wood or plastic with a fine hole bored in one end, ½ inch deep, wide enough to fit over the head of the pin.

Tip—To prevent a heavy specimen from sliding down on the pin, turn the pinned insect over, and place a small drop of white shellac from the tip of a tooth pick at the point on the underside where the pin emerges.

SPREADING—Butterflies, moths, and dragonflies are

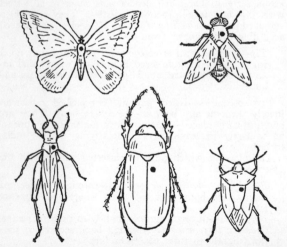

Insect pins are placed systematically, their locations depending on the insect orders, to insure a uniform appearance.

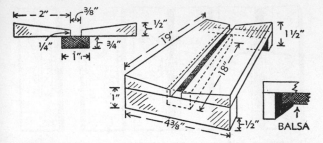

Spreading boards for butterflies and moths are made of two strips of soft wood, nailed parallel, and a pinning strip.

mounted with their wings spread out flat. To accomplish this, they need to be dried on spreading boards.

SPREADING BOARDS—A spreading board consists of two strips of soft wood, nailed parallel on a couple of cross pieces, with a groove between them as wide as the body of the insects to be spread. A pinning strip of cork, balsa wood, or corrugated cardboard is tacked under the groove.

Standard spreading boards are 19 inches long, of widths varying from 3 1/16 inches with a 1/16-inch groove, to 7¾ inches with a ⅝-inch groove. Most useful size is 4⅜ inches wide, with a ⅜-inch groove (see design above).

Tip—Make a number of spreading boards of different groove widths.

METHOD OF SPREADING—Pick up the recently killed or relaxed butterfly with forceps. Squeeze the thorax slightly to open up the wings, then push an insect pin through the center of the back of the thorax. Place the insect body in the groove of the spreading board, and press the pin into the pinning strip. The back of the butterfly should be slightly higher than the surface of the spreading board. "Anchor" the body by pushing a pin in next to the thorax on the side to be spread first, to prevent the insect from swinging on its pin when you start moving its wings.

Cut a number of paper strips, ⅛ inch wide. Pin one end of a strip to the spreading board, ahead of the butterfly's forewing. Move the wing forward, by pushing against one of its heavy veins with a pin, until the rear edge of the wing is at right angle to the insect's body. Move up the hind wing in a similar manner, until its forward edge is just overlapped by the forewing. Be careful not to puncture either wing. Hold the paper strip firmly down over both wings while adjusting them, then

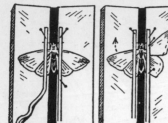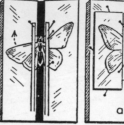

In spreading, hold down wings with paper strips. Open up wings. Keep in place with (a) small glass plates or (b) more strips.

fasten it down by putting a pin through the loose end. Treat the opposite wing pair in the same manner.

The wings are next covered with two more strips of paper, placed further out toward the wing tips, or, as preferred by some collectors, by strips of glass.

If necessary, brace antennae, legs, and rear of butterfly with a few pins, so that they will dry in a natural position.

Tip—Use ordinary pins for fastening down the paper strips, or, better, stiff glass-headed mounting pins.

Put the spread butterflies away to dry from a couple of days to a full week, in a place where they are protected against attacks from ants and other insects, and from mice.

INFLATING CATERPILLARS—It is sometimes desirable to display the caterpillars of butterflies and moths next to the adults of the same species. The most attractive way of doing this is by inflating the caterpillars and mounting them on pins.

The first step is to remove the innards. Place the caterpillar on a piece of paper. Make a slit at the vent with a pin, or with the tip of a knife, then roll a round pencil gently over the body from just behind the head to the tail, thus pressing out the contents.

Insert the tip of a glass tube in the hole at the vent, and fasten the skin to the tube with a tiny wire clip. Inflate the skin by blowing air into the glass tube through a piece of rubber hose, using a double rubber bulb or your mouth. While inflating, dry the caterpillar slowly over a safe heat source—a piece of metal or a tin can with a couple of inches of sand on top of an alcohol lamp or a Bunsen burner, an electrical hot plate, an upturned electrical iron or in a special oven. Turn from time to time,

and watch against scorching. Completely dry, the skin
will hold its shape when blowing stops.

Remove the dried skin from the glass tube. Insert a
balsa wood plug in the hole at the tail and glue it in place
with a drop of shellac. Push a no. 3 insect pin through
the balsa, and adjust the caterpillar to proper pin height.

POINTING—Tiny insects are not pinned on regulation
length insect pins. They are occasionally pinned on especially fine pins, "minuten nadeln," attached by them to
small pieces of cork or pith which, in turn, are impaled
on no. 3 insect pins. More often, tiny insects are "pointed"
—glued to small paper points.

PAPER POINTS—Insect points are cut from stiff, white
paper, or thin cardboard. They may be purchased by the
thousand.

You can make them yourself by punching them out
with a special "insect point punch," or by simply cutting
them from ⅜-inch (8 mm.) wide strips of paper with
scissors or an old razor blade. Do a neat cutting job,
making each point ⅛ inch (3 mm.) wide at the base.

ATTACHING THE POINT—Push a no. 3 insect pin into
the point near its base. Adjust the point to the usual
height of an insect on a pin, ½ inch below the pin head.
Bend the tip of the point downward about 45 degrees.
Touch the tip to a drop of white shellac, then to the right
side of the insect. Adjust the insect so that its head points
straight forward with its body at right angle to the axis
of the point. Put aside until shellac has dried.

LABELING—The notes that have followed the specimens through their temporary storage and their preparation are finally attached permanently to the pins on which

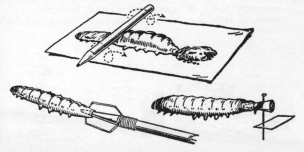

Caterpillars may be emptied with a round pencil, blown up, and
dried, and finally fastened to small plugs of balsa wood.

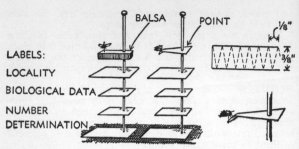

Tiny insects are pinned on "minuten nadeln" or attached to paper points. Place labels properly, as shown to the left.

the insects are impaled. Here custom has established a procedure that provides for exactness and uniformity.

LABELS—The labels considered necessary for satisfactory description consist of:

Locality label, ¼×½ inch, with space for name of locality where found, date, and finder's name. This may be handwritten, but is more satisfactory if printed. The biological supply houses make these available with three lines of 4-point type, according to your specifications, at a couple of dollars a thousand.

Biological data label, a tiny label containing information on host plant or habitat. Not always used, but adding to the value of your collection.

Number label, a small label with the file number of the insect. Used only in large collections.

Determination label, 5/16×11/16 inch, or ½×1 1/16 inch, generally with a black border line, containing scientific name of specimen, original authority, and name of identifier. Also, if ascertained, the sex of the insect.

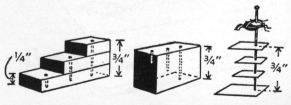

Two pinning blocks: The step block (left) with ¼-inch steps; solid block (center). Right: Correctly placed insect and labels.

PLACING THE LABELS—The labels are placed in their proper positions on the pin by the use of a *pinning block,* a small block of wood, 1⅛ inches thick, 1 inch wide, 3 inches long, with three holes bored in it to depths of ¼ inch, ½ inch, and ¾ inch respectively.

Another type of pinning block is steplike, with the steps ¼ inch, ½ inch, and ¾ inch high, and the holes bored through to the bottom.

Locality label is placed over the ¾-inch-deep hole, and the pin pushed through the center of the label to the bottom of the hole. This sets the label at the proper height.

The biological data label, where used, is set in a similar way, using the ½-inch hole.

The number label is pinned over the ¼-inch hole.

The determining label is placed on the bottom of the storage box, whereupon the pin is thrust through it.

PERMANENT STORAGE

Good specimens deserve good storage, in well-constructed boxes, with tight-fitting covers to protect them against dust and insect attacks.

STORING THE SMALL COLLECTION—The most popular storage box for the small collection is the Schmitt box. This is a wooden box with hinged top that fits tightly over an inside collar. It has a pinning bottom of cork or balsa wood, and is lined with white glazed paper. It is made to a standard size of 9×13×2½ inches.

MAKING YOUR OWN STORAGE BOX—A fair facsimile of the Schmitt box may be made from ½-inch pine boards, cut to size and nailed to top and bottom sheets of Presdwood, Masonite, or ½-inch plywood (see design on page 211). Glue a pinning bottom of celotex (wall board), pressed cork (entomological cork), or balsa wood to the bottom of the box. Paint the inside white, or cover with white paper. Give the outside a double coating of shellac.

> *Tip*—In an emergency, a cigar box may be turned into a short-term storage box. Secure a deep box—the shallow ones are not high enough for your insect pins. Glue two thicknesses of corrugated cardboard to the bottom in such a way that the corrugations of the two pieces run at right angles to each other. Paint inside and outside white. Since a cigar box is neither dustproof nor insect proof, its contents need to be watched carefully against insect attacks.

STORING THE LARGE COLLECTION—As your collection grows, it will pay you to transfer your speci-

mens to drawers in a storage cabinet. The larger biological supply houses carry several models of such cabinets
in stock. Two important models are the U. S. National
Museum model with drawers of 18×18×3 inches outside
measurements, and Cornell University model, with drawers 16½×19×3 inches.

In using drawers, the insects are not pinned to the
drawer bottom, but placed in unit trays of certain standard sizes which, in turn, are placed in drawers. This unit
system permits you to keep your whole collection perfectly arranged at all times.

PROTECTING THE COLLECTION—Certain small
insects take special pleasure in feeding on dried insect
specimens. You need to protect your collection against
them.

REPELLING PESTS—Naphthalene, the ordinary moth
repellent, is commonly used in insect collections. It may be
used in the form of mothballs, or as flakes placed in a
small cheesecloth bag or a perforated cardboard box in
one corner of your collection box.

Tip—To prevent mothballs from rolling around in the
box, pin them in place. Heat the head of a pin in a
flame. When red hot, push it into the mothball. As it
cools, the ball sticks to it. The pin with its mothball
head is then pushed into the bottom of the storage box.

KILLING PESTS—Fine, sawdustlike powder in your storage box tells you that the enemy pests have already made
their inroads. Kill them off immediately.

A teaspoon of carbontetrachloride poured into the box
will do the job. Paradichlorobenzene is another effective
agent. It comes in flakes like naphthalene. Spread a tea-
spoonful of flakes on the bottom of the storage box, and
close it tightly.

Tip—A number of entomologists use a mixture of
equal parts of naphthalene and paradichlorobenzene
flakes to do the double job of repelling and killing.
Paradichlorobenzene cannot be depended on to do the
job alone, because it volatilizes rather rapidly.

DISPLAYING YOUR INSECTS

Instead of storing away your insects, you may be more
interested in putting them on display for yourself and
others to enjoy. Several display methods are old-time
favorites with thousands of insect collectors. New methods make their appearance occasionally.

DISPLAY CASES—Glass-topped wooden and cardboard
display cases are available in a number of different sizes,

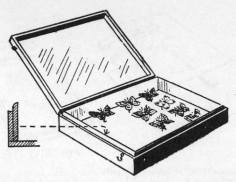

The Schmitt box is the most popular box for the small insect collection. The inside collar helps to keep the box dust-free.

from 9×13 inches to 18×24 inches, ranging in price from $1.50 to $10.00 or more.

You can make your own display cases in the same way you made your storage boxes. But instead of including inside collar and top, fasten a molding along the inside, ¼ inch from the top edge. Cut a piece of glass to rest on this rim.

RIKER MOUNTS—Riker mounts are shallow, cotton-filled cardboard boxes with glass covers. They are usually ¾ to 1 inch deep, ranging in size from 2½×3 inches to 12×16 inches. The insects are arranged on the cotton, then covered with the glass and sealed.

To make your own Riker, buy a piece of window pane, in one of the standard sizes—6×8 inches, 6×12 inches, or 12×16 inches. Make a frame from strips of wood, ½ inch thick, ½ inch wide, of the same outside measurements as your glass. Tack this frame to a bottom of heavy cardboard or ¼-inch plywood.

When assembling, start by placing a pinch of paradichlorobenzene crystals on the bottom. Next put in layers of cotton batting. On top of the cotton, arrange your insects and the labels that go with them. Cover with the glass plate, and seal with strips of 1-inch adhesive tape. Finally, paint bottom, side, and adhesive tape with enamel —black or any other color you may prefer.

Tip—The Riker mount is especially suited to insect life-history displays showing the various stages in the development of a species. Such a display should contain eggs, larva (possibly in tiny alcohol vial), pupa, fully developed insects (male and female) and pressed

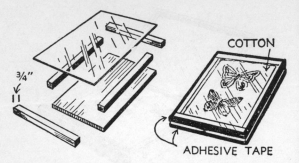

A homemade Riker mount is easily constructed from a frame of wood strips with a plywood backing, and a sheet of glass.

leaf of host plant, with the necessary information on small labels.

PLASTIC BUTTERFLY MOUNTS—Display cases and Riker mounts have the disadvantage that only one side of the insect shows. To offset this, transparent mounts for butterflies and moths have been developed. These are available, in close to a dozen different sizes.

These mounts consist of two identical halves of transparent plastic, with a depression in the middle that fits the body of the insect. The specimen is placed in position on one half. The other is placed on top of it, and the two halves are sealed together by passing a hot electric iron along the edges.

The finished mounts are labeled and placed in special envelopes. They may be stored, file-card style, in filing cases.

EQUIPMENT—Schwartz Transparent Butterfly Mounts ("Transpar" Mounts) New York Scientific Supply Co., or Central Scientific Co. For addresses, see page 28.

PLASTIC EMBEDDING—The most spectacular display method for insects is the embedding of specimens in blocks of water-clear plastic, with smoothly polished surfaces. Embedded specimens can be handled and studied by large numbers of people without damage.

While a great variety of plastics are available, only a few of them are suited for biological embedding. Among them are Ward's Bio-Plastic and Castolite.

In general, the process of making a successful embedding consists of the following steps (complete instructions accompany the materials):

Pick a watertight mold somewhat larger than the specimen to be embedded. A polished glass mold, such as a flat Pyrex dish, is especially good; it will eliminate the job of polishing afterwards. Mix enough uncatalysed plastic and catalyst (setting agent) to make a supporting layer, half the thickness of the final job. Float the insect on the surface of the plastic. Then cover the mold to keep dust off and put aside for six hours at room temperature to let the plastic set.

Mix another batch of uncatalysed plastic with catalyst and pour over the first layer and the insect. Again, put it aside for six to twelve hours to set.

The final process is the hardening of the plastic. This is done by placing it in a covered container in a hot-water bath, increasing the temperature to 170° Fahrenheit (or more, depending on plastic used), and keeping it at this temperature for an hour. A better method is the use of an electric oven.

Tip—A simple electric oven may be made from a two-gallon oil can. Cut off the top. Cut a hole in the bottom to fit over a 75-watt bulb. Punch a few holes in the sides of the can close to the top, and crisscross some wires through them to form a "shelf" for the mold. Put in the mold. Cover the top of the oven with a board. Turn on the light. If you are in doubt about the correct temperature, keep checking it with a candy thermometer.

After the hardening process, turn off the heat and let the plastic cool slowly. In cooling, the plastic shrinks away from the glass, thus making it easy to remove the cast.

The cast may be further shaped with a band saw or a

By embedding insect specimens in water-clear plastic, you produce display items that are spectacular and lasting.

hack saw. If necessary, it may be polished, using tripoli and rouge.

SUPPLIES—*Bio-Plastics*. Ward's Natural Science Establishment, Inc., Rochester 9, N. Y.

Castolite. General Biological Supply House, Chicago 37, Ill.

7. WATER LIFE

A BODY of water under the open sky brings out the kid in each of us—the desire to while away some sunny hours, lying on the belly in front of a lazy pond, watching striders skate across the "dry" surface, diving beetles squirming up and down, tiny fishes moving among the water plants, or wading in a tide pool looking for shells and starfish and sea anemones, or following a stream with rod and reel in hand, hoping for a prize strike, or rocking gently on a boat on the ocean waves, with a school of mackerel flashing by below.

The world under the water's surface is a world by itself—a world of extremes . . . of microscopic creatures in every water drop, and giants in the expanses of the open sea . . . of brilliant beauty and repulsive ugliness . . . of creatures that spend a lifetime burrowed in the bottom mud, and others that travel across an ocean to mate and die.

When once your interest has been aroused you will find water life an unending source of new and intriguing activities. Each body of water is different from any other body and each deserves your study—whether lake or pond, brook or river, meadow or swamp, beach or open sea.

You will quickly have to decide whether your main interest lies in *oceanography*—the study of life in salt water—or whether you favor *limnology*—life in fresh water. Within each of these fields, the opportunity for specialization is tremendous. Just check the possibilities.

In *salt water* you will find a multitude of minute organisms, and then, in ascending scale: sponges—jellyfish, sea anemones—flatworms—starfishes, sea urchins, sea cucumbers—snails, limpets, mussels, clams, oysters, squids—sandworms, bloodworms—barnacles, shrimps, crabs—fishes.

In *fresh water,* the variety is just as great. Here, in addition to numerous microscopic and near-microscopic animals, you will come upon: sponges—hydras—flatworms — threadworms — bristle worms — leeches — fairy shrimps, scuds, crayfish—aquatic insects—snails, mussels —lampreys, fishes—salamanders, frogs, toads—turtles, water snakes.

But do not let the immensity of the subject scare you away from it. Get started—then follow the line that catches your fancy.

BOOKS ON WATER LIFE—J. G. Needham and J. T. Lloyd. *Life of Inland Waters.* Comstock Publishing Company, Ithaca, N. Y.
Augusta F. Arnold. *The Sea Beach at Ebb Tide.* D. Appleton-Century Company.
William Crowder. *Between the Tides.* Dodd, Mead and Company.
E. F. Picketts and J. Calvin. *Between Pacific Tides.* Stanford University Press, Stanford, Calif.
Leonard P. Schultz with Edith M. Stern. *The Way of Fishes.* D. Van Nostrand Company.
John O. La Corce. *The Book of Fishes.* National Geographic Society, Washington, D. C.

WORKING WITH OTHERS

There are many phases of water life that you can undertake on your own—special studies, photography, collections of many kinds. There are others that need to be developed into group projects, still others for which you may require assistance.

Because of the tremendously varied aspects of water life, there may not be any person in your vicinity specializing in the subject you have picked. Nevertheless, it should be worth your while to check up with the local biology teacher or biology professor to get whatever suggestions they may have to offer. If such an approach fails, look through the pages of *The Naturalists' Directory* (see page 31). You will almost certainly find in this book the address of some person interested in your specialty.

If your main pursuit involves fishes, contact your local game warden, and find out whether any federal, state, or private hatcheries are located nearby.

For a more scientific approach to water life, join a national society specializing in the subject, and take part in its work.

SOCIETIES—American Society of Limnology and Oceanography. Hdqrs.: B. H. Ketchum, Woods Hole, Mass. Periodical: *Limnology and Oceanography.*

American Society of Ichthyologists and Herpetologists. Hdqrs.: Philadelphia Zoological Garden, Philadelphia, Penn. Periodical: *Copeia*.

Field Study of Water Life

EQUIPMENT FOR WATER-LIFE STUDY

CLOTHING—Any type of outdoor clothing will do for water-life study, where it is a matter of walking along a lake shore, wading along the beach, rowing or boating. But since you will have to risk getting wet, pick a material that will dry easily—wool preferably. For certain jobs, you may decide to bring along rubber waders.

For more intensive work, where you may have to submerge in order to get hold of specimens, you will, of course, get into a bathing suit. To protect your feet against cuts from barnacles or shells, use a pair of sneakers or, better for walking on wet rocks, a pair of old leather shoes. Add a pair of diving goggles to your outfit, if necessary.

SKIN DIVING EQUIPMENT—Skin diving provides the greatest possible thrill in studying water life, but is *absolutely* and *positively* for expert swimmers only—not for novices in the water. For breath-holding skin diving, diving mask, snorkel, and fins are needed. SCUBA diving (with *S*elf-*C*ontained *U*nderwater *B*reathing *A*pparatus) requires tanks of compressed air and considerably greater swimming ability than regular skin diving.

BOOKS ON SKIN DIVING—Jacques-Yves Cousteau and others. *Complete Manual of Free Diving*. G. P. Putnam's Sons.
Rick and Barbara Carrier. *Dive: The Complete Book on Skin Diving*. Wilfred Funk, Inc.

STUDY EQUIPMENT—WATERSCOPE—Light reflected from the water surface makes it almost impossible to observe the life below, unless you provide yourself with a waterscope. A simple type of waterscope can be made from a wooden bucket. Substitute its bottom for a circular piece of glass. Or, simpler, cut a square hole in the bottom. Cut a piece of plate glass slightly larger than the hole. Fasten it in position with strips of wood, making it watertight with putty or aquarium cement. To use, the bottom of the waterscope is pushed a couple of inches under the water's surface.

Tip—A better waterscope may be made from a piece

of stove pipe, about 2 feet long, with a round piece of plate glass at one end. Rivet two metal handles to the side of the pipe near the top, opposite to each other. Pad upper edge with adhesive tape.

Tip—A deep, flat-bottomed glass dish makes a good improvised waterscope.

FLASHLIGHT—For night hunting of frogs, salamanders, crayfish, and night insects you will need a good flashlight.

Tip—You can use your flashlight for observing under-water life at night. Place the lighted flashlight, with the light switch locked, lens down, in a glass jar. Add a couple of stones for ballast. Screw jar top on tightly. Tie a line around the neck of the jar. When the jar is lowered into the water, the flashlight will light up the surroundings.

MAGNIFIERS—For the identification of many of the minute specimens you come upon, you will need a good magnifying glass. A folding-type pocket magnifier, magnifying up to twenty times, will serve you in most cases (see page 167). A great number of water creatures are so small that they can only be seen in a microscope under laboratory conditions—taking them out of the realm of field study.

WATER-LIFE BOOKS—If you are a beginner, curious about the things you see at seashore, lake, or stream, it pays you to secure a guide book designed to give you just enough information to satisfy you for the time being.

BEGINNERS' BOOKS—Leon A. Hausman. *Beginner's Guide to Seashore Life* and *Beginner's Guide to Fresh-Water Life.* G. P. Putnam's Sons.

For more advanced study, pick a field book that covers the subject in a more complete manner.

FIELD BOOKS FOR IDENTIFICATION—Roy Waldo Miner. *Field Book of Seashore Life.* G. P. Putnam's Sons. Ann Haven Morgan. *Field Book of Ponds and Streams.* G. P. Putnam's Sons.

In case you specialize in certain features of water life, choose a book that treats your specialty comprehensively.

BOOKS FOR IDENTIFICATION—FISHES—Charles M. Breder, Jr. *Field Book of Marine Fishes of the Atlantic Coast.* G. P. Putnam's Sons.
Lionel A. Walford. *Marine Game Fishes of the Pacific Coast.* University of California Press, Berkeley, Calif. J. P. Norman and F. C. Fraser. *Field Book of Giant Fishes, Whales and Dolphins.* G. P. Putnam's Sons. John T. Nichols. *Representative North American Fresh Water Fishes.* The Macmillan Company.

AMPHIBIANS—Anna A. Wright and Albert H. Wright. *Handbook of Frogs and Toads.* Comstock Publishing Company, Ithaca, N. Y.

Roger Conant. *Field Guide to Amphibians and Reptiles.* Houghton Mifflin Company, Boston, Mass.

MOLLUSKS—See page 246.

AQUATIC REPTILES—See Snake Chapter.

AQUATIC INSECTS—See Insect Chapter.

NOTEBOOK—Your notebook will get wet from time to time—you won't be able to help it. So pick a book with a sturdy, waterproof cover, and with pages of good quality paper that won't soak up water and thus obliterate your notes.

CATCHING EQUIPMENT—See section starting on page 221.

FINDING WATER LIFE

"Where'll I find water life?" The answer seems obvious: "Wherever there is water!" Such an answer might be satisfactory in your early hunts. But the moment you want to find specific water creatures, it no longer suffices. You have to look for them in the kinds of water they favor, and the part of such water as suits their living conditions.

WHERE?—SALT WATER—Starting from the SPLASH AREA, where marine fauna meets land fauna in the sea wrack of high tide, you can travel seaward, finding different types of creatures as you move further and still further out.

The LITTORAL ZONE takes in the shore area from high-tide to low-tide level, continuing along sea bottom to a depth of about 300 feet. Its animal life, to a great extent, can be classed as *benthos*—"of the bottom"—moving slowly along the sea bottom, or attached to it.

The PELAGIC ZONE is the open sea, as deep as light will penetrate, with its numerous forms of swimming animals —*nekton*—and still more numerous passively floating forms—*plankton*—ranging from microscopic creatures to jelly fishes up to seven feet in diameter.

The ABYSSAL ZONE refers to the ocean depths, where sea animals live in the darkness, under enormous water pressure.

You will have little chance to study the life of the abyssal zone, unless you happen to be a William Beebe. As far as the pelagic zone is concerned, your studies will have to be by boat, or through the co-operation of the fishermen along our shores. The littoral zone is your most satisfactory hunting ground. Within this zone, the character of the shore and the tide determine the animals you will find.

Generally speaking, shores may be classified as muddy, sandy, or rocky, although there often is some overlapping among them. In mud flats, you will find mostly clams, snails, certain worms, and crabs. The same animals are found along sandy shores—some of them are on top of mud or sand; most of them you will have to dig for. Rocky shores—especially shores with small tide pools— will give you a far better harvest. Here you may find barnacles and periwinkles, limpets and chitons, sea urchins and starfish, sea anemones and crabs, and often specimens of small fishes. Some of the animals are in plain sight; others you discover by turning over rocks and looking among seaweeds. In addition to the shore itself, look for animal life on wharf piles, and on jetsam and flotsam found along the shore.

WHERE?—FRESH WATER—You will find just as many different kinds of living conditions in fresh water as you find in salt. The depth of the water and the speed with which it moves have a profound influence on the animal life.

You will notice a great distinction, for instance, between the water life in a small pond and in a large lake. Certain animals will seem thoroughly at home in the slow waters of a wide river, others in the swift waters of mountain brooks, or fast moving streams.

You will want to search all types of waters, but you will probably find the greatest variety of fresh-water life in the quiet waters of a pond. A pond, as defined by Morgan, is "a body of water that is so shallow that rooted water plants can grow all the way across it." This definition fits bodies of water in meadows and woods, swamps and marshes. In such ponds you may locate the whole gamut of fresh-water life from microscopic protozoans to large fishes—with the exception of fishes that prefer swift water or deep lakes.

Even within a pond, there are several comparatively well-defined zones, depending to a great extent on the plant life. Plants that emerge from the water—cattails, rushes, pickerel weed, and others—harbor certain kinds of animal life attached to their stalks. Plants with leaves that float on the surface shelter a number of fishes, and provide rafts topside for small turtles and young bullfrogs, bottomside for snails and water mites, sponges and eggs. The tangled growth of completely submerged plants is the lurking place for still other types of water creatures. In addition, there are the animals that dig themselves into the pond bottom or hide under rocks, those that travel on or just below the surface, those that spend part of their lives in the water, part of it on the surrounding land.

There are many places to look, each providing its own contribution to your knowledge.

WHEN?—TIME OF YEAR—The best seasons are spring and summer, when water life is at its busiest. Fall is fair, but observations can be made even in winter. There is plenty of life to study in open brooks and under the icy surface of ponds and lakes, although many of the animals have gone into winter quarters deep in the bottom's mud.

TIME OF DAY—The majority of water animals are active in the daytime—especially if the weather is sunny. Some make their appearance mostly at night—frogs, some of the salamanders, crayfishes, certain insects.

CATCHING WATER LIFE

With such great variation in water life, a great variety of catching methods is necessary. Pick the method that best suits your purpose, or combine a number of them to accomplish your aim. Remember that federal and state laws prohibit certain catching methods and govern the taking of some fishes, lobsters and crayfish, edible frogs and turtles, oysters and clams, and a few other water animals. Find out what the laws are and secure the necessary permits.

WATER DIP NETTING—Netting with a dip net is a common method of catching water life.

DIP NET—The aquatic net used for catching water insects (see page 179) is suitable for other water creatures as well. Many collectors prefer a somewhat smaller net— about 9 inches in diameter, 10 inches deep; or even smaller, 5 inches in diameter and 5 inches deep. The

A water dip net is made along the lines of an insect net. A D-shaped frame makes it possible to push it against the bottom.

handle should be 3 to 4 feet long. The same frame may be provided with several replaceable nets of coarse. medium and fine silk bolting cloth or brussels netting.

Tip—A kitchen wire strainer makes an excellent dip net. It may be attached to a handle of suitable length. If the wire screen is too open, line it with cheesecloth.

USING THE NET—The dip net can be used to scoop up small swimming animals. Or it can be used for general water sweeping—moving it back and forth among water plants, from the surface of the water to the bottom, eventually picking up some of the bottom mud.

From time to time, empty the net into a container in which you can study your catch.

PLANKTON SWEEPING—The tiny animals which, with various algae, float in the water are collected with a special type of net.

PLANKTON NET—The plankton net consists of a conical bag made of a rather tightly woven material that permits the water to run through, but retains the minute solid matter. It may be made from silk bolting cloth or woven nylon.

Use 15 inches of yard-wide material. Cut diagonally, then sew the two pieces together into a triangle. Sew the two sides of the triangle together, in this way forming a cone. Cut the tip off the cone, making an opening about ¾ inch in diameter. Hem the material around this opening, and sew on here a 6-inch piece of tape to be used to tie up the opening. Sew the open end of the cone to a brass wire ring, 9 inches in diameter. Fasten three pieces of mason line or thin brass chain, 2 feet long, to the wire ring, equal distances apart. Tie the free ends of the lines together.

USING THE PLANKTON NET—For sweeping a pond, the lines of the plankton net may be tied to a pole and the net, with the tip tied up, moved slowly back and forth in the water. For sweeping in lake or ocean, attach a rope to the net lines and tow the net behind a boat.

After a couple of minutes of sweeping, pull the net out of the water. Let the water drain out, until only a small amount is left. Open up the tip of the net and drop the remaining water with its concentrated plankton contents into a jar.

DIGGING AND TURNING—A great number of freshwater and marine animals spend their life hiding on the bottom. To find them, it is a matter of digging up sand or mud and turning over rocks.

For investigating small quantities of mud, the dip net

or a sieve may be used. In digging for worms and clams, you will need a more substantial tool—a short-handled shovel or a narrow-bladed spade.

> *Tip*—A strong garden rake comes in handy for digging up clams—unless you prefer to secure a regular clam rake specifically designed for the purpose.

PRYING—Animals attached to rocks or wharf piles—sea anemones, barnacles, chitons, limpets, mussels and others —can usually be pried or cut loose with the point of a strong knife. In collecting abalones, a light wrecking bar or a tire iron is in order.

ANGLING—For medium- and large-size fishes, you may have to resort to one of the many forms of angling: *still fishing* with pole and bait, *trolling* from a slowly moving boat, *bait casting* with rod, reel and plug, *surf casting* along the ocean shore, *fly casting* with wet or dry flies.

OTHER METHODS—In addition to the more conventional methods, others may be devised for special purposes.

JACKLIGHTING—Frogs and other amphibians are most easily caught at night—especially during the breeding season of early spring—by hunting for them along the water's edge. Wade slowly, a few feet from the shore, equipped with a flashlight and a bag for carrying your catch. When you locate a frog by its singing, blind it temporarily by playing the flashlight beam in its eyes, then pick it up by hand.

> *Tip*—If you are interested in seeing one of the most beautiful sights in nature, place the battery end of the flashlight at your nose tip while you bend over until the light shines in the bullfrog's eyes. As the frog moves its eyes slightly, you will see brilliant flashes of topaz, emerald, ruby, and sapphire.

> *Tip*—Try a "frog raft": Fasten a lighted candle to the middle of a 1-foot piece of 1-inch board with candle drippings. Float it in the water. Watch for passengers.

TRAPPING—Lobsters, crabs, and octopi are usually caught in boxlike traps—"lobster pots"—made of wire netting or slats, with one or two entrances. The traps are baited with fish heads or entrails and lowered to the sea bottom. "Minnow traps" are used for small fishes.

BAITING—Strips of meat, anchored at the edge of a pond, are almost certain to attract various fresh-water worms and nymphs of aquatic insects.

"WEEDING"—Numerous species of water life attach themselves to stalks and leaves of plants growing in the water. The simplest way of securing them consists of "weeding" the plants by pulling with the hands or with a rake, then picking off the specimens or scraping them off with a fingernail or a dull knife into a dish of water.

COMMERCIAL METHODS—A number of special methods for catching water animals—specifically in the ocean—are employed by professional fishermen. Secure their help if your studies involve the water life of the open sea.

INVESTIGATING YOUR CATCH—Catching water life is to a great extent a matter of "catch-as-catch-can." You grab—and what you get, you get. Your next job is to separate your catch into its component parts and pick out the animals you intend to study.

The simplest method is to drop your catch into a shallow pan—white-painted pie plate or larger—with a small amount of water.

Tip—Photographic developing trays, 6×8 inches, 9×11, or 12×15, make excellent study trays.

For larger specimens and jumping amphibians, use a deep, white-enamel dishpan or an enamel pail.

TRANSPORTING YOUR CATCH—Carry home your catch in mason or mayonnaise jars. It is not advisable to put the top on. Instead, fit a screen-wire lid over the opening. Tie a line around the neck so that the jar can be carried in a hanging position. In this way, there is less chance of the water swishing out.

Fishes may be transported in a pail covered with a perforated lid, or in a live-bait container such as is used by fishermen.

Mollusks and crustaceans should not be carried in water. You have a better chance of keeping them alive if you pack them in wet moss or seaweed. The same goes for many of the salt-water creatures, with the exception of fishes.

Frogs and salamanders, similarly, should be carried home packed in moist moss to keep their skin from drying out. Their eggs and tadpoles, on the other hand, must be transported in water.

WATER-LIFE LISTS AND SURVEYS

In trying to find out about the water life in your territory, you will soon discover that you will have to specialize. The amount of material is just too immense and unwieldy. You can approach the subject from a couple of angles.

You may decide to concentrate on one specific phylum (mollusks, for instance), or a class within that phylum (as represented, in this case, by chitons, snails, tusk shells, bivalves, and squids), or an order within one of these classes (among bivalves you have the choice of mussels, clams, scallops, oysters, and shipworms), or even a single family within an order—and you will still have plenty to do.

Or you may take an ecological approach and attempt to find out all you can about the water life of a tide pool, a forest lake, a brook, a drainage ditch, or whatever strikes your fancy.

LISTING—The only way you can achieve results is by keeping a careful check of your discoveries. Make thorough notebook records of each field trip, with complete listing of species, their location and the conditions under which you found them. By making such a listing on a yearly basis, you will be able to ascertain the fluctuation in water life through the seasons.

FISH SURVEYS—In the field of fishes, you may be of service to your community, and help in the work of your state fish and game department by inaugurating a fish census or a fish-marking project for a club or a youth group, or by assisting in such work.

FISH CENSUS—The main purpose for taking a fish census—"creel census"—of a stream or a lake, is to determine the fish population and, on the basis of the facts revealed, to determine what should be done in the way of improving fish living conditions, fish planting, revising regulations, and so on.

To make a creel census, start off by securing the cooperation of the sportsmen, landowners, visitors who may be fishing in the waters to be surveyed. Develop mimeographed questionnaires, or secure the necessary forms from your state fish department—asking for information on the following points: 1. name of fisherman; 2. date of fishing, and number of hours; 3. catch—name, number, and size of fish; 4. disposition of the catch; 5. miscellaneous information that may be pertinent. Make arrangements to have the questionnaires returned to a general "headquarters." At the end of the season, tabulate the information, and make the findings available to those interested.

REFERENCE—Albert S. Hazzard. *Creel Census*. Sportsman's Club Bulletin, Sports Afield, 405 Second Avenue, S., Minneapolis, 1, Minn.

FISH MARKING—Fish marking is the piscatorial equivalent of bird banding. It is a means of determining life span and rate of growth, and of finding out about range, migration, and many other phases of fish life not too well known.

FIN CLIPPING—Fin clipping is mainly resorted to at the time when hatchery stock is planted in a lake or stream. All the fishes in the batch can then be set out with their fins clipped in the same manner—dorsal fin, or one or more of the paired fins. When fish thus marked are caught later on, and are reported, the pattern of distribution of the original lot can be learned.

FISH TAGGING—A more exact marking method consists in clinching a light metal tag to gill cover or the jaw

Fish are marked for identification upon recapture with light metal tags clinched to gill cover or upper or lower jaw.

—upper or lower jaw, where it will interfere least with the feeding of the fish. This method makes possible the study of individual specimens. The tags come in various sizes—no. 2 for large fish, no. 3 for medium, "fingerling" for small specimens. The tags may be purchased, stamped with appropriate numbers and lettering. A special clincher is used for attaching them.

SUPPLIES—Salt Lake Stamp Company, 43 W. Broadway, Salt Lake City 1, Utah.

A fish-tagging project might be carried out by a group of interested naturalists and fishermen during open season, tagging the catch—then throwing it back. Obviously, few fishermen will like the idea of losing their fish in this manner—even for the sake of science. A better method is to carry on the project out of season, working in complete co-operation with the state's fish department or department of conservation. If done under the supervision of the proper officials, it can probably be arranged to catch the fish with seines—a method otherwise illegal. In that instance, the main part of the project can become a one-day effort of a club or youth group. Have on hand all the necessary equipment for catching, tagging, meas-

uring, weighing, and recording. Distribute responsibilities
for the various jobs, and keep the work humming.

To be successful, effective publicity is necessary. Un-
questionably, local newspapers will be glad to run the
story. In addition, the stream or lake surroundings should
be posted with posters describing the project and with an
earnest appeal for co-operation in sending, to a specified
"headquarters," information in regard to: 1. tag number;
2. size and weight of fish, as well as it can be ascertained; 3. date; 4. location where caught; 5. name and
address of person making the catch. As such information
arrives, correlate it with the original records.

REFERENCE—R. W. Eschmeyer. *Fish Tagging.* Sportsman's Club Bulletin, Sports Afield, 405 Second Avenue, S., Minneapolis 1, Minn.

FIELD OBSERVATIONS

Because of the difficulty of studying water life in the
field, there are great gaps in our knowledge regarding
aquatic animals. Your chances of filling some of these
gaps are excellent. The following listing may suggest
some avenues you may want to pursue.

INFLUENCE OF SURROUNDINGS on water life—What are
the differences between life in forest pond, marsh bog,
lake, meadow stream, mountain brook, and so on? What
causes these differences?

INFLUENCE OF WEATHER—How are water animals in-
fluenced by temperature, sunlight, wind, and other weather
conditions?

LOCOMOTION—What fins are used by various fishes, and
how, at different speeds, for backing, breaking, stopping?
Certain burrowing water animals are said to disappear
with "lightning speed" when exposed. What is their
actual speed?

SENSES—What is the reaction to visual stimuli, to
sounds produced in and outside of water, food of various
smells and flavors, touch?

SITES of various fishes used for feeding, resting, nesting.

MATING HABITS—Courtship, if any, fertilization.

EGG DEPOSITS—Fish eggs, unprotected, hidden, or in
nests. Eggs of insects, snails, amphibians. What methods
of attachment, arrangement, numbers?

LENGTH OF TIME for incubation of eggs. Length of immature stage—nymph, larva, tadpole, etc.

DEPTH STUDIES—What water levels are preferred by
game fishes; by forage ("rough") fishes? What conditions influence these levels?

LENGTH-WEIGHT-AGE RELATIONSHIP in fishes. What

effect has water mass, amount of food, number of specimens, and so on, on fish growth?

> *Note*—Just as a tree age is revealed by growth rings,
> age of certain fish can be read in their scales, through
> a magnifier. At various times during the year, minute
> rings, circuli, form on the surface of the scales. These
> rings develop close together in winter, further apart
> in summer, thus forming yearly growth patterns, an-
> nuli. The number of annuli tells the age of the fish.

"Music" of frogs and toads—Uses of calls—warning, courtship, no apparent use, and so on. When does
singing start, when does it stop; dates; time of day?

recordings—*Voices of the Night*. Calls of 26 frogs and
toads of Eastern North America. Cornell University
Records, Ithaca, N. Y.

Special problems—Feeding cycles and feeding habits.
Parasites and diseases. Hibernation, aestivation—reaction
to freezing and drought.

Keeping Water Life

By keeping of fishes and other water animals it is possible to establish a small world and to observe the life
that goes on in it. The opportunities are as large as your
fancy dictates—from a small tumbler for a culture of
mosquito wrigglers, through aquarium and garden pool,
to a specially constructed pond.

books—*Living Specimens in the School Laboratories*.
General Biological Supply House, Chicago 37, Ill.
J. G. Needham. *Culture Methods for Invertebrate
Animals*. Comstock Publishing Company, Ithaca, N. Y.

Fresh-water Aquarium

The fresh-water aquarium is easy to establish and easy
to keep up, if you follow the simple requirements that
are necessary for success in regard to size of tank, temperature, light, and feeding.

books—William T. Innes. *The Modern Aquarium*.
Aquarium Publishing Company, Norristown, Penn.
Clifford B. Moore, *The Book of Wild Pets*. Chas. T.
Branford Co., Newton Centre 9, Mass.

periodical—*Aquarium Magazine* (Monthly). Aquarium
Publishing Company, Norristown, Penn.

society—Aquarium Society. Headq.: American Museum

of Natural History, 79th Street and Central Park West, New York, N. Y.

AQUARIUM TANKS—The size of the aquarium is governed by the type and amount of water life you expect to study.

All animals require oxygen to sustain life. Water animals meet their needs from the oxygen absorbed by the water through its surface contacts with the air. The larger the water surface, the more oxygen can be absorbed and subsequently the more life sustained. Stating it differently: More animal life can be supported in a certain amount of water in a shallow tank where the surface is large, than can be supported in the same amount of water in a deep tank with a much smaller water surface.

The important thing, then, is to secure a tank that is large enough in water surface area, and at the same time deep enough to make observation possible. Expert aquarists recommend 10 square inches of surface for each inch (not counting the tail) of our native fishes (20 to 25 square inches for warm-water tropical fishes) and a depth of not much beyond 12 inches, unless artificial aeration is provided. In a deeper aquarium, the fishes will come to the top to get their oxygen.

COMMERCIAL AQUARIUMS—All-glass and metal-frame aquarium tanks, stands, and other aquarium equipment may be bought from most of the biological supply houses, as well as from local firms and business houses specializing in aquarium supplies.

SUPPLIES—See list of supply houses on page 28.

Look in your telephone book under "Aquarium" and under "Pets."

Aquarium Stock Company, 31 Warren Street, New York 7, N. Y., and 80/0 Beverly Boulevard, Los Angeles 48, Calif.

M & H Manufacturing Company, 5664 N. Clark Street, Chicago 26, Ill.

ALL-GLASS TANKS—Rectangular all-glass tanks are available in capacities up to 3 gallons (11½ inches long, 8 inches wide, 8 inches deep). Glass tanks of this type crack easily, therefore require extra care.

METAL-FRAME TANKS—The metal-frame tank is the most satisfactory. Modern commercial tanks are usually made with stainless-steel frames, plate-glass sides, and blackboard-slate bottoms.

Common sizes are of the following dimensions:

Approx. capacity	Length	Width	Depth	Square-inch surface area
2 gal.	10"	6"	8"	60
3 gal.	12"	7"	9"	84
5 gal.	14"	8"	10"	112
8 gal.	18"	9"	12"	162
10 gal.	20"	10"	12"	200
15 gal.	24"	12"	12"	288
20 gal.	30"	12"	14"	360
25 gal.	36"	12"	14"	432
30 gal.	36"	14"	14"	504
40 gal.	36"	16"	16"	576

Tip—To find out the capacity of a tank, multiply the length in inches by width and depth, then divide by 231 to get number of U. S. gallons.

For most purposes, you will be better off with several smaller tanks, up to 10 gallons, say, rather than with one or two large tanks.

MAKING A SMALL AQUARIUM—Instead of buying a tank, make your own. You can make a small aquarium of about 3 gallons capacity from six pieces of glass—two 8×8-inch pieces, four 8×10-inch pieces—and strips of *waterproof* adhesive tape, by following the instructions for making a simple terrarium on page 267. The lid is not taped on, but is placed loosely over the aquarium. After the pieces are assembled, paint the adhesive tape and putty all inside corners with aquarium cement.

Tip—To make it easy to move the adhesive-tape aquarium, place it on a 9×11-inch plywood base.

Tip—You can make a better aquarium from pieces of Plexiglass, assembling them with epoxy cement.

MAKING THE METAL-FRAME AQUARIUM TANK—With the many types of metal moldings and angle irons on the market, it is comparatively simple to put together the frame for an aquarium tank. It can be done by riveting together pieces of aluminum or stainless-steel corner bars (inside corner plate, corner molding) with copper rivets, or by riveting or soldering together pieces of ½- or ¾-inch angle iron.

Decide on the size of your tank, and determine what materials you need. Start by making the bottom frame, double-mortising the metal at the frame corners. Fasten the upright corner pieces in position. Finally, attach a band around the tops of the four uprights. Have a bottom of double-thick glass, and four sides of plate glass cut to fit. Put the glass panes in with aquarium cement. This kind of cement does not harden, therefore "gives" if

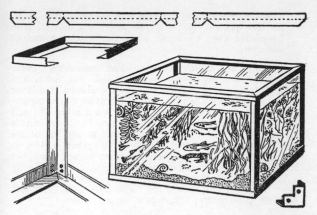

A homemade aquarium frame can be put together from double-mortized pieces of metal molding, bent, and riveted together.

there should be some unusual tension on the tank. Place the finished tank on a mat of solid rubber.

> *Tip*—For a tank larger than 15 gallons, have the angle-iron pieces welded together by a professional welder.

ESTABLISHING THE CONVENTIONAL AQUAR-IUM—Before starting the aquarium, make sure that the tank is waterproof. Fill it and let it stand overnight. If the tank leaks, make the necessary repairs. Then place the aquarium tank in its permanent location and set out to equip it with a sandy bottom, water, water plants, and animal life.

LOCATION AND LIGHT—Place the aquarium where the temperature will be fairly constant—60 to 70° Fahrenheit is ideal. The proper temperature is important for the health of the water life—not just for keeping it normally active, but also for providing the proper amount of oxygen. At higher temperatures, water loses some of its oxygen and does not absorb it as readily.

A certain amount of light is necessary—enough to "read fine print in it," as suggested by Schultz. Sufficient light is particularly important if you intend to have plants in your aquarium. A couple of hours of sunlight a day is all right, but indirect light throughout the day is better. A window to the north or east is an excellent aquarium location.

Tip—If exposure to daylight is not sufficient or feasible, use electric light instead—whether a 40-watt bulb suspended over the tank, or a commercial aquarium reflector.

PUTTING IN SANDY BOTTOM—For anchoring water plants and for providing spawning beds for fishes and hiding places for certain water animals, place a thin layer of coarse sand or fine gravel on the bottom of the aquarium. Clean the sand first by washing it a number of times until the washing water comes out clean. Put it in position in such a way that the layer is 2 inches at one end of the tank, decreasing to about 1 inch at the other. Debris in the finished aquarium will tend to move toward the lower level from which it can be removed.

WATER—When the sand bottom has been firmed down, pour in water, half filling the tank. The water used can be clear pond water, rain water, or tap water.

Tip—To prevent the water pouring from stirring up the sand, place a piece of paper on top of the sand, and pour the water on it. Or place a cup or glass in one corner and pour slowly into this, or use a large spoon to deflect the water stream.

PLANTS—Plants add greatly to the appearance of the aquarium. In addition, they have an effect on the animal life in the water. Plants, under the influence of light, take in carbon dioxide and liberate oxygen. In darkness, they use oxygen and give off carbon dioxide. It appears, therefore, that plants, under proper light conditions, are beneficial to the animal life of the aquarium—not so much by adding oxygen (the water surface should be sufficiently large to take care of this without the help of the plants), but by assisting in removing the carbon dioxide exhaled by the animal life.

The most popular aquarium plants are two ready-rooters with tapelike leaves: tapegrass or eelgrass, *Vallisneria,* and narrow-leaved arrowhead, *Sagittaria;* and three nonrooting, plumelike plants: water milfoil, *Myriophyllum;* fanwort, *Cabomba;* and waterweed, *Anacharia.* You may be able to secure some or all of these in a local pond or lake. Otherwise, buy bundles of one or more plants from each of the two groups from a supply house.

In planting, place the rooting plants in such a way that the sand just covers the roots up to the crown. In the case of the nonrooting plants, push the bottom part of the stalks well down into the sand. If the nonrooters don't seem to stay put, keep them down by tying them to small stones. Do not overplant. A dozen sprays or so is enough for a 5-gallon aquarium. When the planting is completed, pour in more water carefully, until it comes to within approximately 1 inch from the top.

STOCKING THE AQUARIUM—Leave the aquarium for a couple of days to permit the water to clear and the plants to get themselves established. Then introduce the fishes or other water animals.

MAINTAINING THE AQUARIUM

—If the aquarium has been properly established, you should have little trouble maintaining it and keeping your water animals healthy.

FEEDING—In the case of fishes, find out what food they eat in their natural surroundings, by your own investigation or from a field book. If no information is available, experiment. You can be fairly certain that some or all of the following live foods are acceptable: daphnias, cyclops, tubifex worms, aquatic insect larvae and nymphs, mealworms. Most of these you can scoop out of a local pond. Of some of them, you can keep a culture going for all-year feeding—daphnias and cyclops, see page 235; tubifex worms, see page 235; mealworms, see page 188.

Earthworms also rank high as fish food—whole, cut in pieces, or chopped.

Tip—You may be accustomed to dig for earthworms. It is easier to locate them at night, especially after a rain or a garden-hose soaking, when they come up to the surface. Search for them with a flashlight, with the beam covered with red cellophane.

Tip—An earthworm culture may be established in a wooden box or tub. Fill with about 10 inches of good garden soil, moistened but not wet. Place around a hundred earthworms on the soil; cover them with a thin layer of decaying leaves. Every week or so, replenish the diet, varying it with wet coffee grounds, cornmeal, bread crumbs, leftover boiled vegetables. Keep soil moist. Check evaporation by covering container with a burlap bag or a sheet of glass. In wintertime, keep the container in a cool cellar. In the summer, embed it outdoors to within a few inches from the top in a cool, shady place.

Tip—Enchytra worms, "white worms," may be raised in the same manner. Collect the specimens for starting from around a compost heap, or buy them from a supply house.

Although you will probably prefer to use native food for your aquarium animals, you may occasionally have to resort to chopped raw meat, or hard-boiled egg yolk, or to commercial aquarium fish food purchasable from a local pet shop.

The main point in feeding is: DON'T OVERFEED. Feed once a day only. Sprinkle a little of the food on the water and see how it is accepted, then add a little more.

Any food not eaten after about ten minutes should be removed from the bottom of the tank with a glass tube. Cover one end of a regular glass tube or an aquarium dip tube with your finger. Bring the other end down to the refuse on the bottom of the tank. Raise your finger. The water will rush into the glass tube, carrying the refuse with it. Again close the top end of the tube. Lift the tube out of the tank and get rid of its contents.

"GREEN WATER"—Occasionally, aquarium water turns green, and a green film settles on the glass sides and plants. This does not affect the health of the water animals, but makes observation difficult.

The color is caused by green algae. The reason for their development is usually that the aquarium has been exposed to too much light. The best remedy is therefore to remove the tank to a less lighted location where the condition generally clears itself up.

To help clear the water, scrape the algae off the glass sides with a razor blade pushed T-wise into a short stick of wood. When the algae have settled on the bottom, take them out with a dip tube.

> *Tip*—The introduction of half a dozen pond snails into the aquarium will help to check the green water conditions. The snails eat the algae. In addition, they eat the remains of fish food and act as general scavengers.

WATER CHANGING—It should be your aim to have an aquarium that will maintain itself without any water changing. If you follow the recommendations given above, no changing should be necessary. All you have to do is to add a little water from time to time to keep the water level constant.

> *Tip*—To keep the evaporation low and to prevent dust from falling into the water, cover the tank with a piece of window glass. Cement small pieces of cork to the corners so that the glass plate will be raised slightly to permit free access of air.

SPECIAL AQUARIUMS—Practically all fresh-water animals will thrive well in the conventional aquarium. But for a number of them a much simpler arrangement can be used. In all instances, do not keep any animals in the same container with the enemies that prey on them— unless you are planning to study their reaction to each other.

SMALL WATER ANIMALS—Tiny water animals thrive and can be observed in an ordinary water glass, or, better, in a small glass aquarium with straight glass sides. Such aquariums are available in 1-quart size (6 inches long, 2 inches wide, 5 inches deep), and in 2-quart size (4 inches long, 4 inches wide, 8 inches deep).

Some of these animals feed on minute plant and animal life in the water from the pond in which they were found, others—such as the hydras—need a supply of daphnias.

TUBIFEX WORMS—A culture of tubifex worms can be established in a shallow dishpan. Pour in a 2-inch-deep layer of the mud in which the worms are found. Add a couple of inches of pond water.

LEECHES—Leeches can be kept in clear pond water— or in tap water, for that matter—in an ordinary gallon-size glass jar. Place the container in a dark spot. Feed every couple of weeks by placing a sliver of raw meat in the jar. The following day, remove the meat and change the water completely.

DAPHNIAS AND CYCLOPS—For a small culture, sweep daphnia and cyclops out of the pond with a dip net, then place in pond water in a small glass container.

A large culture of 20 gallons or more should be successful in a wooden tub in a cool location. Or try the method suggested by Professor H. Heath of Stanford University, of raising daphnias in a culture medium of 1 ounce of dried sheep manure per gallon of water, adding a few lettuce leaves from time to time.

CRAYFISH—Crayfish can be raised in a gallon jar, a shallow aquarium or in a couple of inches of water in a white-enamel dishpan. Place a couple of handfuls of pebbles on the bottom to provide hiding places. Feed water insects, chopped earthworms, or tiny pieces of meat.

> *Tip*—If some of the crayfish you catch in fall or early spring happen to be females with eggs attached to their swimmerets, you may have the chance to see the eggs hatching into tiny crayfish.

AQUATIC INSECTS—Insect larvae, nymphs, water bugs, and water beetles can be raised in quart jars or quart-size aquariums. Place a small amount of sand on the bottom and insert a spray of some water plant. Part of the plant should be above water so that an emerging adult of dragonfly or damsel fly, for instance, may be able to crawl out of the water. Cover the container with a lid of wire screening to prevent a flying insect from escaping.

The chief disadvantage of the jar or water-glass aquarium is that its cylindrical glass wall makes observation uncertain by distorting the view.

A better aquarium is made from two pieces of glass, preferably plate glass, 6×8 inches, and three pieces of ¾-inch wood, 2 inches wide, two side pieces 8 inches long, and a 4½-inch bottom piece. Smear waterproof household cement on the ends of the bottom piece; then nail the two side pieces to it to form a U. Shellac and let dry. Cement the two glass pieces to the frame. Bind the edges with 1½-inch wide waterproof adhesive tape. Finally paint the tape with whatever color you prefer. Prepare the finished aquarium with sand, water plant, pond water, as described above.

Some of the insects will feed on plant particles and on the algae in the pond water. Others are carnivorous and require small insects, mosquito wrigglers, daphnia, and the like. Dip net sweepings should satisfy most of them.

The peculiar "houses" of caddis larvae can be observed best in a shallow pan, such as a photographic developing tray.

FRESH-WATER SNAILS—Snails will get along well in a container, quart-size or larger, filled with the "green water" of a stagnant pool, or with an inch or so of bottom mud and a couple of water plants.

AMPHIBIANS—Raise salamanders, frogs, and toads from eggs. Locate the eggs yourself during the spring and early summer. Eggs of most salamanders are attached singly on water plants, with a leaf bent down over each of them. Pickerel and leopard frogs lay their eggs in large tapiocalike masses attached to some water plant, bullfrogs and green frogs in floating surface films. The eggs of toads are laid in long, double "pearl" strings. Bring home the eggs in water in a glass jar.

Place the eggs in water in an ordinary gallon jar. Or use a white-glass battery jar. These jars come in three sizes—1-gallon (6 inches diameter, 8 inches deep), 2-gallon (8 inches diameter, 9 inches deep), 3-gallon (9 inches diameter, 12 inches deep).

When the tadpoles begin to come out, plan to keep a couple of dozen only, returning the remaining eggs to the pond where you got them.

Salamander larvae feed on insects and insect larvae, tadpoles live on algae and other water plants. All of them will get along beautifully on dip net sweepings.

Tip—The job of feeding tadpoles becomes even simpler if you raise them on cornmeal. Sprinkle a little meal in the water daily. Remove excess food with a dip tube.

When the tadpoles approach the adult stage, you need to make it possible for the fully-grown amphibians to leave the water. Place a stone in the water with part of

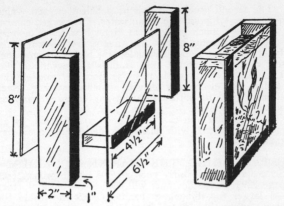

A miniature aquarium for small water animals and aquatic insects
made from glass and wood, or pieces of clear plastic.

it above the surface, or float a piece of wood in it. The
metamorphosis of most amphibians takes place in the
same year. The green frog and the red-legged frog require two years, the bullfrog two to four years.

As the salamanders, frogs, or toads come out of the
water, transfer them to a shallow aquarium in which one
side of the sand bottom has been built up into an above-
water bank, or, better, to a woodland terrarium (see page
267) containing a shallow dish of water. The adult amphibians are carnivores. Feed them live, moving insects,
caterpillars, meal worms, earthworms, slugs, or dangle
tiny pieces of lean meat or liver in front of their eyes.

TURTLES—Small turtles may be raised in the same type
of aquarium or terrarium as adult amphibians. They get
along on a diet of snails, tadpoles, and small fishes.

MARINE AQUARIUM

While keeping the fresh-water aquarium is a fairly
simple matter, the marine aquarium presents two problems that are often hard to overcome.

The first of these is the problem of temperature. Sea
animals are accustomed to much lower temperatures than
fresh-water animals, and unless you can manage to keep
the water temperature around 50 to 60° Fahrenheit, you
cannot expect the animals to thrive. You may be able to
keep the proper temperature in the winter time, but it will
prove a major concern during the summer months. If you
plan to keep warm-water tropical fishes, the water can,
of course, be warmer—70 to 75° Fahrenheit.

The second problem is that of sufficient oxygen. Wind and waves whip air into ocean water. The oxygen content is therefore much higher than in fresh water. You may succeed in keeping marine life alive in fresh ocean water for a couple of weeks. But unless the higher oxygen content can be maintained, your animals will eventually die. You can solve this problem by artificial aeration—by installing an electrically driven air-pump aerator. Such a pump may be purchased from any company handling aquarium supplies.

If you think you can lick these two problems, by all means go ahead with plans for developing a marine aquarium.

ESTABLISHING THE MARINE AQUARIUM— Secure a tank of fairly good size—8 or 10 gallons (see page 229). A smaller tank will soon prove unsatisfactory —a larger too difficult to handle. Check the inside for places where the metal frame may be exposed. Cover exposed spots with asphalt paint or with aquarium cement. Sea water has a corroding effect on metal.

WATER—Bring home salt water from the ocean in glass or enamel containers. If you live inland, you can have sea water shipped in 10-gallon carboys by ordering through a biological supply house.

Pour the water into the tank, and mark the water level on the outside of the tank with a piece of scotch or adhesive tape. This is an important precaution. Some of the water will eventually evaporate, with the result that the mineral concentration will increase, to the detriment of the tank inhabitants. By filling up with distilled water to the marked water level you are assured that the mineral concentration remains constant.

Tip—Cover the tank with a glass plate to slow down evaporation (see page 234).

SAND AND PLANTS—There is no advantage to putting sand into a marine aquarium—unless needed for burrowing animals. Similarly, plants are unnecessary—unless you want them for looks. In that case, float a few pieces of sea lettuce, *Ulva*, or other green algae in the water, or anchor them on the bottom by tying them to small stones. Include a couple of stones for some animals to attach themselves to, for others to hide under.

STOCKING THE AQUARIUM—Marine animals require a larger amount of oxygen than fresh-water animals— therefore a larger water surface. The exact number that you can keep can only be found by experimenting. But in any event, watch out for overstocking.

MAINTAINING THE MARINE AQUARIUM—With proper temperature and aeration taken care of, feeding becomes your only other concern.

FEEDING—Most marine animals will get along on a diet of small pieces of clams, mussels, oysters, and fish.

For sea urchins, sea cucumbers, barnacles, and crabs, place the food next to the animals, with aquarium forceps —two 18-inch strips of wood held together at one end over a thin, wooden wedge, tong fashion. For sea anemones, place the food in the center of the expanded animal. For fishes, drop the food on top of the water so that the fishes may pick it up as it sinks toward the bottom. Food particles not consumed within about fifteen minutes should be removed with a dip tube before it has a chance to decompose.

In feeding starfishes, place a whole, live clam or mussel next to each specimen. Starfishes have their own way of opening shells and getting at the contents.

Marine snails feed on the algae that settle on the sides of the tank.

AQUARIUM POOLS

In many instances, an outdoor pool is preferable to an indoor aquarium tank. Such a pool can be arranged to resemble closely the conditions under which the water life was found in the field.

WOODEN TANK—The simplest outdoor pool is a wooden box, or tub, sunk into the ground in a shady location. Make the box from 1-inch cypress boards. Suitable dimensions are 4 to 6 feet long, 4 feet wide, 15 inches deep. Close all cracks with aquarium cement, and paint with a good quality outdoor paint. Use a light color so that the water animals will be clearly visible.

Tip—To be able to drain the tank, bore a 1-inch hole in the bottom of it. Close it with a cork or rubber stopper. When digging the hole for the tank, deepen it beyond the depth of the box into a stone pit, a "dry well," to take care of the water in draining.

CEMENT POOL—A cement pool may be developed as an expansion of the bird pool described on page 86. By sticking to the idea of sloping sides, but enlarging the pool to a width and length of 6 feet, and a depth of 2 to 3 feet, no form is necessary. Use a 4- to 6-inch layer of cement, smoothing down the surface.

For a pool with vertical sides, you need a form. Excavate carefully, keeping the sides smooth. Put up a wooden wall, 6 inches from the sides, to act as an inside form. Use sheet iron if the pool has rounded corners.

Place chicken wire in the form for reinforcement. Then pour in the cement. The form for the sides can be removed after about 48 hours, whereupon the bottom is poured in. For ease in filling and emptying the pool, you may decide to do a job of plumbing, with a lead-in pipe at one side, a drainage pipe in the bottom.

REFERENCE—*Construction of a Garden Fish Pool*. Fishery Pamphlet, Fish and Wildlife Service, U. S. Department of the Interior, Washington, D. C.

When the pool is finished, fill it with water, and leave it a few days. Flush, and fill again. Repeat the process several times to reduce the alkalinity of the cement. Then put in sand, plants, and water, and, after a couple of days of settling, your animal life.

Tip—To assist in feeding, hang a 50-watt light bulb over the pool, a foot or so above the surface. Lit at night, it will attract insects, which, on tiring, will drop into the water.

Fish Ponds

If you have land available with no natural ponds on it, you may take the next, ambitious step of installing a fish pond. In so doing, you not only provide yourself with the chance to study fresh-water life and have the fun of fishing—you also strike a blow for the cause of conservation.

The simplest way of developing a pond is by diverting water from a stream. But flowing water is not necessary. Surface draining from surrounding territory is often sufficient to maintain the proper water level.

Artificial ponds can vary in size from ½ acre to 2 or 3 acres, in depth from 1½ to 3 feet—5 feet or more in places of drought in summer or of deep freezing in winter.

Before deciding to go ahead, contact the Agricultural Extension Service and Soil Conservation Service of your locality. They will be able to give you valuable advice, and possibly actual help. In stocking the pond, you may get further assistance from your state's fish and game department and from the Fish and Wildlife Service of the U. S. Department of the Interior.

REFERENCES—Verne E. Davison. *Farm Fishponds for Food and Good Land Use*. Farmer's Bulletin 1983. U. S. Department of Agriculture.

John Blosz and Richard F. Dittman. *Construction of Farm Ponds*. Fishery Leaflet 17, Fish and Wildlife Service, U. S. Department of the Interior.

Photographing Water Life

In water-life photography you run up against a snag that you do not often encounter in photography: the problem of overcoming the reflections from a water surface in the outdoors, from the side of a glass tank when shooting indoors. If you remember to keep on watch against picking up these reflections with your camera lens, you should be able to produce some striking underwater shots.

STILLS

EQUIPMENT—CAMERA—To get close enough to your subjects and to be positive that you get what you are aiming for, you require a camera with ground-glass focusing and tripod support. The reflex camera is particularly well adapted to the low-angle shots of amphibians.

Your regular camera lens will do duty for some shots, but for most, you will have to use supplementary lenses or extension tubes. If you hanker to photograph the minute creatures of plankton and of pond mud, you may have to take the step into microphotography, posing your models under a microscope—but that is a science in itself, outside the realm of regular photography.

POLAROID FILTER—There is one accessory that you will bless a hundred times over in your water-life photography: the Polaroid filter or pola-screen. By placing this filter in front of your lens and adjusting it, you are able to cut down a large percentage of reflections and glare, in this way penetrating below the surface film of water and behind the glass of a tank. Some Polaroid filters are visually adjusted—you turn the two sections of the filter while looking at your scene, until reflections disappear—others are provided with a pointer to be turned toward the light source.

In using a Polaroid filter, you do not have to increase the exposure as is the case for other filters. Simply take the meter reading and set the diaphragm and speed accordingly.

EXPOSURES—In exposure meter readings again watch out for reflections. In attempting to take the reading of a fish hovering close to the water's surface you may, actually, be getting the reading of the sky reflected in the water. For safety's sake, use the substitution method, taking your reading on a piece of gray cardboard.

OUTDOOR PHOTOGRAPHY—In outdoor pond photography, concentrate on the life of the water film—striders or whirligig beetles skimming over the surface—and of the first few inches of water just below it. A salt-water tide pool gives you a better chance—provided the weather is still. Ripples on the water will blur your subjects—but may, in some cases, provide an interesting effect.

If you insist on going deeper, use a waterscope as described on page 217. Add an arrangement for attaching the camera on the inside of it, so that you can move the scope about. Of course, you can always go to Florida and photograph the water life of some of its crystal-clear lakes through the special glass-bottomed boats provided for tourists.

UNDERWATER SHOTS—If you are a skin diving expert and want to photograph under water you will need special waterproof casing for your camera, with provision for focusing and for releasing the shutter.

BOOK ON UNDERWATER PHOTOGRAPHY—D. Rebicoff and P. Cherney. *Guide to Underwater Photography*. Greenberg.

NIGHT SHOTS—Frogs are best photographed at night, when a camera with a synchronized flash gun is used.

On a warm spring or early summer night when the frog chorus is at its loudest, go jacklighting for frogs, as suggested on page 223. The blinding beam of a strong flashlight seems to hypnotize a frog—it sits perfectly still as long as the light is in its eyes, giving you time to get within a few feet of it to set up a tripod. Focus your camera on the shining eyes, and take one or more shots —one, certainly, showing the vocal sacs fully extended.

INDOOR PHOTOGRAPHY—Most of your stills of water life will have to be taken indoors, where you can control your subjects and your light.

AQUARIUM PHOTOGRAPHS—Use a tank with one side, at least, of flawless plate glass. Place the tank on a special stand or at the edge of a table. Set up the camera on a tripod and arrange your floodlights—one light as the main light source, the other for a fill-in. The important thing is to place the lights in such a way that they do not reflect against the glass side of the tank into the camera and do not light up the camera itself so that its chromium is mirrored in the glass. You may have to keep the lights to the rear of the tank's front glass, with a large cardboard frame around the tank to prevent the light from striking the camera. Or solve the problem with the help of a Polaroid filter.

Tip—To keep fishes and other water life in focus, place a sheet of glass in the tank, 1 or 2 inches from the front glass. Confine your models between the two glass surfaces.

Tip—Turn off the floodlights when you are not shooting, to prevent them from heating up the aquarium
water unnecessarily.

The shallowness of the depth of field will generally
throw the back of the tank out of focus. If it doesn't,
place a neutral gray background (blue for color photography) or even a few potted plants on the other side of
the tank.

TRAY PHOTOGRAPHY—Some subjects photograph well
from above—directly above or at an angle. Place them
in a shallow glass tray with a couple of inches of water.
Set the tray on a thin layer of pebbles, sand or dirt to
provide a suitable "natural" background.

SHELL PHOTOGRAPHS—Shells are excellently suited for
tabletop photography. Pose them individually on a small
mound of sand. Sidelight or backlight them in such a way
that their texture is brought out to the greatest advantage. Shoot from above, or from a low angle, against a
neutral background.

Shells may also be shot by shadowless photography:
Drape a piece of white material in a U between two
chairs, placed slightly less than 2 feet apart. Suspend
a 2-foot sheet of glass between the chairs. Place the shell
on the glass, focus the camera on it, then arrange two
lights in such a way that the two shadows of the shell
fall outside the field of the camera lens.

MOVIES

With a focusing motion-picture camera, supplied with
a 3-inch or 4-inch telephoto lens in addition to the regular
1-inch lens, you will find water-life moviemaking one of
your most satisfying experiences. You can shoot according to a script and make use of a variety of shooting
methods.

MOVIE TECHNIQUES—Whether you want to take
a movie dealing with a whole water-life community of
brook or lake or sea, or with the life cycle of a single
animal—"From Egg to Frog," for instance—you will
almost certainly want to use a combination of outdoor
and indoor shots—outdoor shots to establish the locale,
indoor for close-ups.

In a movie of, say, "The Quiet Pond," you may establish a mood of tranquillity by starting with "atmosphere
shots" of the pond shimmering in the sunlight, of plants
along its shores waving softly in the summer breeze. The
camera eye then moves down into the water, roaming
here and there, finally showing scene upon scene of dramatic close-ups of the far-from-quiet life-and-death
struggles of the pond's inhabitants.

For the mood shots, you will, of course, make use of the usual technique of the long-medium-close-up shots. When entering the water, use the methods suggested in the previous pages for stills—employing the waterscope for outdoor shots, the aquarium tank for the dramatic sequences taken indoors.

Water-Life Collections

The methods of preparing water-life collections vary with the type of animals.

REFERENCE—Morris Miller Wells. *The Collection and Preservation of Animal Forms.* General Biological Supply House, Chicago, Ill.

DRYING—A few water animals make good collection specimens by the simple process of drying—starfish, sea urchins, and crabs.

Place the animals for a couple of days in a half-and-half mixture of rubbing alcohol and water, or give them a quick boil in fresh water. Lay them out on a board, arrange them in a natural manner, and let them dry in the sun.

LIQUID PRESERVATION—All sea animals can be preserved in formalin or alcohol.

Sea anemones and jellyfish close themselves up, starfish pull in their tube feet when touched or placed in a conserving fluid. By anesthetizing them first, you can keep them extended. To do this, place them in a small amount of sea water, say 1 quart. Slowly add one quarter of this amount (½ pint) of a saturated solution of magnesium sulphate, Epsom salt—made by dissolving 1 pound of the salt in 1 pint of water. Leave the animal in the liquid for six to ten hours, or until it no longer contracts when touched.

Worms, leeches, and small fishes are usually drowned in alcohol.

Frogs and toads die quickly in fresh water shaken up with ether—1 teaspoon ether to 1 quart of water. When a specimen is dead, arrange it in a natural position in a shallow pan containing 10-per-cent formalin (one part commercial formaldehyde, three parts water) and leave it overnight. If the specimen is large, make slits in the stomach wall and underside of leg to give the preservative a chance to penetrate.

Finally, place the specimen in tightly closed jars in 10-per-cent formalin or 70-per-cent alcohol. In the case of jellyfishes and other species that have a large water content, the preserving fluid will have to be replaced a couple of times before the jars are permanently closed.

Tip—For an especially good-looking display, tie or glue your specimens to pieces of regular or opal glass and place in standard biological display jars, as described for snakes (page 162).

PLASTIC EMBEDDING—Small specimens of water life make spectacular displays when embedded in blocks of clear plastics in the manner explained for insects on page 212. A specimen can be placed in plastic within a couple of hours after having received the formalin treatment described above.

Pour a layer of catalysed plastic into a dish and let it stand until quite firm. Pour in the top layer. Blot the specimen to be embedded carefully to remove as much moisture as possible. Let it air-dry for a short while, then dip it in catalysed plastic, and place in position. Work out possible air bubbles. Heat very slowly to 170° Fahrenheit and keep at this temperature for about one hour. Cool slowly.

SHELLS—The study and collection of shells—conchology—has been a popular activity for hundreds of years —with children picking up native species on home beaches, sailors bringing back rare forms from trips around the globe. As in insect collecting, it is common among shell collectors to get together to increase their collections by swapping and bartering.

SOCIETIES—American Malacological Union. Hdqrs.:
    Buffalo Museum of Science, Buffalo 11, N. Y. Periodical: ·*Annual News Bulletin and Report.*
    Conchological Club of California. Hdqrs.: John Q. Burch, 4206 Hallidale Avenue, Los Angeles 37, Calif.

CLEANING THE SHELLS—Shells found empty are seldom satisfactory. They are usually wave or weather beaten and chipped. To secure perfect shells, collect the live animals and clean out the shells.

The one-shelled chitons can be pried off their home bases, and their flesh scraped out with a knife.

Place snails in cold water and heat to boiling point. The soft body can then be pulled out with a bent pin or a small knitting needle. Be sure to keep the "door," operculum, that the live snail may have used for closing itself in. Glue it in position with household cement after the shell has dried.

Tiny snail shells need not be cleaned out. Place them in alcohol overnight, then dry them in the sun.

Bivalves—clams, mussels, oysters—open when you pour hot water over them. Scrape out the meat thoroughly. Some collectors separate the two shells. It is better to keep intact the elastic band that holds the shells together and dry one set of shells spread out flat, another set of the same species closed up. To do the latter, tie a string around the shells during the drying.

Tip—Many of the bivalves open up readily when placed in carbonated water—plain "soda" water.

ARRANGING THE COLLECTION—In developing your collection and displaying your shells, you can use your own ingenuity.

Tiny shells are best kept in small vials with screw caps or corks. Medium shells may fit into match boxes. Larger shells may be kept in cardboard trays of suitable size. The whole collection can then be arranged in shallow drawers. For a large collection, you may want to make use of a system similar to that used in rock collections (see page 337).

Instead of having shells loose, you may prefer to mount your collection. You can attach the shells to a piece of cardboard with household cement. Even better is the use of strips of glass.

Each shell should, of course, be identified and labeled. Write a small catalog number on the shell with India ink. Protect the writing with a dab of white shellac or clear nail polish.

Keep a complete record of the shell under its number, including name, place where found, date, and whatever biological information you may want to add.

BOOKS—Percy A. Morris. *Field Guide to the Shells.* Houghton, Mifflin Company, Boston, Mass.

A. Hyatt Verrill. *Shell Collector's Handbook.* G. P. Putnam's Sons.

FISH DISPLAYS—If you are a fisherman, you may like the idea of turning your prize catch into a display. It can be done by casting or mounting.

FISH CASTS—Get or make up a cardboard box that will hold your fish with room to spare. Fill the box to within 2 inches from the top with moist sand. Smear a thin layer of vaseline over the fish. Lay the fish on the sand and press one side of it completely down into the sand. Make a batch of plaster-of-Paris mixture (see page 133). Pour over the fish to the top of the box and leave it to set. When completely hardened, lift this negative cast off, brush the inside of it with vaseline and make a positive cast in the same way that a positive track cast is produced (see page 135). Paint the finished product in natural colors with oil paint.

FISH MOUNTING—Instead of a plaster facsimile, you

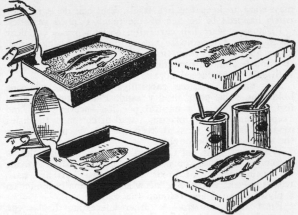

Making a fish cast: pouring plaster on the fish, half embedded in sand; the negative; pouring the positive; final painting.

In preparing a fish for mounting, cut along one side, remove carcass, sew skin together, fill with sand, dry and stuff.

may want to keep the fish itself. You can do it if your catch happens to be one of the tough-skinned varieties.

First skin your fish carefully. Make a cross cut near the tail fin, a lengthwise cut up one side. Using a dull knife and taking your time, skin out the body. Scrape the skin to remove remaining flesh, and rub it thoroughly with salt or powdered borax.

Sew up the incisions carefully. Then, while someone holds the skin, pour in dry sand. Place the sand-filled fish on its side in a natural position—prevent the sand from running out by placing a wad of cotton in the fish's mouth. Use long pins to keep the fins in place. Leave the skin to dry thoroughly.

When dry, pour out the sand. Replace it with cellulose cotton or excelsior, or pour in a plaster "batter," made by mixing plaster of Paris and sawdust, half and half, with sufficient water. Shellac when dry. Finally mount on a plywood panel and retouch the colors.

FISH-HEAD MOUNTS—A rather interesting display can be made of "pickled" fish heads, as suggested by Dave Dunbar.

Cut off the head around the gills and scrape out any remaining flesh. Rub table salt into the head, inside and out, getting it into all crevices. Put a match stick in the mouth to keep the jaws open. Hang up the head by the match stick to dry in the sun for about a week. Brush off the salt and give the head two coats of clear varnish. Mount by tacking it to a piece of wood cut to fit inside the gills.

8. FLOWERS AND FLOWERLESS PLANTS

THE moment you leave city streets behind and set out in the open, you enter into the land of plants. There's the green of the fields, the colors of a multitude of flowers, the arching canopy of trees. Even where nature is not too lavish with her gifts of fertility—on mountain tops and in deserts—you will find plants that make a brave stand under adverse conditions.

Life would be pretty dreary if we couldn't turn to fields and forests, parks and gardens, for recreation and enjoyment—if the green of the out-of-doors should turn to withered brown forevermore.

But even more important, human life would end if plant life should die. The food we eat, the clothing we wear, the air we breathe, the houses in which we live, depend on the plants that grow around us. Even the heat in our homes, the electric light that turns our nights into day, the power of our motors are possible only because of plants of prehistoric days transformed into coal and oil and gases.

There is wonder in the structure of plants, from microscopic bacteria to the tallest tree in the world. There is beauty in colors, excitement in odors, piquancy in flavors. There is healing for body and mind planting a seed in the good earth and seeing it grow.

And there is everlasting mystery in the ability of plants to pick up the energy of the sun and to store it—not just for their own use, but for ours. We are still far from solving the great riddle of plant life: How can a plant take carbon dioxide from the air and water from the ground, and under the power of sunlight and by means of the green matter in its leaves—chlorophyl—combine them into sugar, releasing free oxygen for animals and humans

249

to breathe. Not limited to even that magic, the plant goes on building other substances : starches and cellulose, oil, protein, complex vitamins. How? Eventually we may know.

BOOKS ON PLANT LIFE—Harry J. Fuller. *The Plant World*. Holt, Rinehart & Winston.

Herbert S. Zim. *Plants*. Harcourt, Brace and Company.

Donald Culross Peattie. *Flowering Earth*. G. P. Putnam's Sons.

Rutherford Platt. *This Green World* and *Our Flowering World*. Dodd, Mead and Company.

WORKING WITH OTHERS

Probably no other field of nature has as many followers as the field of botany—plants from the most primitive to the most highly developed, plants of a thousand purposes.

Your local biology teachers will be able to suggest people in your community who are interested in wild plants. Or you may drop a line to the department of botany of your state university, to your state agricultural experiment station, or to your county agent.

You are almost certain to find, right in your own locality, a member club of one of the national garden clubs meeting regularly. While the garden clubs are mainly concerned with cultivated plants, they are also interested in the preservation of native plants. There are people within most of these clubs who specialize in wild flowers and their conservation. Join a congenial group of such people for field trips and other activities.

SOCIETIES—The Garden Club of America. Hdqrs.: 15 East 58th Street, New York 22, N. Y. Periodical: *The Bulletin*.

National Council of State Garden Clubs. Hdqrs.: 160 Central Park South, New York 19, N. Y.

And then, there are scientific organizations working in certain fields of plant life. Many of them publish bulletins and magazines on their special subjects. These organizations and societies are open to interested people.

SOCIETIES—GENERAL—Botanical Society of America. Hdqrs.: Department of Botany, University of Texas, Austin 12, Tex. Periodical: *American Journal of Botany*.

The Torrey Botanical Club. Hdqrs.: Hunter College, New York 21, N. Y. Periodical: *The Bulletin*.

FLOWERS—The Wild Flower Preservation Society. Hdqrs.: 3740 Oliver Street, N. W., Washington 15, D. C. Periodical: *Wild Flower*.

FERNS—American Fern Society. Hdqrs.: 501 University Place, Syracuse 10, N. Y. Periodical: *American Fern Journal*.

MOSSES—American Bryological Society. Hdqrs.: University of Wisconsin, Madison, Wis. Periodical: *The Bryologist*.

FUNGI—Mycological Society of America. Hdqrs.: Michigan State University, East Lansing, Mich. Periodical: *Mycologia*.

Plants in the Field

EQUIPMENT FOR PLANT STUDY

Little equipment is needed to penetrate into the world of plants. As in every other phase of nature, your most important tools are observing eyes—not just eyes that see, but eyes that notice the many details that, together, tell the whole story.

STUDY EQUIPMENT—MAGNIFIERS—Many plant parts are so tiny that they cannot be seen clearly with the naked eye. Some of them may be the final points that determine the plant you are studying—whether tiny hairs, seeds, or number of stamens.

For most work, you can get along with one of the folding-type pocket magnifiers that magnify from 5 to 10 times (see page 167).

If you specialize in plants that have minute parts, you may have to resort to the more expensive Coddington-type pocket magnifier, or the Hastings triplet. These will give you magnifications up to 20✕.

Another type, popular with botanists, is the tripod magnifier. This consists of a pair of lenses in a three-legged mount. The plant part to be studied is placed on a smooth surface, such as a notebook cover. The tripod is straddled over the plant, and the lenses are moved up or down, until the plant part is in sharp focus.

The tripod magnifier is popular with botanists. It consists of a pair of lenses enclosed in a three-legged metal mount.

KNIFE—A penknife with a small blade is satisfactory for opening most flowers to lay open their inside structure, and for making cross sections of stems or branches.

DISSECTING NEEDLE—For very small plants, the knife may be too coarse, and you may have to use a dissecting needle instead. This is just a fine metal point in a small handle of wood or metal, available in scientific supply houses at a dime or a quarter.

Tip—You can make your own dissecting needle by pushing a sewing needle, eye first, into a 3-inch length of ¼-inch dowel stick, with a pair of pliers.

RULE—Your measuring problem will be solved by a six-inch pocket rule, graduated along one edge in·eighths of inches, along the other in millimeters. The most popular type is of flexible, transparent plastic.

PLANT BOOKS—The plant is before you, you have looked at its various parts. Now you want to know, "What is it?"

The number of books for identifying plants is immense. Some of them are simple, others are intended for experts only. Very few cover the whole subject of all plants. Most of them specialize—some in flowers, others in certain flowerless plants.

Your best bet is to pick a well-illustrated book in the subject in which you are interested, and arrive at your identification by comparing your plant with the illustrations, finally checking it against the text that accompanies the most likely picture.

BOOKS FOR FIELD IDENTIFICATION: FLOWERS—F. Schuyler Mathews. *Field Book of American Wild Flowers.* G. P. Putnam's Sons.
Margaret Armstrong. *Field Book of Western Wild Flowers.* G. P. Putnam's Sons.
Edgar T. Wherry. *Wild Flower Guide.* Doubleday & Company.
Samuel H. Gottscho. *Wild Flowers.* Dodd, Mead & Company.
M. Walter Pesman. *Meet the Natives.* (Rocky Mountain Flowers). Published by author, 372 South Humboldt Street, Denver, Col.
Edmund C. Jaeger. *Desert Wild Flowers.* Stanford University Press, Stanford, Calif.

FERNS—Herbert Durand. *Field Book of Common Ferns.* G. P. Putnam's Sons.
Boughton Cobb. *Field Guide to the Ferns.* Houghton Mifflin Company, Boston, Mass.

MOSSES—A. J. Grout. *Mosses with a Hand-Lens.* Distribution: Chicago Natural History Museum, Chicago, Ill.

Henry S. Conard. *How to Know the Mosses*. Wm. C. Brown Company, Dubuque, Iowa.

FUNGI—William S. Thomas. *Field Book of Common Mushrooms*. G. P. Putnam's Sons.

Alexander H. Smith. *Mushroom Hunter's Field Guide*. University of Michigan Press, Ann Arbor, Mich.

LICHENS—G. G. Nearing. *The Lichen Book—A Handbook of the Lichens of Northeastern United States*. Published by the author, P. O. Box 338, Ridgewood, N. J.

ALGAE—Lewis H. Tiffany. *Algae, the Grass of Many Waters*. Charles C. Thomas, Publisher, Springfield, Ill.

ADVANCED BOOK OF IDENTIFICATION—Asa Gray. *New Manual of Botany*. Revised by M. L. Fernald. (Flowering plants and ferns of Central and N. E. U. S.) American Book Company.

Note—For books on the flowers or flowerless plants of your region or your home state, consult your state university or state museum.

NOTEBOOK—And then, of course, the ever-present notebook and pencil—a simple five-and-ten-cent-store affair, or a more elaborate one if your prefer. In this you can keep track of each plant you find—its name, the date you found it, its location, its habitat, and so on.

FINDING PLANTS

The study of plants has two advantages over the study of most other living things: First, plants stay put—you don't have to sneak up on them as on animals, or watch them from afar through field glasses as you do birds, or hunt them with net or line. And, second, you can find plants any time during the year.

WHERE?—The best place to start looking for plants is HERE—right in your own backyard, your garden, or, if you live in the city, the nearest park. These places may be well tended—nevertheless, they will all contain a fair abundance of wild plants. You may think of them as weeds—"a weed is a plant out of place"—but any of them, whether dandelion or mustard, plantain or ragweed, can start you off on your study of plant families.

When you have become acquainted with the plants of your own immediate surroundings, set out on field trips into the different types of plant communities that are found within a couple of miles of your home—whether forest, grassland, marsh, lake shore, seashore, desert, or whatever they happen to be.

Study each type in turn. Discover its dominant plants, become thoroughly familiar with each plant community.

WHEN?—There is no closed season on plants—any time of the year is plant time. There is always something to find—although to find the things that specifically interest you, you may need to pick a certain time of the year.

The season for FLOWERS starts in early spring—mostly with plants of the Lily and Crowfoot families—to wind up in late summer with domineering members of the Composite family.

You can follow the growth of FERNS from spring to fall.

LICHENS and MOSSES may be found in the heat of mid-summer and under the snow of midwinter, ALGAE wherever there is open water—fresh or salt.

Some FUNGI may be located throughout the year. Late summer and early fall are the times for the more spectacular species.

PLANT LISTS AND CALENDARS

LIFE LISTS—By listing in your notebook, or in the margin of your field book, every plant you discover and identify on your field trips, with a notation of date and place, you are building yourself a life list of plants.

Such a listing may be mostly for your own satisfaction, but may occasionally prove of interest to a much larger audience.

REGIONAL LISTS—Your state, through the extension service of its department of agriculture, its department of conservation, or its state university, may already have made a listing of the plants of your region. But conditions change over the years. An old plant community may have given way to a new, plants not previously common to the region may have made their appearance. Many new discoveries are possible—you may be the one to make them!

> *Tip*—Secure from the departments listed above any pamphlets that may have been published on the flora of your state.

CALENDARS—"The flowers that bloom in the spring, tra-la" are possibly the most welcome of all plants. In addition to their beauty, they provide you with a chance to compare their dates of appearing with dates of previous years, in this way giving you an idea of climatic conditions from spring to spring.

FLOWER CALENDARS—The simplest way of keeping track

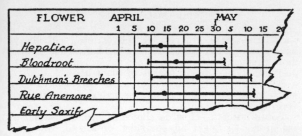

In a flower calendar, aim for three dates: petals open (straight mark), pollen shed (dot), all petals dropped (wavy mark).

of flower openings is to jot down the notes about them in your regular notebook, during daily spring walks:

April 4. Weather: Sunny. Temp.: Appr. 50
    Hepatica. Rue anemone
April 8. Weather: Showery. Temp.: Appr. 55
    Bloodroot. Adder's tongue. Dutchman's breeches ...

Later on, at your convenience, transfer the notes to file cards or looseleaf sheets, one for each flower:

HEPATICA
    April 4.
        Weather: Sunny. Temp.: Appr. 50 ...
    April 6.
        Weather: Cloudy. Temp.: Appr. 55
    April 8.
        Weather: Rain. Temp.: Appr. 45

For a more complete study of spring flowers, aim to get three dates for each flower: 1. Opening of petals; 2. Shedding of pollen (scientifically, a flower is not considered in full bloom until the anthers release their pollen); 3. All petals dropped. In all cases, keep track of weather conditions.

CALENDAR CHARTS—For ready reference, the calendar notes may be transferred to a chart, with flower names opposite the respective dates.

A better system is the use of ruled paper (millimeter paper) on which a line may be drawn opposite each flower name to indicate the full period of flowering.

Tip—A simple calendar chart can be used to advantage in club, school, and Scout work. Rule off a large sheet of cardboard with spaces for:

DATE   NAME OF FLOWER   WHERE SEEN   DISCOVERER
Such a chart may be the basis for a competition.

Field Observations

Field trips for the purpose of learning new flowers, or for checking the progress of the seasons, will always have a certain fascination. But the field trips will be even more productive of results, if the opportunity is taken to peer into ever different phases of plant life.

PLANT DIARIES—Keep track of the development of a single genus of flowering plant through daily observations from budding to fading.

YOUNG SHOOTS—How do shoots of plants push out of the ground—straight up, spearlike, or arched, with bent "backs"? Power of young shoots—moving stones, breaking through concrete, etc.

DESERT PLANTS—Year-round, but specifically a couple of weeks after heavy spring rains: "Belly-flowers"— flowers so tiny that you hardly see them unless you lie on your stomach.

MOUNTAIN PLANTS—Effect of altitude on flower growth.

EFFECT OF INCREASING SHADE—Transformation of forest carpet as year advances. Plant succession as shade increases.

Tip—To determine relative light, use a photographic lightmeter. Take reading against a piece of gray cardboard, on sunny days of observation, at same hour each time.

Wild Flowers around Your Home

Lucky you, if you are close enough to nature to have a piece of dirt of your own, for flowers, fruits, and vegetables. But whether yours is a suburban garden or a country estate, a section of it should be set aside for a display of native wild flowers and ferns. You may be able to find, and transplant whatever plants you need from the wild—with permission of the property owners, of course. Or you may secure nursery-grown specimens —or possibly even raise your own from seeds or cuttings.

On the other hand, if you happen to be an apartment dweller, you can still get a lot of satisfaction from wild flowers, by raising them indoors and following their growth.

Your Wild Flower Garden

You can turn the wild-flower corner into the most fascinating part of your whole garden. In doing it, you get more than the usual enjoyment out of gardening. You have the added thrill of the hunt—of hiking through neighboring or faraway fields and forests in search of specimens and of matching your skill against nature in your efforts to effect a successful transplanting.

BOOKS—George D. Aiken. *Pioneering with Wildflowers.* Published by author, Putney, Vt.

Norman Taylor. *Wild Flower Gardening.* D. Van Nostrand Company.

DEVELOPING THE WILD FLOWER CORNER— To be a successful wild-flower gardener, you need to start out by developing a section of your garden to fit the living conditions of the plants you intend to introduce.

Many wild plants transplant with gusto to the perennial border of the ordinary garden—but they look out of place there, and often take on a different character. Wild columbine, for instance, dainty in the wild where it lives on a lean diet, becomes husky in company with its cultivated relatives.

If you want to have your wild plants look the way they do in their natural habitat, you must imitate that habitat as closely as possible in your garden. This means special attention to exposure, moisture, and soil reaction.

EXPOSURE—Some wild flowers are open-field plants exposed to the sun all day long, others grow in the deep shade of dense forests. You should have no trouble in providing for the former. The latter need to be shaded— preferably under the spreading branches of native shrubs and trees that are their natural neighbors.

MOISTURE—From desert plants to floating bog specimens—your choice is great. You wouldn't expect cacti to thrive in marshy ground, nor water lilies to get along in dry sandy soil. You will have to decide whether you want to use your garden as you have it, or whether your ambition calls for the development of a desert section, a rock garden, a marshy area.

You might feel that the best arrangement would be to have all possible conditions present. Such a garden can be developed best when a fairly large area is available. If your space is limited, you may solve the problem by a series of terraces, separating them by rocks or old logs.

SOIL REACTION—Some wild flowers are at home in alkaline soil, some like their soil neutral, others prefer acid soil. In spite of their apparent native preferences, a number of plants will get along seemingly well in whatever soil you provide. Others are more fussy—they will go on a hunger strike and die unless the reaction of the soil to which they are transferred matches their original surroundings.

Tip—Alkalinity and acidity are described in chemical language by pH numbers: pH 1 to 6 indicate acid reactions, pH 7 neutral, pH 8 to 14 alkaline conditions. The reaction is determined by the change in color of certain dyes. Purchase a soil-testing set. Or, cheaper, a soil-test paper. Use long-range 4- to 9-pH test paper. Mix a small amount of soil with an equal amount of rain water or distilled water. Immerse a strip of paper in the mixture. Match the color the paper has turned against a scale that comes with the paper, to find pH number.

SUPPLIES—pHydrion Soil Tester. Doughten Seed Co., Jersey City, N. J.

The safest way to satisfy your wild flowers is to bring them into the garden with plenty of the soil in which you found them growing.

If that is not possible, you may have to change the reaction of your garden soil.

You can make it *more alkaline* by adding crushed limestone.

You can make it *more acid* by mixing in leaf mold from oak or coniferous forest. OR by raking sulphur into the top—3 to 5 pounds to 100 square feet. OR by sprinkling aluminum sulphate on the surface—3 to 5 pounds to 100 square feet. OR by watering with a solution of 1 pound tannic acid to 5 gallons of water.

SECURING PLANTS—With the garden spot prepared, you are ready to move in the plants.

PLANTS FROM THE WILD—It used to be a fairly simple matter to secure plants for a wild-flower garden from woods and fields. It isn't any more—unless you happen to be or to know an owner of country property. Because of population growth and real-estate and park developments, going to "the country" to collect wild flowers now involves the risk of trespass on private, state, or federal property—where what looks like native plants may actually have been planted by owners or rangers.

Respect other people's property. Trespass by arrangement only, and get permission, in advance, to remove those plants that you would like to transfer to your own garden.

Tip—You can often do a service for protection of wild flowers by removing them (by permission) from places where real-estate development or highway construction threatens their complete destruction.

Know and follow the laws of your state in regard to wild flowers. In order to protect rare and disappearing species of wild flowers, several states have enacted laws for their protection. Some states protect all wild flowers along the highway right-of-way and forbid the moving of plants from public lands.

But whether your state has such laws or not, you will certainly want to do your part to perpetuate its wild plants. Find out which flowers in your territory are so plentiful that they can be picked freely, those that should be picked in moderation only, and those that should be left undisturbed in their natural habitat. Choose your flowers from the first category, and, with care, from the second, but leave those in the third alone.

REFERENCES—*Helpful Hints on Conserving Wild Flowers.* Free. Conservation Committee, The Garden Club of America, 598 Madison Avenue, New York 22, N. Y.

Helpful Hints on Conserving Wild Flowers of New England. Free. New England Wild Flower Preservation Society, 300 Massachusetts Avenue, Boston, Mass.

Wild Flowers of California—Suggestions for Conserving Them. Free. California Conservation Council, 912 Santa Barbara Street, Santa Barbara, Calif.

Wild Flower Protection Lists— Northeastern, Southeastern, and Western editions. Wild Flower Preservation Society, 3740 Oliver St., N. W., Washington, D. C.

EQUIPMENT—You will need a few pieces of equipment for transferring plants to your garden: A small *garden trowel*, a flat *basket*, *newspaper* to wrap around the roots, a *notebook* for writing down the living conditions of each plant.

Tip—Aluminum foil is considerably better than newspaper. It is easier to wrap and is waterproof and airproof.

TRANSPLANTING—Your success in transplanting depends on your care in digging up the plants, the way you transport them and replant them.

Remove dead leaves, debris, and stones from around the plant. Make a circular cut with your trowel around it, then lift it, very carefully, with a fair-sized ball of soil attached to the roots. Wrap the roots immediately in newspaper or, better, in aluminum foil.

In bringing your plants home, protect the top against damage, and the plant as a whole against wilting. If you have a long trip before you, wet down the paper- or foil-wrapped roots to prevent them from drying out.

Plant the flowers as soon as possible after you get home. Set them to the same depth as you found them in the wild and in the same general living surroundings. Water them, then mulch around them with leaves or grass clippings, to prevent too quick evaporation.

BUYING PLANTS—Occasionally, you may be able to secure plants that appeal especially to you, through barter with another wild flower enthusiast. More often, you may have to buy them from a nursery specializing in wild flowers. Usually it is much easier to work with nursery-grown plants than with wild specimens. They will have been transplanted several times, and therefore have a root system that can be disturbed without ill effects.

NURSERY PLANTS—George D. Aiken Company, Putney, Vt.

Gillet Fern and Flower Farm, Southwick, Mass.

Charles G. Curtis Company, Callicoon, N. Y.

Rex D. Pearce, Moorestown, N. J.

Vicks' Wildgardens, 632 Montgomery Avenue, Narbeth, Pa.

Nik-Nar Nursery, Ashville, N. C.

Gardens of the Blue Ridge, Ashford, McDowell County, N. C.

Lester Rowntree and Company. Carmel, Calif.

Carl Purdy, Ukiah, Calif.

PROPAGATION OF WILD PLANTS—When once you have your wild-flower garden established, you can increase the number of plants by various types of propagation—among them division, slips, layering, and seeds.

DIVISION—The simplest way of propagating many wild flowers is by division. This consists in digging up the roots, after one or two growing seasons, dividing them into several parts, and planting these separately. The job should be done in late summer, after the foliage has turned brown, or in early spring.

CROWNS—If the root appears like a tangled mass of rootlets, all you have to do is usually to break or cut the crown vertically, to get several sections. Make sure that each section retains one or more buds.

ROOTSTOCKS—Branching, horizontal rootstocks or rhizomes are cut in portions, each with a bud. Plant the sections horizontally.

BULBS—Bulbous plants often form small bulbs, bulblets, below ground—some even above ground at the leaf bases. Each of them is a potential new plant. If the bulb is scaly, as in the case of lilies, break off the scales, and plant them, along with the core.

CUTTINGS—ROOT CUTTINGS—Some plants with deep taproots may be propagated by root cuttings. Cut the root into 2- to 3-inch-long sections. Bury these out-of-doors, to form calluses, in a mixture of leaf mold and sand. Transplant them the following spring.

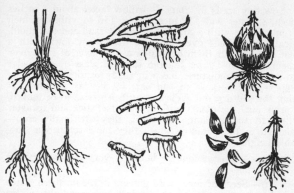

Propagation by division: breaking a crown apart, cutting a root-
stock into sections, separating the scales of a lily bulb.

GREEN CUTTINGS—Green cuttings, or slips, are made by
snipping off tips of branching plants to a length of 3 to
4 inches. Pull off most of the leaves. Push the ends
about 2 inches down into a mixture of sand and leaf
mold. Keep the mixture moist until the cuttings have
rooted.

Tip—To speed up rooting, dip the bases of the slips
in plant hormone for rooting, before planting them.

LAYERING—Many ground-hugging plants propagate
themselves by sending out horizontal shoots that root
where they touch the ground. Runners already rooted
can be separated from the mother plant and planted.
Rooting can be encouraged by pinning down runners with
sticks, covering them at the pinned-down points with
soil.

SEEDS—Wild-flower seeds may be collected in the fall
and sown like ordinary garden seeds. Pick seeds of rare
plants carefully, or not at all—the plants may have a
better chance to survive when the seeds are permitted
to fall where the plants grow.

You will simplify matters for yourself by purchasing
seeds from one of the seed houses that specialize in wild-
flower seeds.

SEEDS—Rex D. Pearce, Moorestown, N. J.

Colorado Seed Company, Denver, Col.

Theodore Payne, 2969-99 Los Felix Boulevard, Los
Angeles 26, Calif.

Sow tiny seeds in "flats"—shallow boxes about 3 inches deep, 8 inches wide, 12 inches long. Fill to within an inch from the top with a mixture of moist sand and leaf mold. Scatter the seeds over the soil, firm them down with a flat board, cover them by sifting a thin layer of sand over them and firm again. Place a sheet of glass over the flat to retain the moisture. Keep in shady location until shoots appear, then expose to sun part of the day without letting the soil dry out. When of sufficient size to be moved, "prick out" the plants with a small flat stick and transfer them to another flat. From this they are finally transplanted to the outdoors when they have reached a suitable height.

Tip—A plastic squeeze bottle is very satisfactory for watering.

Tip—Seeds of most wild flowers in the northern states drop to the ground in the fall and spend the winter exposed to freezing and thawing, snow and rain. Seeds collected from such flowers may not germinate unless they have gone through this natural process of "stratification." To stratify them, prepare the seed flats in the fall and place them in the ground out-doors. Cover with burlap to protect them against driving rain and with window screening to save them from rodents.

Tip—Artificial stratification may be accomplished by keeping the seeds in a refrigerator for a month or so, shifting them between the freezing compartment and humidifier from time to time.

Large seeds are more easily sown in a seed bed in the open. Sow them in the fall, so that they will be exposed to all kinds of winter weather. Sift a layer of sand over them to the thickness of the seeds themselves. Firm it down with a flat board. Cover with burlap and wire screening.

Tip—If you are successful in propagating your wild flowers, why not think of repaying nature for your pleasure by planting some of them back where you found the mother plants? You may want to go further and work with a local garden club or youth group to establish a *Wild Flower Sanctuary* in a community park or camping area.

RAISING FERNS—Ferns are raised from spores collected from the spore cases found on the fronds. Because of the way in which ferns develop, their cultivation is quite different from that of seed plants.

Fill a flat bulb pot half full of pebbles. Cover with a layer of mixed sand and leaf mold. On top of this,

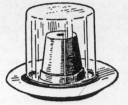

Ferns may be raised from spores in a covered bulb pot, or, better, on the outside of a flower pot, as suggested by Costello.

sprinkle fine sand. Sterilize everything by baking the pot in an oven for ten minutes or more. Cool completely. Place in a pan of water. When the soil is moist throughout, sprinkle the spores over the surface. Then cover the pot with a piece of glass and place it in a warm, shaded spot.

> *Tip*—Or use the Costello method: Fill a flower pot with sphagnum moss. Sterilize it with hot water. Also sterilize a saucer and a bell jar. Cool. Invert flower pot in the saucer. Sprinkle spores on the wet surface of the pot. Fill the saucer with water. Cover the pot with the bell jar.

In a few weeks, a green film forms on the surface. Look at it closely with a strong magnifier, and you will see that it consists of numerous flat, generally heart-shaped *prothallia*—minute plants a single cell layer thick. In another week or more, tiny fronds begin to appear.

When the small new fern plants are large enough to be moved, transplant them to a seed flat, and treat them as regular seed plants. Eventually, set them out in your fernery.

REFERENCE—*Growing Fern Prothallia in the Laboratory*. Turtox Service Leaflet No. 44. Free. General Biological Supply House, Chicago 37, Ill.

WILD PLANTS IN YOUR ROOMS

Wild flowers brought indoors are always welcome. In the spring, they herald sunny days ahead. In the fall, they tell of Indian summer. A myriad of decorative schemes are possible—from floating a single large flower in a glass bowl, to arranging a spectacular display of autumn asters.

There are a number of other possibilities that are often overlooked:

DRIED WEED STALKS—There is a very special beauty

in the winter stalks of many of our wild plants—of
cattails and milkweed, yarrow and evening primrose,
Jimson weed and goldenrod and pampas grass.

Most of them can be brought indoors and arranged
with no preparation. The grasses need to be treated to
prevent shedding, by spraying them with a fixative of
thinned lacquer or shellac. Cattail heads are kept intact
by giving them a quick dip in the fixative.

Tip—Look into the windows of commercial florists
in the winter, and you will see large bouquets of prepared dry flower stalks, many of them in bright colors.
You will recognize many weed stalks among them,
painted or sprayed with quick-drying enamels. If you
prefer the pastel tones, try some of the new water
paints, either painting or dipping the stalks.

POTTING—You may want to raise a few wild flowers
indoors to follow their blooming closely, from budding
to fading.

One way to do this is to pot the plants in the spring,
as soon as they show the earliest sign of life. Dig them
up carefully, with a good ball of earth adhering to the
roots. Plant them in ordinary, unglazed clay pots, 6 to
8 inches in diameter, with about 1½ inch of pebbles on
the bottom for good drainage. Keep the soil moist by
placing the pots in saucers with a small amount of water.

For earlier bloom, plant your pots in the fall, but
leave them outdoors all winter, dug down with the top
flush with the ground. Bring them into an unheated room
or porch early in February, then into a warmer room
when the buds show.

TERRARIUMS

An even more spectacular display is possible with a
terrarium—a covered glass container with a miniature
garden of soil and plants.

Nathaniel Bagshaw Ward, an English doctor, started
the terrarium idea more than a hundred years ago. Ward
noticed that ferns and grasses kept right on growing in
a tightly closed glass container in his home. He realized
that the plants stayed alive because the water that tran-
spired from the leaves and evaporated from the soil condensed, and kept the moisture content constant. The prin-
ciple made possible the successful transportation of plants
on long ocean journeys—rare specimens from everywhere
to botanical gardens in England, coffee plants from
Arabia to Brazil, rubber plants from South America to
the East Indies.

TYPES OF TERRARIUMS—Almost any glass container that can be made fairly airtight can be turned into a terrarium, or "Wardian case."

BELL JARS—A bell-jar terrarium is possibly the easiest one to make. Simply develop a miniature garden in a glass or metal tray that fits the circumference of the bell —then place the bell over it. Be sure that the plants do not touch the sides. Somewhat Victorian—and rather expensive.

> *Tip*—For a modern counterpart, make the garden in a circular cake tin. Cover with a transparent plastic plant cap such as is used for raising tender vegetables in the garden.

BOTTLE GARDENS—All kinds of bottles and glass containers can be used for decorative indoor gardens—from 10-gallon carboys, 5-gallon distilled water bottles, to carafes, globular glass bowls, and brandy inhalers.

It takes a bit of imagination, patience, and ingenuity to develop this type of terrarium. Begin by lining the bottom of the container with a thin layer of moss, green side down, for looks. Then pour in a layer of pebbles, for drainage, and one of leaf mold, or place in position with a teaspoon on a long handle. Then insert the plants with the help of slender wooden forceps—homemade to fit your container. Tamp down the soil with a dowel stick. Fit in small pieces of moss to hold plants in place and give a more finished look to your planting. When it is necessary to water, use a rubber bulb spray.

> *Tip*—You can make an interesting bottle garden from a 1-gallon mayonnaise jar. Lay it on one side, cradled

Numerous types of bottle gardens are possible. Especially good is a 1-gallon mayonnaise jar cradled on two wooden supports.

on two wooden supports. Then arrange soil and plants in it.

COMMON TERRARIUMS—The most common terrarium is a rectangular glass case, either of solid glass, or of glass panes fitted into a framework of metal molding. Ready-made terrariums of this type, of many different sizes, are available commercially through scientific supply houses, as well as through stores selling aquarium supplies.

Tip—An old discarded, even leaky, aquarium will make an excellent terrarium case.

MAKING A SMALL TERRARIUM CASE—You can make a small terrarium case from six pieces of window glass and a spool of 2-inch adhesive tape—waterproof, preferably.

Pick one of the commercial window pane sizes—6×8 inches, 8×10 inches, 10×12 inches. When you buy them, have two pieces cut square.

Lay out the pieces, as shown in the diagram on page 267. Place them as far apart from each other as the glass is thick. Fasten the four side pieces together, then to the bottom piece with strips of adhesive tape cut to proper length. Reinforce with tape along bottom and top edge. Place tape around the edges of top piece, then hinge this in position as a lid with another piece of tape.

Tip—A stronger terrarium case results, if you tape four sides only, then sink their bottom edges into a one-inch layer of newly mixed plaster-of-Paris batter in a bake dish of suitable size. Let·set and dry, then waterproof the plaster with melted paraffin. Reinforce the top edge with a strip of adhesive tape. Place a sheet of glass over the case.

MAKING THE FRAMED TERRARIUM CASE—With the many types of aluminum, brass and stainless-steel molding available today, it is quite easy for anyone with a small amount of skill in metal working to put together the frame for a good-sized terrarium case, along the same lines as the aquarium cage on page 230.

Start by making a bottom frame out of an aluminum corner bar, double-mortising it at the frame corners. Rivet pieces of similar bars upright at each corner. Finally rivet a band around the tops of the four uprights. Have cut to fit a bottom and four side pieces of double-thick glass. Put the glass panes in with aquarium cement or hold them in place with pieces of aluminum cove, bolted to the corner bars. Fit still another piece of glass over the finished case.

Tip—For an easier job, cut a piece of 1½-inch board

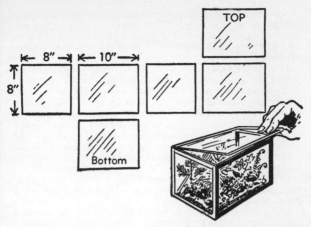

A small terrarium case results when you tape two square and four rectangular glass pieces together with adhesive tape.

to suitable size (10×14 inches, for instance). Get four pieces of slotted aluminum molding (12 inches long, or thereabouts). Screw them to the corners of the board. Fit four pieces of glass into the frame. Fasten with aquarium cement.

PLANTING THE TERRARIUM—When the container is completed, the satisfying job of planting it is before you. In planting, remember that your goal is to create a bit of nature that will greet you daily during the lean months between October and May. You have the choice of many different habitats, from humid bog to arid desert.

WOODLAND TERRARIUM—A 2-inch layer of gravel or pebbles first—mixed with a bit of charcoal, if you like, to keep the terrarium "sweet." On top of this a couple of inches of leaf mold, moistened so that it forms a ball when squeezed in the hand. Then woods plants, the number depending on the size of the case, arranged in a pleasing, natural manner, placing taller specimens toward the back. Finally a thin layer of green moss as a plush carpet around the base of the other plants, and maybe a couple of small rocks and lichen-spotted sticks to clinch the effect.

Keep covered and in cool, semishade most of the time. If "sweating" occurs, push a match stick under the cover to raise it slightly.

BOG TERRARIUM—Place 2 inches of gravel in a waterproof terrarium case. Cover with 2 to 3 inches of wet sphagnum moss. On this fill in several inches of the soil you collected with your bog plants. Set the plants as deep as you found them in the wild. Keep covered with a piece of glass.

DESERT TERRARIUM—Cover the bottom of the terrarium with 2 inches of gravel, then with 2 to 3 inches of a mixture of sand and soil. Plant cacti and other desert plants to the original soil lines that show on them. Place a few stones, pieces of dead cactus and yucca stems, and the like on the ground, to give an "artistic" effect. Cover with glass. Sprinkle ground around the plants with water every couple of weeks. Keep in sunny location.

If moisture condenses on the inside, remove glass entirely.

SURVEY TERRARIUM—A terrarium provides an opportunity for a thorough survey of the small plants of a given area.

Make a terrarium case that will enclose 1 square foot (144 square inches) of ground (12×12 inches, or 10×14 inches, or 8×18 inches), or ½ square foot (6×12 inches, or 8×9 inches). Cover bottom with 1 inch of gravel. Place on top of this a 3-inch thick sod of grass, or piece of forest carpet, cut to the size of the terrarium. Make every effort to keep the sod intact while putting it in.

Sprinkle thoroughly with water. Cover, and keep in semishade, in a fairly cool spot. See what develops. In addition to plant life, you will discover much animal life in your survey terrarium. Keep a record of the insects, centipedes, spiders, mites, and others that may emerge.

REFERENCE—*The School Terrarium.* Turtox Service Leaflet No. 10. General Biological Supply House, Chicago 37, Ill.

The Terrarium. School Nature League Bulletin, Series 4, No. 3. National Audubon Society, 1130 Fifth Avenue, New York 28, N. Y.

Flower Photography

"WORK WANTED—Photographic model, of exceptional beauty, with natural, inborn grace, colorful, able to pose untiringly without temperamental upsets, no compensation asked. . . ." The photographer's dream come true!

Few human beings would fit such an ad. But most flowers do. That is what makes flower photography such a pleasant occupation.

With just enough technical skill to know how your camera works, with a certain amount of "feel" for composition and light-and-shadow values, and with ability to pick interesting "models"—and almost all of them are!—

you have all the qualifications that are needed to make a good flower photographer. If you know something about flowers besides . . . magnificent! If you don't, you'll soon learn.

STILLS

EQUIPMENT—CAMERA—For flower photography, use a camera that makes it possible for you to fill the whole negative with a single flower head—you will not always want to do this, but it should be possible for you to do so.

That means a camera with close-up attachment, extension bellows, extension tubes, or one with a telephoto lens. It also means a device whereby knife-sharp focusing can be done—either on ground glass, or by focusing attachment.

TRIPOD—For focusing purposes, you also need a tripod. The ordinary tripod is of no help, unless its legs can be folded all the way out, completely flat. Best is a special, low tripod, the kind used for tabletop photography. Flower photography is belly photography. You need to get down where you can be on eye height with your subjects—or lower.

TAKING STILLS—LIGHTING—Your best lighting is forenoon and afternoon sunlight; the best time a couple of hours before and after high noon. At those hours, the light strikes the flowers from the side, modeling them with a rather soft shadow effect. Noon itself is not very satisfactory—the light is harsh, it hits your flowers from above and casts dense, unpleasant shadows.

Move around the flower you intend to photograph. Look at it from all angles until you have found the most striking effect. Many flowers photograph best when back-lighted, with the sun shining through their petals.

Tip—To soften the shadows, use a metal reflector, 10×14 inches, or so. Crinkle up a piece of aluminum foil, smoothe it out somewhat, paste it on cardboard. Prop up the reflector with the help of a short stick.
Tip—Use a Polaroid filter for white flowers in bright sun, for better modeling of their structure.

BACKGROUND—The proper background is of great importance in flower photography. The subject should stand out clearly against its surroundings.

A single, brilliantly colored flower may stand out against almost any background, but a less conspicuous plant will disappear in a jumbled net of crisscross lines, unless you give it special attention:

THE SKY AS BACKGROUND—Tall plants appear even taller and more spectacular when photographed from a low angle against a blue sky, or a sky with a few scattered clouds. Shoot through a light or medium-yellow filter.

OUT-OF-FOCUS BACKGROUND—A sharply delineated flower will stand out effectively against a background of soft, blurred masses. To achieve this effect, focus critically on the center of the flower, then open up the diaphragm wide enough to throw everything else out of focus.

SHADOW BACKGROUND—Compose your shot, with the camera lens slightly higher than the flower. Look through the focusing device and determine what surroundings constitute the background. Throw a shadow over those surroundings with a piece of cardboard. In this manner, your flower stands out brightly against a much darker background—as long as you watch out that the shadow does not hit the flower itself.

Whatever you do about backgrounds, p-l-e-a-s-e use nature's own. Don't detract from a good flower portrait with a cardboard or cloth background—except in those rare instances where an artificial background may mean the difference between a picture and none at all.

EXPOSURES—In taking an exposure reading with a meter, remember that you get the reading not just from the flower itself, but also from its surroundings. If the flower is light, close down the diaphragm accordingly.

The correct exposure is, of course, especially important in color photography. Although front lighting is usually preferred, you can get striking effects with side and back lighting. If you have arrived at the proper stop for front lighting, open up one full stop for a side-lighted, two full stops for a back-lighted subject.

Tip—Flowers with finely veined white petals, or of a pale hue, often appear "washed out" in color, even though the exposure is correct. By underexposing slightly—one-half stop, for instance—you are able to deepen the color. But don't overdo it!

Watch your time setting. If you decide on a small aperture, you may have to shoot at 1/20 or 1/10 of a second. This is O.K. on a perfectly still day, but not on a windy day. A slight breeze will require 1/50 of a second or less. If the wind is stronger, either protect the plant with a screen, wait for a lull, or come again some other day.

WHAT TO PHOTOGRAPH—Instead of setting out on an indiscriminate hunt, specialize from the beginning.

FLOWERS AROUND THE YEAR—Starting in early spring, photograph the flowers as they appear.

A movie titler, with its extra lens and its framing device, will simplify your early efforts in flower photography.

FLOWERS OF A CERTAIN REGION, of a certain plant family, of plants of certain specific uses.

SYMMETRY OF NATURE—The almost architectural effect of opening buds, unrolling fern fronds, veination in flower petals, structure of seed pods, and so on.

SERIES—Whole plant, leaf detail, flower, fruit of a number of different plants—probably the most revealing and profitable kind of plant photography.

SEQUENCES—From tight bud, through blossoming, to seed, of the same plant.

THE UNUSUAL—The tiny, dark purple flower in the middle of a Queen Anne's lace's flat-top flower cluster, the real flower of skunk cabbage or Jack-in-the-pulpit, the violet flower that never opens, tiny ferns, and many more.

> *Tip*—When photographing small plants, it is often well to include a familiar subject in the picture—a leaf, a twig, or the like—to indicate relative size.

MOVIES

EQUIPMENT—CAMERA—In movies, as well as in stills, you will find wild flowers easy to work with—provided you have the right camera. You need to get close to your subject for best effect. The lens for the usual family movie won't get you there.

In the beginning, you can make use of your titler with its extra lens and framing device. Compose your picture within the frame. What you have in your frame is what you get in your shot.

Sooner or later, you will want to get closer to your flowers for more spectacular effects. You will then require supplementary lenses, an extension tube or telephoto lens. You will need a focusing device to be positive that you not only get what you aim for, but get it in sharp focus.

For many of your shots, you will want a low tripod.

MOVIE TECHNIQUES—With much nature movie-making, you have to grab what you can get, when you can get it. For flower movies, you can develop and follow a script for a complete film. It can be simple—"A Day in Spring"—or complex—"The Glory of Creation." It can be close to home—"Our Wild Flower Garden"—or of social significance—"Saving Our Heritage."

SEQUENCES—As you take your shots, you will probably work in sequences of medium shot, close-up, extra close-up. But don't stop with a single angle. Move around your subject and shoot it from several sides. Add a few distance shots to establish locale and provide atmosphere.

MOOD—There are moods to flowers. Try to catch them. The proud sunflower—make it look taller by shooting it from a low angle. The shy arbutus—show it hiding among dead leaves. The pink lady's-slipper—make those colors sing! The Cinderella idea: a casual shot of a dandelion—then a single head filling the whole screen in its golden glory!

Tip—"Dew-kissed" flowers photograph well. If nature doesn't supply the dew, a spray gun or atomizer will.

MOTION—Movies should be motion pictures. The breeze that might spoil a still is your best ally in taking movies. A soft stir is pleasing, but watch out for gusts that may throw your subject out of the view of your lens.

STOOGES—Where there are flowers, there are insects. Let them come around, then shoot while they visit your flower subject. They will add further motion and interest to your film. But don't get insects into every one of your shots. It is a flower film you are aiming for, not an insect picture.

TIME-LAPSE PHOTOGRAPHY—Time-lapse photography is the most tedious form of nature photography, but the result is usually truly extraordinary: a tight flower bud suddenly bursting into full bloom before your eyes . . . a sprout shooting out of the ground and continuing its growth like Jack's bean stalk . . . a fern frond unfurling . . . just to mention a few.

Time-lapse photography is the reverse of slow-motion photography. In slow motion, the film is shot at high speed (say, 64 frames a second) and shown at regular home-projection speed (16 frames a second). The result is the appearance of greatly slowed-down action (in this case, 64 divided by 16, or one fourth the speed of the actual action). In time-lapse, the film is shot at very slow speed (say, 1 frame every minute—every 60 seconds) and projected at regular speed (16 frames a second). The action will appear tremendously accelerated (in this case, 60 multiplied by 16, or 960 times as fast as the original action).

Four things are necessary for successful time-lapse photography: 1. a camera with single frame action; 2. a solid tripod that will keep the camera in the exact position throughout the filming; 3. a steady subject—which rules out outdoor shooting; 4. a uniform light source for all frame exposures—which means artificial light.

LINING UP THE ACTION—For your first attempt in time-lapse photography, pick a fast-opening flower.

Some morning, bring a bud indoors for study. Place it in a dark room. Light a 100-watt bulb near it. Find out how long it takes this sample to open fully by the light and heat of the bulb. Then decide how long you want the action to occupy the screen. You find, for instance, that it takes the bud two hours—120 minutes to open. You want the scene to last 15 seconds. Projected at regular home speed of 16 frames a second, 15 seconds means 240 frames. To cover the action, then, you need to take 240 frames in 120 minutes. Divide number of frames into number of minutes—240 into 120. The answer is ½. By taking a frame every ½ minute, you get your scene: two hours' action condensed into fifteen movie seconds.

SETUP AND EXPOSURE—When you have your figures straight, set up your camera firmly on a tripod, and focus it on the now faded stand-in flower. Get the best possible composition. Put up a single photoflood to simulate sunlight, with a reflector on the other side of the flower to soften the shadows. Take an exposure meter reading, and set your lens opening accordingly.

Note—In taking single frames, the shutter speed is slower, than when the camera is running at full speed. Compensate for the resulting *increased* exposure, by *decreasing* the lens opening ⅓ to ½ stop to prevent overexposure.

Turn off all lights. You are all set for shooting the following day.

TAKING THE SCENE—Next morning, bring in a new bud. Put it in place, and turn on the 100-watt bulb. This bulb will remain burning throughout the action. Check your focus and your exposure.

Turn on the photoflood bulb. Take a single frame. Turn

off photoflood. Wait until almost ½ minute is up. Turn on photoflood. Snap a single frame. Turn off photoflood. And so on, until the bud is fully opened and the action completed. Tedious . . . it certainly is! But wait until the scene comes back from processing!

AUTOMATIC TIME-LAPSE OUTFITS—After having tried time-lapse a few times, you may either decide that you have had enough, or become so intrigued with the possibilities that you want to go deeper into the subject.

In the latter case, you will want to develop a method that will eliminate the tedium of having to flick a button every so often. The way to do it is to devise a gadget that will do the job for you automatically.

If you are electrically and mechanically inclined, you should be able to figure out such an apparatus. The basic element will be a solenoid that, energized at regular intervals, will release the camera shutter. Plans for such outfits have appeared in national movie-making magazines. Check with the publishers of these magazines for back copies.

REFERENCE—Cooper Jenkins. *A Basic Time Lapse Control.* Service Pamphlet of Amateur Cinema League, 420 Lexington Avenue, New York 17, N. Y.

An electrical time-lapse outfit is available commercially, designed for scientists and professional photographers. It is—at least for the time being—outside the scope and the pocketbook of any but the most ardent and well-heeled amateur flower photographer.

Plant Collecting

Plant collecting is probably the easiest and least expensive of all types of nature collecting. You can start anywhere, and the equipment for preparing a satisfactory collection is found in the ordinary household.

Note—Know your state laws in regard to protected flowers, and respect other people's property when collecting. A true botanist and plant lover is eager to "Save the wild flowers." Therefore, never pick a flower unless six are seen, never collect a plant with root unless ten are found. *Refrain from collecting rare plants threatened with extinction* (see page 259).

THE HERBARIUM

The most popular type of plant collection is the herbarium—pressed, dried plants, mounted on sheets of thin cardboard. When carefully done, a herbarium may be valuable for years to come to show the plant life of a certain region—some European herbariums established almost five hundred years ago are still in excellent condition.

You can start a simple herbarium around your home or around camp with whatever materials you have on hand, or you can go in for expert methods from the start, developing or purchasing the necessary equipment.

Whatever you do, there are four simple rules you need to follow to make a good herbarium: 1. Collect whole plants. 2. Dry them thoroughly under pressure. 3. Mount them carefully. 4. Label them correctly.

REFERENCES—I. M. Johnston. *The Preparation of Botanical Specimens for the Herbarium*. The Arnold Arboretum of Harvard University, Jamaica Plains 30, Mass.

S. F. Blake. *Directions for Collecting Flowering Plants and Ferns*. U. S. Department of Agriculture, Bureau of Plant Industry (Office of Economic and Systematic Botany), Washington 25, D. C.

SIMPLIFIED HERBARIUM METHODS

If you are interested mostly in making a collection of plants from your immediate vicinity, you can generally dispense with the kind of collecting equipment that an expert botanist would take along. As a matter of fact, if you are working with a group of youngsters, you will find it a deterrence to collecting if you insist on carting equipment along every time you go hiking. Although expert botanists will frown on the idea of bringing home a wilting bouquet of field flowers, it is the simplest way of getting started—provided your bouquet consists of

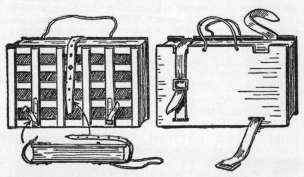

Two types of field presses: lattice-frame press (left) of ¼-inch strips of wood, solid-side press (right) from plywood.

carefully collected whole plants. The specimens may have wilted a bit on the way home, but they will usually regain their freshness if placed in water for a short while, whereupon they are ready for pressing.

PRESSING THE FINDS—Make up two pressing boards, 12×17 inches, by nailing together a few pieces of scrap wood or slats from an orange crate. Open up some newspapers and make 16×23-inch sheets—the standard newspaper size—by cutting along the left folds. Tabloid newspapers are already cut to size and need only be taken apart.

Put one of the pressing boards on the table. Fold three newspaper sheets in half and lay them on the pressing board.

Spread a newspaper sheet before you, and place your first plant on the right half of it, arranging it in a natural manner. Fold the left half of the paper over, and write the name of the enclosed plant in the right hand corner of this folder. Place this specimen folder on the press, and cover it with a layer of three newspaper sheets folded in half. Continue in this manner, alternating specimen folders with layers of newspaper.

When your stack is ½ foot high (or less), place the other pressing board on top of it. Finally, put a weight on top—stones for instance—or strap the whole pile tightly together with two straps—web or leather—or Scout belts.

Give the plants a first pressing for about fourteen to eighteen hours. Then replace all papers in the pile with fresh, dry sheets. This goes for your specimen folders as well as for the drying sheets. Rearrange the specimens, if necessary, in the new specimen folder. Remember to transfer the plant names to the outside of the new folders.

After another twenty-four hours, open up the pile again. This time, leave the specimen folders intact, simply renew the drying sheets.

Follow the same procedure every twenty-four to forty-eight hours, until the plants are thoroughly dry. The job should be completed in a week or ten days, unless the weather is exceptionally humid.

STANDARD HERBARIUM METHODS

Herbarium methods vary somewhat among the experts, but generally follow these lines:

COLLECTING EQUIPMENT—For collecting, the most common piece of equipment used today is the *field press* or *collecting portfolio*. The collection box, or *vasculum*, once the trademark of the botanist, is now used mainly for bringing home fresh specimens that are to be studied and analyzed before pressing—or discarding.

Drying press of latticework. Check order of driers and corrugated ventilators, above and below specimen folders.

A field press can be made from two pieces of heavy cardboard or ¼-inch plywood, cut to a standard size of 12×18 inches. Or rivet or nail 1½-inch-wide, ¼-inch-thick strips of wood together into two 12×18-inch lattice frames, keeping the strip approximately 2 inches apart.

Between the two sections of the field press, place a dozen or more specimen folders made from unprinted newsprint or old newspapers, and just as many pieces, plus one, of "driers"—heavy blotting paper, gray "building felt," or "carpet paper," cut to 12×18 inches, or standard herbarium driers. Hold everything together with two web straps. For comfort in carrying, you may want to add a shoulder strap.

In addition to the field press, you will need a *trowel* for digging up roots, and a sharp *pocket knife* for snipping large plants into sections and for trimming down bulky specimens.

And then there's your perpetual companion: your *notebook*—preferably a stiff-cover booklet, for keeping notes of plant names, locality, growing conditions, and so forth.

COLLECTING TECHNIQUES—To be perfect, a specimen should show all the features of the plant: root, stem, leaves, flower, fruit.

Dig up each plant carefully, then place it in a specimen folder of newsprint. Spread out the plant to reveal as much as possible of the structure. Make it look natural. Keep away from the outdated and unlovely "walking stick" style. Arrange some flowers face-up, others face down, and some of the leaves with underside showing.

The latter is especially important when pressing ferns.

Small species will fit readily into your specimen folders. So will any plants up to 3 feet—provided you bend its stem into a sharp-angled V, $\wedge$, or N.

> *Tip*—If the springiness of a bent stem tends to throw part of the plant outside the folder, cut a slit in a small piece of stiff paper, and bring the slit paper down over the bend.

Write a serial number on the front of each specimen folder, and jot down all necessary data about the plant in your notebook under the corresponding number.

Place the specimen folders in the press, alternating them with herbarium driers. Close the press and tighten the straps around it.

The plants may be kept in the field press until the morning after your field trip, but preferably not any longer. They should be transferred to the drying press as soon as possible.

PRESSING—The usual drying press is similar to the lattice-work field press, only made of heavier material—½-inch wood strips, spaced about 1 inch apart.

Place a herbarium drier on one of the press sections. Put on top of it a specimen folder with the first plant in place in it. Then another drier, another specimen in its folder, and so on, finishing with a drier and the other press section. Strap tightly together, or place heavy weights on top of the pile.

After about twenty-four hours, replace the herbarium driers with fresh sheets, and strap up the pile again. Dry the moist driers for future use. Repeat with twenty-four-hour intervals, until the specimens are thoroughly dried. They are dry when they no longer feel cool to the touch, and when a stem snaps when bent.

> *Tip*—The drying process may be speeded up by the use of "ventilators" of double-surfaced corrugated cardboard—bought or cut out of cardboard boxes—with the corrugations running crosswise. The sheets are then placed in the press in the following order: ventilator, drier, specimen folder, drier, ventilator, drier, specimen folder, drier, ventilator, and so on.

For extra-quick drying, the "ventilated" press may be placed in direct sun, on top of an idling automobile motor, a safe distance over a stove.

When the plants are dry, go carefully through the specimen folders and write out a 2×3-inch label for each plant, with name of plant, where collected, date, collector's name.

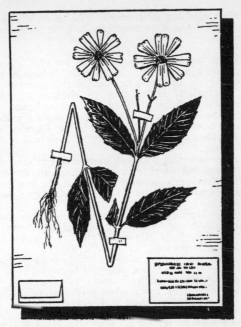

A well-arranged, well-pressed, well-mounted plant specimen. Notice N-shape of stem, seed envelope at left, label at right.

MOUNTING—For mounting, use regular herbarium mounting paper. This is thin cardboard, cut to standard size of 11½×16½ inches. It pays to buy a good quality if you intend your collection to last.

The specimens are mounted on the mounting sheets by gluing, taping, or tying—whichever you think best.

GLUING—The method of gluing the whole plant to the sheet is easy after a little practice, and undoubtedly produces the neatest display. The disadvantages to this method are that you can never transfer the plant to another sheet without damaging it, and that only one side of the plant can be studied. Nevertheless, it is a method commonly used by expert collectors.

To do a good mounting job, get a piece of glass, 12×17 inches. Spread a thin layer of glue evenly over the glass, with a broad brush.

Tip—Slightly diluted Le Page's glue and special herbarium glue are satisfactory. Still better is so-called "tin paste"—used commercially to glue labels on tin cans.

Pick up the plant specimen with forceps. Place it, bottom-side down, on the glue. Use the forceps to press all parts down into the glue. Lift up the specimen, and lower it carefully to the mounting sheet in a pleasing arrangement. Moisten the specimen label and paste it in the right-hand corner. Cover the sheet with a piece of unprinted newsprint or other white paper. Place a heavy book, marble or cement slab on top of it to hold it down while drying.

Continue mounting your specimens in this manner, placing one finished sheet over the other with protecting sheets of newsprint between them. Run the brush over the glass from time to time to keep the glue layer smooth and even.

TAPING—Taping is a more tedious process than gluing. In this method, the specimen is fastened to a herbarium sheet with thin strips of gummed cloth in strategic locations, across stems and, occasionally, leaves.

Gummed cloth comes in sheets and in tapes ¾ inches and 1½ inches wide. Cut a supply of ⅛-inch-wide strips, and keep a wet sponge handy for moistening them.

TYING—Especially coarse plant parts may refuse to be stuck to the mounting sheet with glue or tapes. In that case, you will have to tie them on.

Thread a needle with a piece of strong, green thread. Push the needle through the mounting sheet, from the top, at one side of the plant part. Bring the thread in from the back on the other side of the plant part. Tie the two ends of the thread together over the plant part, then trim off the excess thread. Use as many loops of this kind as may be necessary.

SPECIAL METHODS—Most flowering plants and such flowerless plants as ferns give no trouble in pressing and mounting. But some plants and plant parts require special treatment.

FLESHY PLANTS—Plants with thick, succulent stems and leaves will dry slowly, at best. They often keep on living even in the drying press—sending out new shoots, refusing to give up. Before placing them in the press, dip them in boiling water for a few moments. That kills the cells and makes drying easier. As far as possible, keep the flowers of such plants above the surface of the boiling water, or pick extra flowers to press separately.

PLANTS WITH THICK PARTS—Some plants have heavy stems, thick roots, large flower-heads, bulky fruits that

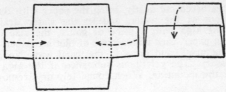

Seed envelopes may be made from pieces of white paper, cut and folded as shown. They are glued to the left on mounting sheet.

do not press flat. Trim down the thickness by slicing off the back half—the part that will not show when the plant is mounted. Then press in the usual manner.

SEEDS—Seeds are often important in the identification of a plant—but they have the bad habit of falling off the specimens. They are therefore placed in small envelopes of white paper, cut and folded as shown in the diagram on this page, or in small cellophane envelopes. Paste seed envelopes in the left-hand corner of the mounting sheets.

MOSSES AND LICHENS—Mosses and lichens should be picked in "fruiting" condition as far as possible. Dry under very light pressure, otherwise important characteristics of growth may be obliterated. Large specimens may be mounted on regular mounting sheets. Smaller specimens are usually kept in envelopes of a standard size of $4 \times 5\frac{1}{2}$ inches.

ALGAE—Coarse seaweeds are dried in the usual manner. But delicate algae, with thousands of threadlike parts, would look miserable if pulled out of the water and slapped on to a piece of mounting paper. Instead, float the alga in fresh water in a shallow dish. Slip a piece of mounting paper under the alga. Hold the end of the stalk against the paper, at an appropriate point. Move the paper gently, setting the alga in motion. When

Delicate algae are floated onto their mounting papers so that they will have a chance to spread out in a natural manner

it has feathered out neatly, bring the paper with the alga slowly out of the water, and let the water drain off. Cover the alga with a piece of gauze, the size of the mounting paper, then with a piece of blotting paper. Place in drying press, and press in the usual way. No gluing is necessary. The gelatinous substance of the alga takes care of the mounting. When completely dry, remove the gauze.

STORING—When your mounting sheets are ready, sort out your plants, following the order in your botany manual.

Place all the plants of one genus together in a *genus folder*—all the goldenrods, all the asters, and so on. This is a manila folder slightly larger than the mounting sheets, 12×17 inches.

The genus folders, in turn, are placed in *family folders* or portfolios made of cardboard sides with cloth backs.

The complete herbarium is finally stored in a suitable container—a cardboard or wooden box for a small collection, a cabinet with 12½×17½-inch shelves or drawers for the large collection.

Tip—To protect the collection against insects, place a small amount of a mixture of paradichlorobenzene and naphthalene crystals, half and half, on the bottom of your storage container, in a cloth bag.

Displaying Pressed Plants

You may consider it a pity to store away some of your most beautiful specimens on a shelf or in a drawer, where few will have a chance to see them. Also, you may need your specimens for demonstration or instruction—yet want to protect your plants against injury. There are several ways of solving these problems.

Cellophane sheet covers—For handling mounted plants safely, cover the mounts with a thin sheet of cellophane. Such sheets may be cut out of rolls, or bought, cut to 12½×17½ inches size, from a scientific supply house.

Lay a cellophane sheet over the mounting sheet. Fold about 1 inch of cellophane over at the top, and glue this to the back of the mounting sheet. Fasten the lower front edge of the cellophane to the herbarium sheet with a couple of short strips of scotch tape.

Botanical riker mounts—A Riker mount for a botanical specimen is easily prepared. All you need is a piece of glass or sheet plastic, a piece of cardboard of the same size, a thin layer of cotton batting, also cut to size, and a few feet of black *passe partout* (gummed paper tape) or masking tape.

Place the cardboard on the table, and cover it with the cotton batting. Arrange the plant specimen on the cotton, and press the glass down over it. Seal it along the edges with the moistened *passe partout* or with masking tape.

SPECIAL MOUNTS—You may make an airproof mount by placing your plant specimen between two pieces of wax paper, fusing them together with a warm iron. An even better mount is made with adhesive plastic sheets.

SUPPLIES—*Plain-Vu* self-laminating plastic sheets. A C Industries, Box 5102, Newark 5, N. J.

OTHER COLLECTIONS

SEEDS—Small seeds and flat seeds may be kept in cellophane envelopes. Seeds with fluff, spines, wings, or the like might suffer from this treatment—they are better off in short, round, straight-walled vials with corks or screw caps.

> *Tip*—Many collectors keep all types of small seeds in vials, labeling around the top with narrow labels—Dennison No. 261, for instance.

For display purposes, seed vials may be wired to sheets of plywood or heavy cardboard.

FLESHY FRUITS—Fleshy fruits that would shrink up and become unrecognizable in drying may be preserved in glass jars in 10-per-cent formalin.

> *Tip*—The trouble with formalin is that it almost always bleaches out the natural colors of specimens kept in it. To keep some of this color, try adding 10-percent ordinary cane sugar to the solution.

FUNGI—Mushrooms present one of the toughest problems for the collector. Here are a couple of methods.

DRIED MUSHROOMS—The most common way of pre-

When protected against draft, the spores from a gilled mushroom will fall into an intricate pattern, forming a spore print.

serving mushrooms is through drying. One way of doing this is by stringing them on heavy thread and suspending them over a hot stove until they are dry.

For a more efficient method, spread the specimens on a piece of cloth over an open rack. Place in the oven. The proper temperature for drying is between 130 and 160 degrees. To arrive at the desired temperature, the oven must be set at its lowest heat and the oven door kept open. It is a matter of slow drying, not baking.

When thoroughly dry, the specimens may be kept in cellophane envelopes. Or you may decide to flatten them down a bit and mount them on regular herbarium sheets or special cards.

SPORE PRINTS—During its short life span, spores by the millions drop from the gills of a gilled mushroom. By catching the spores as they fall, they create an intricate and beautiful pattern. But great care is needed— the slightest draft sends the microscopic spores flying.

Spread a very thin coat of mucilage-water mixture, half and half, or egg white stirred liquid with a fork, over a piece of thin cardboard. Cut the stem of a mature, fully opened mushroom directly under the cap. Place the cap, bottom down, in the middle of the cardboard.

Tip—If the gills protrude below the edge of the cap, so that they will fold under when placed on the paper, the whole cap needs to be kept slightly raised over the paper. Push three toothpicks into the side of the cap and keep it suspended on these by resting them on small wood or cork supports.

Cover the layout with a turned-over glass dish, and leave undisturbed for 24 hours.

During this time the spores will fall down and will stick in the mucilage, made moist from the natural moisture of the mushroom. Lift the cap off, and let the sheet dry in the air.

The spore print may be further fixed with ordinary fixative, or clear shellac, sprayed on it from an atomizer or brushed on carefully with a soft camel's hair brush.

Colors of spores vary from white, through pink and rusty brown, to black. To have your spore prints show up, use a dark-colored or black paper for mushrooms with light spores, and vice versa.

Tip—No mushroom has blue spores. So why not use a medium-blue paper for all your spore prints?

9. TREES

FOR recreation and pleasure, we take to the woods. There's a certain primitive enjoyment in walking along a half-hidden trail under the green canopy of tall trees, listening to the forest murmurs . . . the wind in the tree-tops, the calls of birds . . . the footfalls of animals scampering away before your approach.

In almost all nature activities, sooner or later you will be drawn to the woods—into the closely knit community of trees and shrubs, with the myriads of other plants that make up the forest carpet, the soil from which they all spring, the creatures that live in it, the lakes and streams that traverse it. The forests of our country hold an un-ending fascination to all who enter them.

And then, some day, you may stop under a mighty tree in wonder, thinking of the forces that send the sap surg-ing from the deepest root tip to the highest twig, the power of the green leaves to pull nourishment out of the air, the riddle of bud opening and leaf falling, and a hundred other things.

Or you may listen to the voice of the trees, as ex-pressed by an unknown author:

Ye who pass by, harm me not. I am the heat of your hearth on cold winter nights, the friendly shade screening you from the summer sun. My fruits are refreshing draughts quenching your thirst as you jour-ney on. I am the beam that holds your house, the board of your table, the bed on which you lie, the timber that builds your boat. I am the handle of your hoe, the door of your homestead, the wood of your cradle, the shell of your coffin. I am the gift of God and the friend of man. Ye who pass by, listen to my prayer.

In spite of the fact that we depend so much on trees, we have not played fair with our natural treasures. We have cut and burned and wasted a large part of our original heritage.

Fortunately, we are waking up! Today the importance of conserving and perpetuating our forest resources is recognized by every thinking citizen.

BOOKS ON TREES—Rutherford Platt. *This Green World*. Dodd, Mead & Company.

Trees. The Yearbook of Agriculture, 1949. U. S. Department of Agriculture. $2 from Superintendent of Documents, Washington 25, D. C.

WORKING WITH OTHERS

Getting to know the trees may be a personal pursuit—whether you do it in the form of walks in the woods or growing trees in your home garden or wood lot. On the other hand, you may be one among the many who have their interest in forestry awakened to the point of determined community action. The need for such action is becoming more and more evident—not just for the sake of beautification, but also to provide recreational facilities and forestry products for the future.

You will find youth groups, schools, service clubs willing to listen to suggestions for projects for planting trees, and eager to get to work. Plans of this type, carried out successfully in numerous communities, have involved such varied aspects as the establishment of a memorial grove, the improvement of school grounds, ball park, and Scout camp grounds, creating a springtime display of flowering dogwood along the main approach to the town, willow planting along river banks to stop erosion, developing a community forest.

In all such projects, whether for your home grounds or on a community scale, your county agent and the agricultural experiment station of your state are ready to help you with expert advice. In many instances, they are also able to provide you with tree seedlings, at low cost. You can secure further ideas from the U. S. Forest Service of the Department of Agriculture, the National Park Service of the Department of the Interior, both with headquarters in Washington, D. C., and from national associations interested in trees.

SOCIETIES—The American Forestry Association. Hdqrs.: 919 17th Street, N.W., Washington 6, D. C. Periodical: *American Forests*.

The Wilderness Society. Hdqrs.: 2114 P Street, N.W., Washington 7, D. C. Periodical: *The Living Wilderness*.

Trees in Field and Forest

Equipment for Tree Study

The main pieces of equipment for tree study are the same that you would use for studying herbaceous plants.

STUDY EQUIPMENT—Magnifiers—Any of the magnifiers described on page 251 is suitable. You may never need one for the identification of a tree, since most trees have a number of readily seen identifying marks— but you may want it to catch the beauty of often tiny and inconspicuous tree flowers, and to study wood and tree rings.

Knife—A penknife with a strong, sharp blade is necessary for making cross sections of branches to find out their structure and to determine color and consistency of their sap.

Measuring devices—Foresters use special gadgets for measuring diameter, height, and board-foot volume of trees—caliper, tree scale or cruiser's stick. You can get along with a tape measure for measuring diameter, and a foot rule for finding the height.

Measure a tree's diameter at breast height (d.b.h. for short)—4½ feet above the ground. Take the girth of the tree with your tape measure, then divide by 3 to get a rough diameter, by π (3.1416) for a more exact measurement.

To measure the height of a tree, make a chalk mark on the trunk at your own height. Step back. Hold the ruler upright with your hand outstretched at full arm's length before you. Close one eye. Continue to step back until

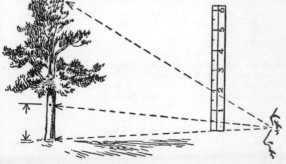

Measuring tree height: One-half inch covers your height indicated on the tree. Multiply your height with number of half inches.

½ inch of the ruler covers the distance from the ground to the chalk mark on the trunk. Now measure the whole tree, on the ruler, from the same position. Multiply the number of half-inches by your height to get the height of the tree.

TREE BOOKS—For the specific trees of your region, drop a line to the forestry service of your state. It probably has available, free or at low cost, a booklet on the forest trees of your section.

For a more comprehensive view, get a good field book of common trees, and carry it with you on your field trips.

BOOKS FOR FIELD IDENTIFICATION—F. Schuyler Mathews. *Field Book of American Trees and Shrubs*. G. P. Putnam's Sons.

George A. Petrides. *Field Guide to Trees and Shrubs*. Houghton Mifflin Company, Boston, Mass.

William M. Harlow. *Trees of the Eastern United States and Canada*. Whittlesey House.

N. A. Bowers. *Cone-Bearing Trees of the Pacific Coast*. Whittlesey House.

Willard Ayres Eliot. *Forest Trees of the Pacific Coast*. G. P. Putnam's Sons.

Charlotte H. Green. *Trees of the South*. University of North Carolina Press, Chapel Hill, N. C.

When it becomes a matter of identifying trees of the rather uncommon species, you may have to resort to Gray's *New Botany* (see page 253) or to Sargent.

BOOK FOR ADVANCED IDENTIFICATION—Charles S. Sargent. *Manual of the Trees of North America*. Houghton Mifflin Company, Boston, Mass.

NOTEBOOK—Your notebook may be a small bound volume or a loose-leaf book in which you can keep a record of the names and important details of the trees you discover. Include a number of map sketches among your notes, with the location of prominent trees clearly indicated so that you can find them again.

FINDING TREES

WHERE?—The answer to the Where? is easy: "Wherever they are!" If they are found at all in your locality, you will certainly know about them.

In the beginning, get to know the trees of your immediate vicinity. Find out what species associate to make up your local woods, and learn some of the reasons why

these specific trees grow and thrive in your region—soil
conditions, temperature, light, rainfall, and so on.

Having once started on the subject of trees, you will
want to expand your circle of knowledge ever farther
and farther afield—to your county, your state, eventually
to famous trees and forests of our country.

Your vacation trips will take on new meaning as you
add to your list of tree acquaintances. You have a life-
long hobby before you, with breathtaking sights and quiet
excitement—Eastern dogwood and Southern magnolia in
bloom, scarlet fall flames of sugar maples over New England, splashes of golden-yellow aspen among the dark-
green ponderosas on a Rocky Mountain slope, cypresses
of Monterey with their gnarled limbs, royal palms of the
Everglades in their slender beauty, mangroves and sequoias and mesquites and Joshua trees. Historical trees,
unusual trees, the world's tallest or oldest trees—you will
find them scattered throughout the length and breadth
of our country, in state and national forests and parks.

REFERENCES—Charles E. Randall and D. Priscilla Edger-
     ton. *Famous Trees*. Miscellaneous Publication No. 295.
     U. S. Department of Agriculture. 15 cents from
     Superintendent of Documents, Washington 25, D. C.
     Herbert S. Zim. *Plants*. Chapter XX, "Plant Local-
     ities Worth Visiting." Harcourt, Brace & Company.
     Devereux Butcher. *Exploring Our National Parks*.
     Oxford University Press.
     Map of National Forests, and information pamphlets.
     U. S. Forest Service, Washington 25, D. C.
     List of National Parks, and information pamphlets.
     U. S. National Park Service, Washington 25, D. C.
     State Forests. Write your state forestry service.

WHEN?—If you are concentrating on a single phase
in the lives of trees, you will have to watch your season.
Otherwise, trees are there to be studied year round: the
unfolding of the leaves in the spring, formation of flowers
and fruit in summer, fall coloration of foliage, twigs,
and wintering buds—and, starting all over again with the
sap running in the old trees, the first tiny sprouts of the
new seedling.

TREE LISTINGS AND SURVEYS

LIFE LISTS—Your list of trees discovered and observed
will grow from field trip to field trip—in the beginning
in spurts, then slowly, until you have located and become familiar with all local species.

You will, of course, keep a record of your finds in your

field notebook. In addition, develop a separate list to be left at home, to which you can add new species as you come upon them in your wanderings. Such a listing may take the form of marginal notes in your field book of trees, or it may occupy a special notebook.

SURVEYS—It often becomes of interest to make a thorough tree survey of a given area—school grounds, city park, camp. The effectiveness of such a survey depends on the size of the area covered, and the number and skill of the people participating in the survey.

> *Tip*—Get the co-operation of local groups interested in nature—nature clubs, biology classes, Boy Scouts and Girl Scouts, garden clubs, and others.

GENERAL SURVEY—For a thorough, general survey of an area, divide it into squares with sides approximately 100 feet long (40 average walking steps), marking the corners of each square in a conspicuous way, such as, for example, with sticks with paper streamers if the survey is an open area, with strips of gauze bandage tied around trees in a forest. Place two or more investigators in each square, with instructions to pick a leafy twig of each different tree and shrub they find, and bring in their haul to a central spot at a certain time. Arrange all specimens according to species and have the experts catalogue them.

TREE CENSUS—A census of local trees is another job that might be undertaken by a nature club or youth group.

Get a street map of your community, or a topographic map of the area. Divide it into sections—in town by the middle of streets, in the field by paths, streams, or other landmarks. Send a couple of investigators into each section, with instructions to count all trees present that are at least 4 inches thick, indicating number of each species. Tabulate the result.

In a survey of this type, reported by Jaques, of the trees of Mt. Pleasant, Iowa, it was found that this community of less than 4,000 people had 15,998 trees 4 inches or more in trunk diameter. Apple trees led the list with 3,369, followed by American elm, 2,137, and silver maple, 1,846. More than 100 species were represented.

> *Tip*—In this kind of survey, you may succeed in locating, as a by-product, the thickest tree, the tallest tree, the tree with widest spread, within the community.

TREE MAPPING—In making a survey of a certain area, it may prove beneficial for future work to know definitely where representative specimens of trees are located.

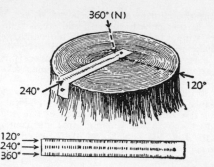

In making a tree-ring record, use adding machine paper. Rub three radii, with 120-degree intervals, onto the paper.

The simplest way to accomplish this is to draw in the position of the trees on a large-scale map of the territory. A surveyor's map is suitable. Even better is a map made especially for the purpose on which the trees can be indicated by regular map signatures and by numbers. If an artistically inclined person is connected with the project, the result should be even more attractive.

TREE-RING STUDY—In investigating the trees of your community, you may start to wonder about the age of the more impressive ones. You may come upon tree stumps that show the yearly growth rings of trees of similar size. You count them—and possibly think of the days long past of which those tree rings could tell. You have entered into the subject of *dendrochronology*—from *dendros,* tree, *chronos,* time.

The chief proponent of this science is Dr. A. E. Douglass of the University of Arizona. He has made new use of an old knowledge: that tree rings are narrow in years of drought, wider in years of normal precipitation. By fitting together the tree-ring patterns of old trees from the same area of the Southwest, he and his associates have developed a record of dry and wet years going back to the time of Christ. By matching the year rings of the timbers of an old Spanish Mission against the tree rings of this record, it is possible to ascertain in which years the timbers were cut, and hence the approximate year in which the building was erected.

The same method has been found to work in varying degrees in other sections where forests exist or formerly flourished. It was used a few years ago in a project sponsored by the American Philosophical Society of Philadelphia and directed by Dr. Edward E. Wildman to find out about the climate of the Delaware River Valley as revealed in the growth rings of old trees, found in the form of stumps and as timbers in old buildings.

To make a record of the tree rings of a stump, you require a few feet of adding-machine paper (purchasable in a stationery store), a couple of thumbtacks, a soft pencil, and a compass.

Smooth down the surface of the stump with sandpaper, or, possibly, with a plane. Tack a strip of adding-machine paper to the stump, placing ½ inch of one edge of the paper over the radius running from the center toward the north. Rub the pencil over the paper, the way you make a rubbing of a penny, until the tree rings show up clearly. Move the paper so that the middle of it rests over the 120-degree radius. Take your second, ½-inch-wide rubbing here. Move the paper next to the 240-degree radius for a third rubbing along the other edge of the paper, opposite to the first rubbing. In this way, the rubbings of the three radii will lie parallel to each other on the paper strip (illustration, page 291).

When the rubbings are made, write in the compass directions of the three radii, and complete the record by adding the name of the tree, location, altitude, soil, probable year when tree was cut.

> *Tip*—A stump "museum" can be made a special feature of a nature trail. Smooth down surface. Varnish. Indicate rings representing historical events with arrows and markers.

TREE CALENDARS—A tree calendar may be developed along the lines suggested for flower calendars and calendar charts (page 254). But rather than taking calendar notes of trees in general, you will find it more interesting concentrating on specific trees of home grounds, school grounds, or camp.

The notes here may include: 1. unfolding of first leaf; 2. flowers in bloom (shedding of pollen) ; 3. fruits ripe; 4. first indication of fall coloration; 5. all leaves shed.

FIELD OBSERVATIONS

Your early field trips will be mostly for the sake of locating and identifying the trees of your neighborhood. When that has been accomplished, you may want to delve deeper into the life of a single tree or of a tree association—trees that live together because they require the same living conditions of soil, moisture, and light.

TREE ASSOCIATIONS—What are the main tree associations in your area—beech-maple-hemlock, oak-hickory, pine, or what? How do they differ? Why do they differ?

TREE DIARY—The life of a tree for a full year, based on once-a-week observations.

TREE COMMUNITY—Not just the tree itself, but other plants and creatures that live on and in it.

BUDDING AND LEAFING—How are leaves arranged in the bud? How does the bud open?

FLOWERS—How pollinated? By insects? Wind? Self-pollination?

SEED DISPERSAL—How dispersed—by wind, water, animals, birds?

OTHER REPRODUCTION—By suckers, sprouts from stump, and so on.

BARKS—How do they differ? Thickness of bark—thickest in what compass direction?

FALL COLORATIONS—Listing of trees by colors—from light yellow of poplars and birches, through orange and red of sugar maple, to flaming scarlet of scarlet oak and tupelo. Influence of weather—light, moisture, temperature.

TREES IN WINTER—Recognition by silhouettes, bark, buds, leaf scars.

DYING AND DEAD TREES—What caused death—old age, insects, fungi, weather, fire, man?

STUMP DETECTING—Study stumps and, by observation and deduction, decide the facts of the tree's life and death. The following questions, adapted from William Gould Vinal's *Nature Recreation,* show the possibilities:

1. What kind of tree was this?
2. How old was it when cut?
3. How much was its average annual increase in diameter?
4. In what year did it grow most rapidly?
5. Approximately when was it cut?
6. (a) What tools were used? (b) In what order?
7. (a) Number of workmen? (b) Amateur(s) or woodsman (or men)?
8. Where did he (or they) stand?
9. In what direction did the tree fall?
10. Was it cut during a strong wind, or a calm?
11. Was it cut before or after it died?
12. If after, why did it die?

Tree Photography

Tree photography has an appeal not only to the person whose main interest is a set of documentary shots of tree details, but also to the landscape photographer who may look at a tree mainly as a valuable prop to improve the composition of his pictures.

Whatever your approach, you will find that one of the great advantages of tree photography is that it can be an all-year hobby. There is always some phase of tree life in season to be photographed.

STILLS

EQUIPMENT—CAMERA—Tree photography is one of the few types of nature photography in which the average snapshot camera feels at home. If you know what to photograph and how to go about it, you should be able to take an excellent series of shots of tree silhouettes and of tree trunks even with the cheapest Brownie. But use a yellow filter to darken the sky, and a fine-grain film so that good enlargements may be made.

For complete coverage of a tree, from its shape to the tiniest flowers, you need a better camera, equipped with the same features for close-up photography as are required for flower photography (see page 269).

WHAT TO PHOTOGRAPH—If you are familiar with trees and have an eye for their pictorial possibilities, you will never run out of subjects.

BOOK OF TREE PHOTOGRAPHS—G. H. Collingwood and Warren D. Brush. *Knowing Your Trees*. American Forestry Association, Washington 6, D. C.

SEQUENCES AND SERIES—Single, casual tree pictures are of little value. Think from the start in terms of *sequences* —several shots of the same tree, its shape, trunk, bark, buds, leaves, flowers, fruits—and of *series*—silhouettes of a number of different trees, close-ups of as many types of bark, tree flowers, fruits. Sequences and series develop together—by the time you have taken a number of sequences, you automatically have your series as well.

TREE SILHOUETTES—A set of twin shots of the same tree, one taken in summer, the other in winter has a greater appeal than a single shot. Such sets are most effective when taken from the identical spot, so that there is no question of the shots being of the same tree. If taken at the same time of day, so much the better.

Tip—Don't stake your spot. The stake won't be there when you return half a year later! Instead, add to your exposure notes, the compass bearing from which the shot was taken, determined with a pocket compass, and the distances in number of steps.

Silhouette shots are generally taken of trees growing in the open, to get their characteristic forms—the vase shape of the American elm, the wind-blown effect of the sycamore, the dense, globular crown of the sugar maple, the cone shape of firs and spruces, and so on.

Aim, as far as possible to have the sun strike the tree at an angle somewhere between 30 and 60 degrees to the line between camera and tree. Sidelighted to this extent, highlights and shadows of trunk and crown will give the tree a molded and alive aspect.

Watch your background. Place your camera in such a position that you avoid distracting background features of buildings, wires, poles. Many of them may be eliminated by taking the photograph from a low angle. Your best background is a blue sky, clear or with scattered clouds. Use a medium-yellow filter to darken the sky.

Tip—An unusual set of tree photographs results from using infrared film and red filter. The green foliage will appear almost white against a black sky background.

TRUNK AND BARK—The rough bark of many trees will test your photographic skill. In strong light, the deep fissures will turn into black masses. To get details in the shadows, it is advisable to photograph tree trunks and barks in diffused light—by waiting until a cloud covers the sun, shooting on a hazy day, or throwing a shadow on the bark with a scrim or gauze screen.

BUDS, LEAVES, FLOWERS, AND FRUITS—Follow the same procedure as for photographing flowers (page 269). You may find it necessary to tie down the branch you are photographing, to keep it in focus, and to tie up overhead branches to prevent them from casting distracting shadows.

FALL FOLIAGE—All the above subjects are suited to color photography as well as to black and white. When it comes to photographing fall foliage, it is a different matter. The brilliant colors add little to a black-and-white photograph, but make all the difference in a color transparency. A series of such transparencies, thrown on the screen, is a marvelous sight. But stick to close-ups for your greatest effects.

MOVIES

EQUIPMENT—CAMERA—The motion-picture camera with the usual, 1-inch lens for amateur movies can be used to excellent effect for taking tree movies.

Shoot the whole tree the way you would a medium landscape, the trunk the way you would photograph a person full size. Moving closer, to about 5 feet, you can get bark and branch features.

By placing a portrait lens over the 1-inch lens, you can get within about 2 feet of leaves, flowers, and fruits. The latter will not fill the frame as in a real close-up, but will give you a satisfactory medium shot. Your titler

can be used in a similar manner and has the advantage
that the framing device tells you exactly what you get.

For close-ups of tree flowers and fruit, you will need
extension tubes or a 3- or 4-inch telephoto lens and a
focusing device. A wide-angle lens will come in handy
for silhouette and crown shots.

YOUR TREE MOVIES—In making movies of trees, it
pays to develop a script in advance. Individual shots may
be technically perfect, but it is the way they are tied
together that makes entertainment or education out of
them.

The variety of possibilities is inexhaustible. It ranges
the whole way from "Trees in Spring" or "Flames of
Autumn," through "Our American Forests" or "Mighty
Sequoias," to "At Home in the Woods."

Use your imagination in making the script. If you do,
you come to fully realize that a tree is not just a tree—
it is a wildlife community in itself, exposed to the elements and probably inhabited by mammals, birds, insects,
flowerless plants such as mosses and lichens. You can
build a whole film around a tree. Take a clue from
Kilmer and show the tree through the seasons—in winter
with snow on its "bosom," in summer as it "intimately
lives with rain." Mix medium shots of the tree lifting
its "leafy arms to pray," with close-ups of the "nest of
robins in her hair," and of flowers and fruits.

Tip—One of the few places where SLOW panoraming
may be justified is in showing the height of a tree,
sweeping the lens from the base up into the crown.

Growing Native Trees

Plant a tree and follow its growth—you will never get
closer to nature than that. As the tree grows, your appreciation of living things will grow with it. You will be
proud, too: "When I planted this tree it just came up
to here . . . now look at it!"

We had a Johnny Appleseed once whose vision was a
flowering America. We need many more Johnny Apple-
seeds today to keep America green. The trees you plant
in your front yard will help. A back-yard arboretum or
a farm wood lot is the next step. But don't stop until
you have helped in the creation or upkeep of a town park
or community forest, and in the work of your federal and
your state's forestry service.

NATIVE TREES FOR YOUR GROUNDS

In deciding on trees for your home grounds, keep in
mind that the trees you plant will only thrive if your
locality provides the climate that matches their natural

living conditions. You will have no luck attempting to grow a species native to the North in the all-year warmth of southern Florida. Neither can you expect a Southern tree to survive the harshness of a New England winter.

Before you plant, therefore, note what trees are already doing well in your locality, or check with local nurserymen or other authorities and get their recommendations. Write to your state forester, or contact your local agricultural agent. Their advice is yours for the asking.

TRANSPLANTING TREES—You will know that the climate is suitable, if you transplant native trees or shrubs into your garden from your immediate vicinity—with permission, of course, if from someone else's property.

TIME FOR TRANSPLANTING—The best time for transplanting trees is when the running of the sap is at the lowest ebb—from September or October to early in the year. Late fall is the generally recommended time, but much transplanting is done in early spring.

Don't accept this as an arbitrary rule. Trees can be moved successfully at almost any time of the year, if the proper care is taken.

TRANSPLANTING HINTS—As a general hint for transplanting—don't bite off more than you can chew. In other words, don't attempt to move a tree that's too large to stand successful transplanting. As a rule of thumb, it is not wise to try to move any tree larger than 1 inch in diameter—unless the job is handled by expert tree movers.

Select a sound tree, with strong buds. Make a circular cut in the ground around it, 1 foot or more in diameter,

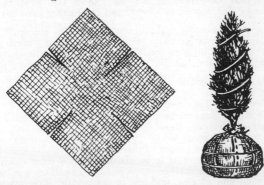

To protect the roots, dig up a tree with a ball of dirt. Wrap the ball in burlap. For ease in fastening burlap, cut it as shown.

depending on the size of the tree. Then cut in under the roots. In transplanting, it is very important that the roots be prevented from drying out. Keep as large a ball of earth as feasible attached to them, and tie up the ball in burlap for transporting.

In spite of all care, it often happens, in digging out a tree, that the dirt falls away from the roots, especially in dry weather. Don't despair at this. Wrap up the roots tightly in wet burlap, bring the tree home, and plant it immediately.

For planting, dig a hole large enough to permit the roots to spread out in their natural position. Hold the tree upright, and fill in around it with dirt taken from the spot where the tree grew. Add *no* fertilizer. Then give a plentiful soaking with water. Keep watering thoroughly for several weeks to encourage root growth.

If a number of roots have been cut off in digging up the tree, compensate for them by pruning back the top to a similar extent.

NURSERY STOCK—Rather than attempting to transplant wild trees, you may have more success with planting nursery-grown stock. From a nursery, you may purchase local trees of almost any size you desire—from a few large ones for your garden corner, to thousands of seedlings for the establishment of a wood lot, for reforestation, or for creating a community forest.

For an extensive planting, the recommended stock is one-year-old hardwood seedlings and two- to four-year-old conifer seedlings or transplants (transplants are plants that have been grown for one or two years as seedlings, then moved to another bed for further growth).

Tip—Many states make available seedlings and transplants free or at cost. Write to your state forestry service for information. It is advisable to file your request in the fall for spring delivery.

PLANTING SEEDLINGS—Determine the location of the wood lot. Figure out the size of it, then order the right number of seedlings (see page 392).

When seedlings arrive, get them into the ground as quickly as possible. Keep their roots moist in the meantime with wet moss or by "puddling"—placing them in a pail in a liquid mixture of dirt and water.

Lay out the first row to be planted. This is most easily done by placing a marker—a piece of red cloth on a stick —at each end of row, and one in the middle. This gives you two markers in sight, at all times.

A mattock or grub hoe makes a good planting tool.

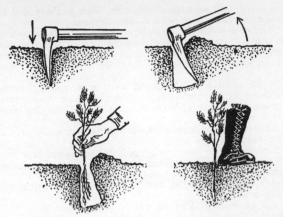

In tree planting with a mattock, drive mattock straight down, raise handle to widen hole, place seedling, firm the dirt.

Drive the blade straight into the ground, with the handle horizontal. Raise the end of the handle, thus widening the hole at the bottom. Remove the mattock. Flick the roots of the seedling into the hole, with the root "collar" at ground level. Use mattock to push dirt in around the seedling. Finally firm the dirt with the foot. Be sure that no air space is left around the roots at the bottom of the hole.

TREE CUTTINGS—A number of wild deciduous trees and shrubs can be propagated from cuttings.

WINTER CUTTINGS—The time to take cuttings is late fall, after the leaves have fallen, or any time during the winter.

Choose sound, pencil-thick twigs for your cuttings. Cut the twigs into pieces, 6 to 8 inches long. Tie the cuttings into bundles of a dozen or so, and bury them in sand. Store for the winter in a cool cellar—keeping the sand moist, but not wet.

In the spring, set out the cuttings in a rather sandy soil bed. Transplant after a year into nursery or permanent location.

FORCING SPRING CUTTINGS—Twigs of a number of trees are suitable for forcing, especially those that have catkins —willow, poplar, alder, hazel. Collect them when the buds have started to swell—late January or February.

Cut them off with diagonal cuts with a sharp knife. Place in water in a not-too-warm room.

Within a week, you will have a touch of early spring to enjoy in your room—and in a couple of weeks, possibly rooted cuttings. Let them get a good start, then plant them out in your wild garden.

TREES FROM SEEDS—It may give you an extra thrill to raise your own seedlings in your own home nursery—to see your trees develop from their first tiny green shoots.

CONIFERS—Conifers—pine, spruce, fir—are easily grown in a small nursery area.

Determine the number of seedlings you want to grow. Then figure on 50 seedlings to a square foot. For large numbers, prepare a seed bed the way you would a vegetable bed. For smaller numbers, you will be better off using a frame.

As an example, let us say you want to grow 200 plants. That will take 4 square feet—a plot 2×2 feet.

Select a spot ½ foot larger in all directions than your growing area—in other words, 3×3 feet. Cultivate it to a depth of 1 foot, removing all stones.

Make a frame of scrap wood, 3×3 feet, about 10 inches high. Place it around the growing area, sinking it down 4 inches. Smooth down a 2×2-foot patch in the middle of the framed-in area. Sow the seeds over this patch in drills 4 to 6 inches apart, about ¼ to ½ inch deep—approximately twice the diameter of the seed. Firm the ground around them with a board, then cover them with a ½-inch layer of sand. Press the sand down with the board. Cover the seed bed with brown building paper, or burlap. Finally, place a piece of ½-inch hardware cloth (wire mesh) over the frame to keep out rodents and birds.

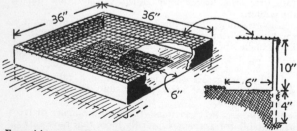

For raising a small number of conifer seedlings, prepare a seed bed. Surround it with a frame, and cover with wire mesh.

When the seeds start to sprout in the spring, remove
the paper, but keep the wire screen on. Place strips of
lath across the frame, lath-width apart to give half shade.
During the summer, weed and water regularly.

The seedlings should be ready for transplanting the
second spring into a transplant bed, or into permanent
location.

HARDWOODS—The seedlings of maple, birch, elm, ash,
dogwood, and several other hardwoods may be grown
in a vegetable bed, or in a frame as suggested above.

The nut-bearing hardwoods—oaks, hickories, walnuts—
are better sown directly where you want the mature trees
to grow. The seedlings develop a deep taproot the first
growing season, which makes it difficult to transplant
them successfully. Cultivate small spots of ground, 12 to
18 inches in diameter, to a depth of 12 inches. Plant the
acorns or nuts in the fall, soon after they are ripe. Place
3 to 5 in each spot to assure success in case of non-
sprouting of some of them and mice and squirrel destruction of others.

Tip—To protect the nuts against rodents, make a cross
slit in the bottom of an empty tin can, then press the
can down over the nuts until the bottom is flush with
the ground. Or use a dome of wire mesh instead.

As the sprouts come up in the spring, keep weeds away
from their immediate surroundings to get them well established.

Tree Collections

Tree collecting offers a greater variety of possibilities
than other types of nature collecting. You can make a
herbarium with exhibits showing all the parts of individual trees, or you can specialize in different aspects of
trees—in their leaves, twigs, roots or fruits.

THE TREE HERBARIUM

The making of a herbarium of tree specimens follows
closely the development of a plant herbarium, as described
on pages 274 to 280. The equipment is the same, and the
procedure follows the same general pattern, with only a
few variations.

SPECIAL METHODS—Cut sprays of branches and twigs
to a length of 10 to 12 inches so that they will fit properly
on the regular herbarium sheet. If at all possible, get
branches with flowers and with fruits in their early
development, as well as leaves. This is not always possible. In some trees, the flowers appear and fade before
the leafing, in others, the pollen-bearing and seed-bearing
flowers are found on separate trees. In such cases, it will

be necessary to secure several sprays to get all features of the tree included. Prune off excess twigs and leaves, if necessary, so that the remaining will show up clearly.

In drying the specimens, the woody stems may give you some trouble because of their thickness. They just won't press flat, with the result that the leaves shrivel up instead of drying flat. You can solve this problem to a certain extent by whittling down the back of the stem to half thickness. If that is not enough, have on hand pads of newspaper strips of various sizes that you can build into the same thickness as the stems and place these over the leaves to flatten them down.

In mounting your specimens, you may find that you will have to use a combination of the mounting methods described on pages 279 to 280. If you prefer to stick to a single method, you will probably have to resort to tying.

Small, flat seeds and fruits can be mounted on the herbarium sheet with the specimen itself. Large, dry fruits will have to be stored in boxes, fleshy fruits in glass containers in a formalin preservative (page 283).

LEAVES

Leaves may be pressed, or reproduced in a number of different ways. Leaf reproductions may have little scientific value, but they combine enjoyable activities with gratifying results.

PRESSED LEAVES—It is easy to make a good collection of pressed leaves. All you need in the line of collecting and pressing equipment is a couple of pulp magazines among whose pages you can place the leaves, and some heavy books for keeping them flattened. Change the leaves into another magazine after a first pressing of about twenty-four hours, and finish the drying there.

For perfect specimens, pick your leaves in early summer, before they have been chewed by insects. Or maybe you will like to make a collection of leaves in their most spectacular fall coloration.

MOUNTING LEAVES—Individual leaves may be glued to full-size or half-size herbarium sheets, or to thin cardboard of any size you like—5×7-inch filing cards, for instance.

OR fuse them between two dry-mounting sheets or pieces of waxpaper or cellophane (see page 283).

OR attach them with scotch tape to the insides of plastic envelopes. Such envelopes of clear, .005-gauge plastic are available at stationery stores in several sizes, punched for insertion in loose-leaf binders.

Four leaf prints: Top—ink print and spatter print. Bottom—blueprint (or photo negative) and driprint (or photo positive).

Tip—Pressed leaves have many decorative uses, from lamp shades to glass-covered tabletops.

LEAF PRINTS—A leaf print can be made in a rather casual manner by pressing a leaf against any smeared surface—a large inkpad, a sheet of carbon paper, a piece of newly painted wood—then by transferring the ink or paint that has been picked up by the leaf veins to a piece of clean paper. If you want better prints, use a more exacting inking method, or go in for photographic reproductions.

Settle on a definite size for all your prints—5×7 inches is especially good. Photographic papers come in that size.

SMOKE PRINTS—Smoke printing is a backwoods

For smoke printing, smoke up cardboard. Press leaf in soot. Move leaf to white paper, press down leaf to make print.

method for which you only need a few pieces of white paper and a candle stub. Rub candle wax in a thin layer over a sheet of paper. Smooth it down with a finger, rubbing it in thoroughly. Light the candle stub. Move the paper, horizontally, through the flame, with the waxed surface down. If done carefully, the paper will pick up a thin layer of soot. Place paper on a smooth surface, sooty side up. Lay the leaf on the paper, veiny side down. Cover with a sheet of paper. Rub the leaf through the paper to make it pick up a thin coating of soot. Place the leaf, sooty side down, on piece of clean paper, cover with another sheet, and rub firmly but carefully with the fingers of one hand while keeping the leaf in place with the fingers of the other.

INK PRINTS—For ink printing, purchase from an art supply store a tube of linoleum-block printing ink—

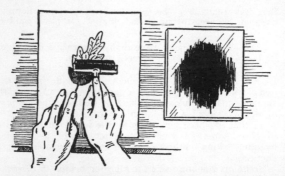

In ink printing, spread ink on glass plate. Roll ink on leaf. Place leaf on white paper. Transfer the ink from leaf by rubbing.

black, green, or brown, water soluble or oil base—or get
a dab of regular printer's ink from a local printer. You
further need a small rubber roller (brayer), a piece of
glass, several sheets of white paper, and pieces of newspaper.

Squeeze half an inch of printing ink onto the glass plate.
Spread it into a thin, even layer by rolling the roller over
it, back and forth and cross-wise. Place a leaf, veiny side
up, on a piece of newspaper. Ink the veins with the rubber roller. Place the leaf, inked side down, on a sheet
of clean paper. Cover with a piece of newspaper. Roll
the rubber roller over the newspaper, pressing the leaf
under it firmly against the printing paper. Remove newspaper. Pick up the leaf carefully so that you do not
smudge the print.

BOOKS—David S. Marx. *Learn the Trees from Leaf
    Prints*. Botanic Publishing Company, Cincinnati, O.
    David and Jean Villasenor. *How to Do Nature Print-
    ing*. Foster Art Service, Laguna Beach, Calif.

SPATTER PRINTS—Spatter printing is an outlining process. The finished print shows the leaf in white silhouette

Two ways of making spatter print: with toothbrush and leaf
held in position with pebbles (left), with spatter screen box (right).

against a background of minute ink drops. Ordinary ink
is not suitable. You need a thicker-flowing ink, such as
India ink, or slightly diluted poster colors.

TOOTHBRUSH METHOD—Place a leaf on a piece of construction paper or mimeograph paper, holding it down
with pebbles or pins. Dip the tip of an old toothbrush
in a small amount of ink in a saucer. Shake off surplus
ink. Point the toothbrush at an angle toward the leaf,
bristles up. Rub a nail or stick over the bristles, from

the tip of the brush toward the handle. As the bristles snap back, they spatter drops of ink on the paper. Continue until a satisfactory print has been made.

Tip—The spatter process can be greatly simplified and speeded up with the use of a spatter screen box. Replace top and bottom of a cigar box or a cream cheese box with wire screening, stretching it over the frame and tacking it in position. Arrange a leaf on a sheet of paper. Place the screen box over it. Rub the inked toothbrush over the top until the print is completed. The screen adds an interesting pattern to the print.

SPRAY-GUN METHOD—Pour the ink into a spray gun or atomizer. Tack the leaf with pins to a sheet of paper on a supporting background of cardboard. Stand the cardboard on end. Shoot a fine spray of ink at the leaf from the spray gun, from a distance of a foot or more.

Tip—Even simpler than a spray gun is the use of paint or enamel in an Aerosol can. Experiment until you arrive at the right distance for spraying.

BLUEPRINTS—In blueprinting the finished product shows a white leaf against a blue background. Blueprint paper may be purchased from artists' and architects' supply stores. Most of it comes in large rolls, but you will probably be able to persuade the dealer to sell you a few feet. Cut it to whatever size you want for your collection. All handling of blueprint paper must be done in subdued light.

You need a printing frame also. You can buy a 5×7-inch or larger photographic printing frame for about a dollar. Or you can get along with a piece of ½-inch plywood or corrugated cardboard, 6×8 inches, hinging a pane of glass of equal size to it with adhesive tape, and using one or two spring clothes pins, or large rubber bands for clamping the parts together.

In shade, pull out a piece of blueprint paper from the light-proof envelope in which you keep it. Place the leaf to be printed on the coated side of the blueprint paper, and put both of them in the printing frame with the leaf against the glass. Close the frame. Expose to direct sunlight until paper has turned from cream through blue to an ashen gray. Remove the paper. Place it face down in a pan of water for ten minutes or more. During the washing, the exposed part of the paper turns blue again. Blot between pieces of newspaper, and dry between more sheets under slight pressure.

Tip—When printing, place a small rectangle of paper in the right-hand corner. When completed, you will

have a white space here for your identification notes.
Tip—Blueprints may be intensified by immersing them
in a solution of potassium bichromate (1 level teaspoon to 1 gallon of water) for about five minutes,
before the final washing.

DRY PRINTS—Dry-printing paper—"Driprint," "Ozalid"
—is also used by architects. It is dry-developed, and produces a positive—a brownish-red, blue, or black leaf
silhouette against a white background, depending on the
type of paper used.

SUPPLIES—Eugene Dietzgen Company, 218 East 23rd
Street, New York 10, N. Y.

For the printing, proceed as in blueprinting. Expose to
sun or a photoflood bulb for twenty to forty seconds, until

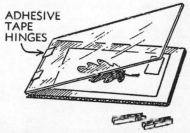

ADHESIVE
TAPE
HINGES

A simple printing frame for blueprinting and photo printing can
be made from a piece of glass, adhesive tape, and cardboard.

the yellow color has disappeared. Then, in a subdued light,
attach the exposed paper to a piece of cardboard with a
couple of small tabs of scotch tape. Rest it face down on
the edges of a shallow pan with about ½ inch of concentrated ammonia, bought at the drugstore—the household kind is not strong enough. Fume it for a couple of
minutes until a clear image has formed. No washing is
needed afterward.

Tip—If the odor of ammonia bothers you, use the
tube method instead of the open tray: Pour ammonia
into a small glass dish, such as a custard cup. Roll up
the prints to be developed inside a tin can of a diameter
slightly larger than the glass dish. Place the can over
the ammonia dish, and fume the prints until they are
correctly developed.

PHOTOGRAPHIC PRINTS—Instead of blueprint paper, use

proof paper, such as is used by portrait photographers for making preliminary prints of their negatives. This is a printing-out paper, turning dark when exposed to the sun. It is not developed afterward, only fixed.

The printing method is similar to blueprinting. A short exposure to the sun or strong artificial light will result in a white leaf outlined against an almost black background. By a longer exposure, you will get a complete negative photograph of the leaf, with all veins showing.

When the exposure is completed, fix the paper for five to ten minutes in regular photographic acid fixer (hypo), then wash for fifteen minutes or more before drying.

Tip—If you have a photographic darkroom at your disposal, you can do the printing here, using contact paper and contact printer, or enlarging paper and enlarging easel.

Small leaves may be placed in the enlarger head itself and projected as a regular negative, to make an enlarged print.

Tip—A photographic leaf print may be used as a paper negative to produce a positive print. Place it face to face with a piece of unexposed paper in the printing frame, with back of original print toward the glass. Expose, then fix and dry.

"ETCHINGS"—Heatforming plastics, such as Lucite and Plexiglass, make it possible to produce a plate from which a number of "etchings" may be made.

Heat a sheet of plastic, ⅛ or 3/16 inch, 6×6 inch, in a kitchen oven, or in a top-of-the-stove oven, at a temperature between 220 and 300 degrees, until it has become soft enough to be marked easily with a finger nail.

Tip—Instead of using an oven, soften the plastic under an infrared bulb, suspended about 1 foot above it.

Working fast, take out the softened plastic and place it on a flat, hard surface. Lay the leaf on it, underside down. Place sheet of metal or heat-resistant glass over leaf and plastic. Apply pressure—heavy books, clamps, letterpress. When cooled, remove leaf. Your plate is ready. From here on, it is printed like a regular etching plate.

Spread a small amount of printer's ink over the plate with a straight rubber squeegee, filling the lines of the leaf design. Wipe surface ink off with a wiper block, made by wrapping a couple of layers of newspaper around a small piece of wood. Dampen the back of a piece of good quality engraving paper. Place it over the plate, then cover it with a couple of pieces of blotting paper, thin felt or sheet rubber. Make the impression by rolling the "sandwich" firmly with a rolling pin, by sending it through a wringer, or by putting it in a block-printing press or in an engraver's press.

When you have taken as many impressions as you desire, clean the plate with carbon tetrachloride. Then heat it again. By the "elastic memory" of heat-forming plastics, it will turn back into a smooth sheet ready for further use.

SKELETON LEAVES—Skeleton leaves are occasionally found in the woods, where insects, fungi, and moisture have done the skeletonizing. You can do a quicker job yourself.

Pick a leaf with rather tough veins. Place it on a piece of cloth or soft felt. Hold one end of a hand brush or hairbrush loosely between the fingers of one hand. Tap the bristles of the opposite end of the brush firmly and repeatedly against the leaf. The bristles will slowly pick out the fleshy part of the leaf, leaving even the finest veins intact. When the leaf is completely skeletonized, dry it under pressure, the way you would an ordinary leaf. Mount the pressed leaf between glass or cellophane.

Tip—For a quicker job, boil leaf for a couple of minutes in a solution of 4 ounces household lye in 1 pint of water—in an enamel or glass pot, NOT in aluminum. Wash thoroughly in water before using brush.

Twigs and Winter Buds

TWIG COLLECTIONS—Select a twig that is truly representative of the tree, then cut it off. Trim it with a sharp knife to fit the size of the sheets on which you plan to mount your twigs. Make the trimming cut on the slant, and in such a way that it will face out when the twig is mounted, to show the inside structure.

Mount the twig on the sheet with strips of gummed cloth or adhesive tape, or by tying (see page 280).

Tip—Instead of mounting the twig in a separate collection, you may want to place each twig next to the leaf of the same tree species, in your leaf collection.

Wood Specimens

WOOD COLLECTIONS—If there is lumbering, clearing, or thinning going on in your neck of the woods you have a good chance of securing a collection of wood samples of local trees. No nature lover would cut down a live tree just for the sake of adding a wood specimen to his collection.

Cut foot-long sections out of thick branches or young trees, 2 to 4 inches in diameter, leaving the bark intact. When you get the blocks home, trim them down to the

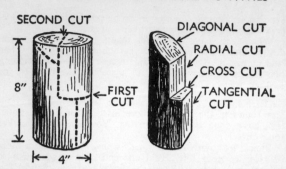

Make your wood specimens to size shown, or to your own standard size. Cut as indicated. One half of cuts may be varnished.

standard length you have set for all your wood samples —6 to 10 inches. Season them for a month or more in a spot where they will dry slowly.

Finally, turn each of your samples into a display piece that will show the different grains: Make a cross cut to the center, half the length of the block down, then a radial cut from the top until the saw meets the cross cut. Saw off half of the bottom "step" in a tangential cut. Cut the top diagonally, at a 45 degree angle. Sandpaper all cut surfaces.

Tip—If you like, you can leave the left half of the exposed surfaces unfinished, and coat the other half with varnish or lacquer to show how the grain of that particular wood takes a finish.

Mount the specimens by wiring them to plywood panels, or by standing them upright, secured with screws, on pieces of 1-inch board.

10. ROCKS, MINERALS, AND FOSSILS

LOOK wide over the countryside—and whether you
 stand on the highest peak of the Rockies or the lowest
point of Death Valley, in the most undulating part of
New England or the flattest of Kansas, all around you
are rocks, rocks and more rocks. Some of those rocks
are the solid masses of the hardest granite, others the
loose powder of the softest sand. Some of them are the
original bedrock or "country rock" of the landscape,
others make up the mantle rock of loose material, formed
from the bedrock on which it lies by weathering or
carried in from afar by ice or wind or waves.

Rocks are of a thousand uses. They give us directly
the stones for building blocks and the coal for our fur-
naces. Through various processes they supply us with
our metals—iron for our skyscrapers and our cars,
copper for our electrical fixtures, aluminum for our
cooking pots and our planes, silver for our coins, uranium
for our atomic reactors. They give us the chemicals for
our industries, the fertilizers for our farms, the plastics
for our homes. They provide us with the implements of
peace and the arms of war. But more important than
anything else: they indirectly sustain our life—the soil
in which our plants grow is made up of particles of
rocks and fragments of minerals, mixed with decomposed
plant matter and animal remains.

The moment you become interested in rocks, and in the
minerals or prehistoric plant and animal life that form
them, the whole field of *geology* opens up before you in a
vista of a score of roads all leading out from a main
center.

In the beginning, your interest may consist in hunting
for the most beautiful or most unusual rocks or minerals

in your locality and preparing them for the most effective display. But collecting alone will soon prove of little satisfaction to you unless you can identify your specimens —and so you delve into *mineralogy, petrology,* or *lithology.* With your interest once aroused you may start wondering about the origin of your rocks and minerals and fossils. How were they formed? By what forces did they come into being? This curiosity of yours may lead you into a study of the formation of the landscape and its underlying structure, *geomorphology,* or of the past ages of the world, of *historical geology* and *paleontology.* Or you may wonder about the uses to which rocks and minerals are put and look into *economic geology* as it deals with metal ores or coal mines, quarries or mineral fields, oil or gas deposits, or some other of its multitudinous phases.

The field of geology is as big as the earth—it *is* the earth!

BOOKS—GENERAL GEOLOGY—Carrol L. Fenton and Mildred A. Fenton. *Our Amazing Earth.* Also *Earth's Adventures.* Doubleday and Co.

Gary G. Croneis and William C. Krumbein. *Down to Earth.* University of Chicago Press, Chicago, Ill.

ROCKS—Carrol L. Fenton and Mildred Fenton. *The Rock Book.* Also *Rocks and Their Stories.* Doubleday and Co.

MINERALS—George L. English and D. E. Jensen. *Getting Acquainted with Minerals.* McGraw-Hill Book Co.

Herbert S. Zim and Elizabeth K. Cooper. *Minerals.* Harcourt, Brace and Co.

FOSSILS—Carroll L. Fenton and Mildred A. Fenton. *The Fossil Book.* Doubleday and Co.

Ruben A. Stirton. *Time, Life and Man: The Fossil Record.* John Wiley and Sons.

METEORITES—Harvey H. Nininger. *Out of the Sky.* University of Denver Press, Denver, Colo.

WORKING WITH OTHERS

It is, of course, possible for you to pursue your interest in geology alone. But you might as well realize from the beginning that the instant you show the least bit of interest in rocks, minerals, or fossils, you have automatically entered the vast fraternity of "rockhounds," or, at the junior level, "pebble pups."

What are rockhounds? Some time ago, *Desert* Magazine presented an illuminating description of those peculiar critters:

Rockhouns is queer animals. They was made to walk standin up strait, but when in action they doubles over, or crawls aroun on all fours. They all has excepsnal eyesite, but carries an extry eye in a pocket for lookin on all sides of every spessimens. Also, they drapes theirselves with sacks to carry home their plunder in, and sometimes can scarce stagger under its weight.

A mere whisper to rockhouns about availluble materiel is jest like a red flag to a bull. They chases it. It don't make no matter if it's rainin er freezin er so hot that nails melt out of boards; if rockhouns hears about somewhere they kin find new and diffrunt rocks, they travels there pronto! When on the scent they never stops till it gets too dark to see, and then they talks about what they've found till about daylight an time to take the trail agin.

So, if you are a rock-and-minerals enthusiast, make the most of it. Join with others in a local branch of one of the national societies. If no nearby branch exists, find out through your state university or natural history museum the addresses of local organizations. Practically every state has one or more of them. Then sign up and take part in the deliberations of the group, and in its field trips.

SOCIETIES—American Federation of Mineralogical Societies. Hdqrs.: 3366 N. E. Beakley Street, Portland 13, Ore. Periodical: *Gems and Minerals.*

Mineralogical Society of America. Hdqrs.: 12 Geological Museum, Cambridge 38, Mass. Periodical: *The American Mineralogist.*

In addition to meeting and exploring with like-minded individuals, the true rockhound spends much of his time in correspondence and in exchanging his own specimens for specimens from rock-and-mineral collectors in other states or other countries. If you are interested in this kind of pursuit, you will find a great number of addresses in a current issue of one of the periodicals that cater to hobbyists interested in geology.

PERIODICALS—*Rocks and Minerals.* Box 29, Peekskill, N. Y.

The Mineralogist. 329 S. E. 32 Avenue, Portland 15, Ore.

The Earth Science Digest. Box 1357, Chicago 90, Ill.

Lapidary Journal. Del Mar, Calif.

The Desert Magazine. Desert Press, Palm Desert, Calif. Of special interest to westerners.

If your interest in geology runs toward exploring the more exciting aspects of the subject rather than to the usual type of field trips and collecting, you may want to get into contact with mountain-climbing geologists who scale the highest peaks of our country, or with speleologists—"spelunkers" for short—who penetrate into the wonderland of the deepest underground caves.

SOCIETIES—American Alpine Club. Hdqrs.: 113 East 90th St., New York 28, N. Y. Periodical: *American Alpine Journal.*
National Speleological Society. Hdqrs.: 125 Tapawingo Road, S. W., Vienna, Va. Periodical: *NSS Monthly News.*

Geological Field Work

EQUIPMENT FOR FIELD WORK

CLOTHING—The usual kind of outdoor clothing is suitable for average geological field work, but if you intend to go in for more intensive work it will pay you to secure clothing that is tough enough to take it. Excellent is an outfit of sturdy, extra-heavy denim, as long as it does not fit too snugly—you have a lot of bending to do. For climbing, it is important that your clothing be without any kind of trim that may snag on projecting rocks.

Tip—Reinforce the knees of trousers with patches of soft leather to strengthen them for all the kneeling you will be doing.

For footwear, pick a pair of sturdy hiking shoes or climbing boots.

Much of your field work will be under the open sun, so protect your face with a broad-brimmed hat or a vizored cap. If you expect to be working under a protruding overhang, bring a hard fiber hat.

TRAVELING EQUIPMENT—Rock hunting will take you far afield, way off the beaten track. It is important for you to get there, and to return safely.

MAPS—Take along a map of the territory you expect to cover. Before setting out, study the map and familiarize yourself with the main features of the landscape so that you will have a general idea of the lay of the land— the direction of its ridges, the streams and main roads that traverse it. In addition to using the map for finding your way, use it for marking your route and the locations of your finds.

Excellent for your purpose are the topographic maps produced by the U. S. Geological Survey to the scale of

1:24,000 (1 inch on the map is equal to 2,000 feet in the field). Drop a postcard to Map Information Office, United States Geological Survey, Washington 25, D. C., and request a free *Topographic Map Index Circular* of the state in which you are traveling. From this index, decide on the maps you need, then order them, following the instructions for ordering given in the index circular.

COMPASS—When traveling cross-country you will need a compass for "orienting" your map—that is, turning the map so that north on the map points in the same direction as north in the field. You will also need a compass in case you want to determine the directions in which certain geological features run and for preparing a simple sketch map that will make it easy for you to return some other time to your "strike"—if any. A compass can also be used to determine whether a mineral is magnetic or not.

> *Tip*—For general cross-country traveling and for simple map sketching, pick a compass based on the "Silva" system, such as Pathfinder, Explorer, or Huntsman. The built-on base plates of these compasses function as protractor and simplify the job of determining your bearings.

FIRST-AID ITEMS—Bring along a pocket supply of a few adhesive bandages and a couple of ampules of some disinfectant. A sprained ankle is always a possibility while climbing, therefore include the materials for laying a sprained ankle bandage—a bandana or a Scout neckerchief.

SPECIAL EQUIPMENT—For mountain climbing, you may need climbing boots with crampons, mountain ax, pitons, spring hooks, and climbing rope.

REFERENCE—Kenneth A. Henderson. *Handbook of American Mountaineering*. Houghton Mifflin Co., Boston, Mass.

For cave exploring, you will need the same kind of special equipment as for mountain climbing and, in addition, flashlights (head type) and spare lights (candles and matches). As an added safety feature, most spelunking parties equip themselves with field telephones by which they keep in continuous contact with a post at the cave entrance.

REFERENCES—Franklin Folsom. *Exploring American Caves*. Crown Publishers.
   Charles E. Mohr and Howard N. Sloane, eds. *Celebrated American Caves*. Rutgers University Press, New Brunswick, N. J.

STUDY AND COLLECTING EQUIPMENT—In the beginning of your geological pursuits you can very well get along with an ordinary hammer, a cold chisel, a couple of newspapers, and a knapsack. When you have decided that rock hunting is the hobby for you, you will probably want to secure better equipment.

HAMMERS—The favorite geology hammer or "mineral hammer" weighs about 1½ pounds. It comes in two different shapes. In both, one end of the head is square and flat; but in one, the opposite end is chisel-shaped, while in the other the opposite end terminates in a sharp pick point. The chisel-shaped hammer is particularly suited for splitting stratified rocks (limestones, shales, etc.). The pick-pointed hammer is excellent for digging out minerals and for loosening fossils. Many rock hunters carry both.

> *Tip*—For more extensive work, a regular pick, a chisel-pointed steel bar ("moil"), a sledge hammer, and a spade may be called for. They are heavy, so watch your transportation problem.

CHISELS—A $\frac{7}{16} \times \frac{1}{2}$-inch and a $\frac{5}{8} \times \frac{3}{4}$-inch cold chisel are valuable in cases where more exact chipping is necessary than can be done with the edge of the mineral hammer, or in places, such as cavities, where the hammer will not reach.

POCKET KNIFE—An ordinary pocket knife will be found helpful for digging crystals or small fossils out of soft rocks.

GLOVES—If your hands are tender-skinned, protect

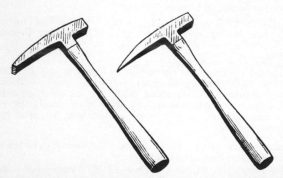

"Mineral hammers" come in two shapes. One has a chisel-shaped head; the other is pick-pointed. Many geologists use both.

them with a pair of cheap cotton gloves when handling rock specimens.

GOGGLES—If your work involves much pounding or chipping with the hammer, it is advisable to protect your eyes with a pair of goggles.

LABELING MATERIAL—Use adhesive tape or masking tape for marking the specimens you collect.

> *Tip*—Cut ½-inch tape in as many ¾-inch pieces as you expect to need. Stick them to a piece of wax paper or plastic or discarded film for easy carrying. Number them with India ink.

NOTEBOOK—Carry a pocket-size notebook for taking general notes of the trip as well as detailed notes on the specimens collected, numbering the notes to coincide with the numbered labels you stick on the specimens.

MAGNIFIER—One of the magnifiers described on page 167 with magnifications from about 5× to 10× will make it possible for you to see the individual mineral crystals of which many rocks consist.

FIELD BOOK—For tentative identification in the field of rocks and minerals which you come upon, you will probably want to bring along a suitable field book.

BOOKS FOR IDENTIFICATION—Frederic B. Loomis. *Field Book of Common Rocks and Minerals.* G. P. Putnam's Sons.

F. H. Pough. *Field Guide to Rocks and Minerals.* Houghton Mifflin, Boston, Mass.

D. K. Fritzen. *The Rock-Hunter's Field Manual.* Harper & Brothers.

Richard M. Pearl. *How to Know the Minerals and Rocks.* McGraw-Hill Book Co.

Herbert S. Zim and Paul R. Shaffer. *Rocks and Minerals.* Golden Press.

WRAPPING MATERIALS—Bring old newspapers for wrapping rock specimens, paper toweling or cleansing tissue for minerals, cotton for protecting crystals.

> *Tip*—Some rock collectors place their rock specimens in individual paper bags (No. 1) after wrapping and put all rocks found in a single locality in a larger bag (No. 5).

FIELD BAG—For carrying home your loot, take a sturdy canvas musette bag, preferably divided into several compartments, with a strong shoulder strap; or a stout knapsack. You should be able to pick up one at a nearby army surplus store or in the Boy Scout or Girl Scout section of a local department store.

Tip—Many collectors pack a cigar box in their field bag for the safe carrying of rocks that have a tendency to crumble or rocks with loosely imbedded crystals. A molded wood pulp egg box, with separate compartments, is particularly good for safeguarding delicate minerals. Small plastic boxes or glass vials may be needed for sediments, soils, and crystals.

SPECIALIZED EQUIPMENT—The days of the old-time prospector with his burro are long past. Modern prospecting—exploring for commercially valuable deposits of rocks and minerals—has become a highly specialized part of economic geology. Only a couple of items used by professional prospectors are of interest to amateurs.

ULTRA-VIOLET LAMP—A portable ultra-violet lamp (see page 342) will permit you to locate fluorescent minerals in a rock pile, but only in the blackness of a dark night.

GEIGER AND SCINTILLATION COUNTERS—These instruments—ranging in price from $100 to $1,000 and more—are indispensable to the geologist or prospector specializing in locating radioactive minerals—minerals containing uranium and thorium.

REFERENCES—Max W. Von Bernewitz. *Handbook for Prospectors.* McGraw-Hill Book Co.

H. C. Dake. *Popular Prospecting.* J. D. Simpson & Co., West 19-27th Ave., Spokane 41, Wash.

A. W. Knoerr and G. P. Lutjen. *Prospecting for Atomic Minerals.* McGraw-Hill Book Co.

A portable ultra-violet lamp makes it possible for you to determine if a rock pile contains fluorescent minerals.

U. S. Atomic Energy Commission and U. S. Geological Survey. *Prospecting for Uranium.* For sale by Superintendent of Documents, U. S. Government Printing Office, Washington 25, D. C., for 30 cents.

Finding Rocks and Minerals

WHERE?—Where to start? Right outside your door if you live in the country; down the street at the nearest building excavation or in the nearest park if you live in town. Everywhere you go, geological formations lie before you.

Whether you are interested in the field of geology as a whole or in collecting geological specimens, start off by getting a thorough understanding of your own immediate vicinity—how its hills and valleys, its mountains or plains, its bedrock and its soils came into being. Such an understanding will help you immeasurably to know what outcrops may occur and where you have your best chance of finding specimens of certain rocks and minerals or fossils.

When you know your own locality and your own state, your eyes will have a keener perception of the geological wonders of our country's variegated surface and its hidden underground treasures. You will thrill to the sight of Mount Washington rising in the mist and to the Half Dome of Yosemite silhouetted against a blue sky. You will marvel at the incredible immensity of the Carlsbad Caverns in New Mexico and at the puzzling pinnacle of the Devil's Tower in South Dakota, at the seemingly bottomless gully called the Grand Canyon and at the hot springs of Yellowstone. You will ponder the forces that shaped the granite coast of Maine and the sandstone caves of southern California, the delta of the ever-flowing Mississippi and the dried-up ocean bed that is now the salt flats of Utah. And you will marvel at the rich mineral wealth of our country—from its soft, humus-laden soil to its massive building blocks, from its luster-less metal ores to its brilliant gem stones, from its coal deposits to its reservoirs of petroleum (literally "rock oil").

REFERENCES—*Geologic Map of the United States.* 4 sheets, each 27×47 inches, showing more than 160 rock units, distinguished by patterns printed in 23 colors. $2.50 from U. S. Geological Survey, Washington 25, D. C. *Geological Maps* of your state. Write to your state geological survey department, at your state capital, for lists of geological folios and reports.

Rock sources—Wherever you travel through the countryside there will be rocks aplenty. Some of them may form the very surface on which you walk, others may be outcrops laid bare by erosion or by the work of man. "Layered" *sedimentary* rocks are distributed throughout America. The heat-formed *igneous* rocks and the "changed" *metamorphic* rocks crop out mostly in mountain territory—you will have no luck searching for them in the Mississippi valley or in the Great Plains regions. In the northern section of our country, you will come upon boulders and rock fragments and sediment which were not part of the native ground but were carried in by glaciers and deposited during the glacial age.

You can start your study and collecting practically anywhere. But for the greatest yield, look particularly in places such as these:

Raw CUTS of completed roads or roads under construction.

EXCAVATIONS for new buildings, highways, railroads, bridges; tunnel construction; harbor deepening.

Waste heaps of broken rocks around QUARRIES; slag dumps around MINES.

WARNING—Never enter quarries or mines without explicit permission of those in charge. There may be danger of rock slides, blastings, or unexploded charges. Quarry and mine foremen are often exceedingly helpful to rockhounds; they may even have on hand especially interesting samples which they themselves have collected.

WELL CUTTINGS and DRILLINGS from water wells and oil wells.

Eroded HILLSIDES, RIVER BANKS and GORGES, CANYONS and "BADLANDS."

BEDS of stony streams, whether water-filled or dry.

Exposed CLIFFS and the debris slopes below them—TALUS SLIDES.

OUTCROP LEDGES on cliffs, in hillside pastures.

In parts of the country once covered by glacier, investigate GRAVEL PITS, GLACIAL TILL, LOOSE BOULDERS, edge-of-glacier MORAINES.

MINERAL SOURCES—Where you find rocks you find minerals—that's what the rocks are made of. The listing above of places for finding rocks holds true, then, for minerals as well. But when it comes to discovering good specimens rather than tiny crystals and poor fragments, you need to keep your eyes peeled for special conditions or special formations:

CRACKS and CAVITIES—"vugs"—in granite and trap rock, in lavas and limestone.

CONTACT LINES between two kinds of igneous or metamorphic rocks, or between an intrusion of igneous rock into sedimentary rock.

PEGMATITE DIKES—the coarsely crystalline veins that cut the mountain face in light bands with almost parallel sides.

GRAVEL and SAND in stream beds, draws and gullies, and on ocean beaches.

Deposits in CAVES and around HOT SPRINGS in limestone districts.

Odd-looking pebbles or rocks, loose or in residual clay, may prove to be mineral-lined GEODES, or minèral-filled AMYGDULES, or agate NODULES; break them open.

The temporary lakes—called PLAYA—of some of our southwestern states may yield water-soluble minerals—such as halite (common salt) and borax—on going dry.

In desert territory, look for "FLOATS," minerals found lying loose, eroded out of the ground by wind action. Where you find floats, you may hit upon still better specimens by digging. Or you may come upon the abandoned dumps of old-time prospectors.

REFERENCES—Minerals, by Zim and Cooper (page 312), contains a twenty-page listing of important localities in the United States and Canada.

Publications of the Geological Survey (free on application to Geological Survey, Washington 25, D. C., or Denver Federal Center, Denver, Colo.) contains lists of books, pamphlets and circulars describing rock and mineral locations.

FOSSIL SOURCES—Probably the smartest procedure for finding fossils is to eliminate first the places where you will NOT find them: in igneous rocks. Fossils are the petrified remains of plant and animal life of ages past, and it is obvious that they could never have survived the heat of the molten magmas and lavas that formed the igneous rocks. You need to search for them in sedimentary rocks.

LIMESTONE and SHALE DEPOSITS, in natural outcrops or exposed in road cuts, quarries, excavations, mines, tunnels, would be your prime choices for investigation. The finer the grain of limestone or shale, the more successful you will probably be; but don't expect to find fossils in all limestone or shale.

Fine-grained SANDSTONE DEPOSITS may contain fossils; coarse sandstone seldom does—yours may be the exception, though, so better examine anyway.

VOLCANIC TUFA—rock formed from the ashes of volcanic eruptions—sometimes contains fossils.

Around COAL MINES, check the slate and shale debris

around the breakers. Also look for "coal balls"—hard masses occurring in coal seams.

Occasionally, fragments of fossilized bones are found in debris at the foot of CLIFFS of sedimentary rock, in gorges, badlands, canyons. They may lead to the discovery of the layer in the cliff above where the remaining parts are deposited.

Working in shale, you may come upon CONCRETIONS—rounded masses, harder than the surrounding shale—in which fossils may be imbedded.

Fields of PETRIFIED FORESTS in the West, not under federal, state or local protection, will yield silicified or opalized wood.

Fossil sharks' teeth are found in great numbers in PHOSPHATE BEDS in our southern states and along the SEA SHORE in certain sections of the country.

Preserved footprints of prehistoric animals come to light from time to time, such as in the RED SANDSTONE DEPOSITS of New England.

REFERENCE—Richard Cassanova. *Illustrated Guide to Fossil Collecting.* Naturegraph Co., San Martin, Calif.

SOCIETY—Paleontological Society. Hdqrs.: Harvard University, Cambridge 38, Mass. Periodical: *Journal of Paleontology.*

METEORITES—On one of your field trips you may accidentally stumble upon a meteorite—the unburned or unevaporated remains of a meteor or "shooting star" from outer space. Meteorites are more commonly found in desert or plains territory than anywhere else—not because more of them fall there, but simply because they are more conspicuous there, and therefore more easily spotted than in mountainous or wooded areas.

SOCIETY—Meteoritical Society. Hdqrs.: Department of Astronomy, University of Southern California, Los Angeles 7, Calif.

WHEN?—TIME OF YEAR—Any season is geology season —the landforms are there to study, the hills and mountains and plains. As far as collecting is concerned, rock-hounds are busy the year round, with the possible exception of collectors in the northern parts of the country in the dead of winter when snow covers their hunting grounds.

TIME OF DAY—The proper light conditions play an important part in finding rocks and minerals. A cliff wall with a western exposure would be in deep shade in the forenoon but lighted by the sun in the afternoon—so, obviously, the afternoon is your choice for studying it. Horizontal ledges on a south-facing bluff cast readily seen shadows when the sun is at zenith, but vertical fissures will show up much more clearly in the slanting rays of the sun in early morning or late evening. Front-lighted permatite dikes may look of little promise, while the same dikes side-lighted may reveal a wealth of worth-while specimens. The same holds true for floats on desert plains—they are most easily found by the shadows they cast in morning and evening.

If your hobby is the collecting of fluorescent minerals, you may want to go hunting for them at night, with a portable ultra-violet-ray lamp as a main part of your equipment.

A period of clear weather immediately following a heavy rain is particularly propitious for rock hunters. The rain will have washed exposed surfaces free of dust, making it much easier to locate good specimens. Also, a heavy rain may have exposed a new batch of minerals from the sand or clay in which they were embedded on hillsides or in stream banks.

FIELD OBSERVATIONS

While the United States Geological Survey and your state geologist have probably made a general study of the geology of the territory in which you do your field work, there is still much detail work to be done. The findings of amateur geologists may help toward a clearer understanding of the landscape, and to a more exact listing of local rocks, minerals and fossils. Many valuable museum finds have been made by amateurs.

LAND FORMS—Find out by personal investigation the formations of the bedrock of your territory, and the mantle-rock that covers it. With this knowledge you have the basis for making conclusions on the underlying formations, and for determining what rocks and minerals you are likely to find, and whether fossils are present.

ROCK FORMATIONS—Make a listing of the deposits you investigate, with notes of their location, types of rocks, detail sketches of bedding, layers, folds, faults, joints, dikes, and so on.

OUTCROPS—Map the main rock outcrops of your area by "walking the outcrop" to determine the direction of each "strike"—the direction in which the outcrop extends from one edge to the other—and measure its width; and to determine the amount of the "dip"—the angle expressed in degrees at which the outcrop rises from the ground. You can find the directions of the strike with a

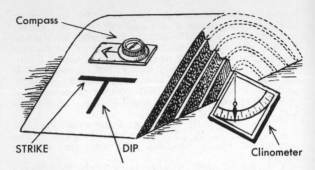

The "strike" (direction of an outcrop) is determined by a compass; the "dip" (angle at which outcrop rises), with a clinometer.

compass and the angle of the dip with a clinometer—from *klino,* to incline, *metron,* measure.

> *Tip*—You can make a simple clinometer from a piece of thin wood, 4×4 inches, a five-and-ten-cent-store protractor, a small nail, a thin string, and a small lead sinker with eye. From the protractor, cut a quarter circle marked from 0 to 90 degrees, and tack it to the board in such a way that the zero is at the bottom edge. Hammer the small nail into the board at the center of the protractor circle, and suspend the sinker (whittled into a small plumb bob) in the string from this nail as a pointer. When measuring, place bottom edge of clinometer on the dip, and read the degrees where the pointer indicates it to be.

MINERAL DEPOSITS—Visit the location of the more important minerals of your state to ascertain the conditions under which they are found, what varieties occur together, and their relative abundance.

WEATHERING—Study the effects of weathering on the surface of rocks found in your region.

AGE OF SEDIMENTS—Locate deposits of shale and slate, and attempt to determine their age from the fossils found in them.

SOIL PROFILES—Measure the depth of each type of soil as it appears in a raw road cut, or in a hole dug in the ground—from the top layer of darker-colored loam, through the layers below it of lighter-colored subsoil, for a distance of a couple of feet, or until you strike bedrock.

WELL LOGS—In oil regions, you may have a chance to

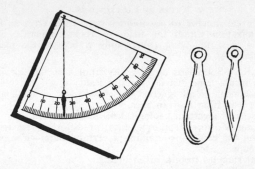

A simple clinometer may be made from an inexpensive protractor, a piece of wood, and a lead sinker whittled into a plumb bob.

join the "mud smellers"—the geologists who investigate the core and sludge from rotary drills, or the cuttings from churn drills, and interpret the information gained. In this investigation, it is particularly important to know from what depth the material is brought to the surface, the type of material, the character of it, the depth at which the material changes from one type to another.

Geological Collections

The collecting of rocks and minerals and fossils is about the least expensive hobby you can think of. To start with, your equipment may be only an old hammer and an old chisel, and your storage cabinets a few cigar boxes. It is only when you get deeper and still deeper into the subject that you may decide to secure more adequate collecting equipment and better facilities for storing and displaying your specimens.

By then, you will also have to make up your mind in what direction your collection should go—before the ever-growing piles of rocks and minerals drive your family from house and home.

A beginning collector is apt to pick whatever comes his way or whatever catches his fancy. But he soon becomes critical and starts to choose perfect specimens only. At the same time, he realizes that he cannot hope to cover the whole field of geological collecting, and concentrates on those rocks and minerals that fit into the type of collection he visualizes for himself.

BOOK ON COLLECTING—William B. Sanborn. *Crystal and Mineral Collecting.* Lane Book Company, Menlo Park, Calif.

Types of Collections

A great number of possibilities open themselves up for specialization within the fields of rocks, minerals, and fossils. The following covers only a few of the many possibilities.

ROCKS—Specimens of all rocks from a certain locality —township, mine district, county, state.

Specimens of all igneous *or* sedimentary *or* metamorphic rocks from a given area.

Rocks of a certain geological formation or era.

Samples of ores from one state; or different ores from around the country containing a certain metal—iron, silver, copper, etc.

Soil samples from a given area.

Representative rocks, personally collected, from states and foreign countries visited.

MINERALS—Specimens of all minerals from a certain locality—township, mine district, county, state.

Minerals of one certain distinguishing characteristic—such as color, luster, hardness, fluorescence, etc.

REFERENCE—Fritzen's *The Rock-Hunter's Field Manual* (see page 317) has the minerals arranged according to color: black, blue, brown, colorless, gray, green, purple, red, white, yellow.

Specimens to show all the main crystal systems; or minerals representing one single crystal system—cubes, tetragons, hexagons, etc.

Minerals representing all the groups, according to chemical composition, of Dana's system of classification; or minerals of one single chemical group—sulphides, oxides, carbonates, silicates, etc.

REFERENCES—Pough's *Field Guide to Rocks and Minerals* has the minerals arranged according to Dana's system.

Note—A complete "Dana" collection is hardly within the reach of the amateur collector—it would involve a specimen of each of the more than 4,000 minerals described in the three-volume standard work on minerals: James D. Dana's *System of Mineralogy,* revised by Charles Palache, Harry Berman, and Clifford Frondel. John Wiley and Sons.

Specimens of the several forms in which a single mineral may be found—various forms of calcite, for instance, or quartz, garnet, barite, etc.

Minerals containing a certain metal—calcium, zinc, manganese, etc.

Gem stone minerals.

FOSSILS—Specimens of all fossils from a certain locality—township, county, state.

Collection of specimens of fossilized plants *or* invertebrates *or* vertebrates from a given area.

Fossils representing the main geological eras, or fossils from one single era—Pre-Cambrian, Paleozoic, Mesozoic, Cenozoic; or from one single period within an era—Cambrian, Silurian, Devonian, etc.

Collecting Techniques

The methods of collecting various types of geological specimens vary somewhat, calling for an ever-increasing amount of care in the field preparation.

ROCK SPECIMENS—Find a place on the rock surface (outcrop) where the texture of the fresh, unweathered rock appears characteristically and to best advantage. Then break loose, with hammer and chisel, a specimen that shows, in the case of igneous rock (granite, basalt), the alignment of the grain; in the case of sedimentary rock (sandstone, limestone), the layering; in the case of metamorphic rock (slate, marble), the banding or folding. Trim the specimen down roughly to the standard size which you have set for your collection (see page 332).

> *Tip*—Expert collectors do little field trimming, preferring to do the job at home. For amateurs it may be advisable to do the trimming on the spot. If you spoil one specimen, there are others available.

Next stick a number marker on the specimen—a numbered strip of adhesive tape or masking tape (see page 317). Immediately, open your notebook and write down

Use newspaper sheet for wrapping a rock. Fold paper up from bottom, then fold it over from sides, finally roll rock up in paper.

details pertaining to the specimen : 1. its number ; 2. name —if you know it ; 3. exact location where found so that you might be able to return to the same spot again ; 4. structural feature of the rock mass of which the rock is a sample and of other types of rock associated with it ; 5. date of collection.

Finally, wrap the rock specimen in a half section or quarter section of a newspaper sheet to prevent it from getting damaged rubbing against other specimens. Put the package in your knapsack for transportation home.

If you are collecting sediments, sands or soils, newspaper wrapping is unsuitable. Instead use small screwcap jars. Stick number marker on outside of jar.

MINERALS—Exert great care in collecting and transporting minerals to prevent them from being scratched or broken.

In the case of a float, stick a number marker on it as for a rock specimen (see above). Then wrap it in tissue and place it in a box (cigar box or egg box) in your knapsack.

When it comes to a mineral attached to a rock formation, do not attempt to knock the mineral itself off with a hammer ; instead, use chisel and hammer at a safe distance around the base of the mineral and remove a piece of the rock to which it is fastened—the "matrix." Refrain from any further trimming in the field. Stick a number marker on the specimen and wrap it carefully.

Especially fragile minerals should be placed in cotton —or in moss or grass if you didn't bring cotton—before they are wrapped in tissue. Tiny crystals are better transported in small vials, stoppered with cotton to prevent them from shaking around and breaking.

FOSSILS—Where fossils appear in fairly soft rock, they may be exposed by splitting open the layers between which they lie with chisel or wedges and hammer. Be certain to keep both of the counterparts—one may contain the fossil itself, the other bear an impression of it. Don't skimp on size, even in the case of small fossils. A slab showing how such fossils as trilobites and ammonites lay on the ocean floor is more valuable than a single perfect specimen.

If your fossil occurs in a hard rock substance, don't attempt to chisel out the fossil ; instead, cut well beyond the outline of the fossil so that there will be no danger of damaging it, and leave the main job of trimming to be done at home.

As in the case of rocks and minerals, stick a number marker on each fossil specimen and make notes of all pertinent information, including details about the strata between which it is found.

FOSSIL SKELETONS—Of all geological specimens, fossil bones require the greatest care in their collection. As a matter of fact, if you should ever have the luck of hitting upon the skeleton of a prehistoric animal you may do a great service to science if, instead of attempting to dig it out yourself, you report your find to the nearest museum and let its trained paleontologists do the job of recovering it.

ADDING TO YOUR COLLECTION

Few rockhounds are content with just the geological specimens they find themselves. Sooner or later, they want to complement their collection with rocks and minerals from other states or countries around the world. The most interesting way of doing this is by personal bartering with local collectors or by swapping through correspondence with rockhounds at home or abroad (see page 313).

Where personal contacts or correspondence are not feasible, the solution to the problem is by purchase through a reputable dealer in rocks and minerals.

REFERENCE—*Rockhound Buyers Guide,* published annually by *Lapidary Journal,* Del Mar, Calif., contains an extensive listing of dealers. Addresses may also be found in the magazines listed on page 313.

MINERAL DEALERS—Ward's Natural Science Establishment Inc., P. O. Box 1712, Rochester 3, N. Y.
Schortmann's, 6 McKinley Avenue, Easthampton, Mass.
Odoms, Star Route A, Box 32C, Austin, Tex.
W. H. Wright, The Prospector's Shop, 201 W. San Francisco St., Santa Fe, N. M.
Gritzner's, Mesa 7, Ariz.
J. M. Grieger, 1633 East Walnut St., Pasadena, Calif.
Minerals Unlimited, 1724 University Avenue, Berkeley 3, Calif.
Ward's of California, P. O. Box 1749, Monterey, Calif.

IDENTIFYING YOUR SPECIMENS

Before preparing your specimens for storage or display, you want to have them correctly identified. In the beginning, seek the help and advise of some local geologist or a fellow rockhound. Then, as you become more proficient, you will be able to do your own identifying.

EQUIPMENT FOR IDENTIFICATION—For complete identification of your specimens, you will turn to books, sample collections, and various types of testing equipment.

BOOKS—Books are available on all phases of geology. For general identification, almost any of the field books on rocks and minerals, listed on page 317, will suffice. For exact identification, you may require a more technical book that describes the various physical and chemical tests that will definitely establish the identity of a rock or mineral specimen.

BOOKS FOR LABORATORY IDENTIFICATION—Pough's *Field Guide to Rocks and Minerals* (see page 317) explains the tests for identifying most American rocks and minerals.

   E. S. Dana and C. S. Hurlbut. *Manual of Mineralogy.* Also *Minerals and How to Study Them.* John Wiley and Sons.

SAMPLE COLLECTIONS—Book descriptions and illustrations are not always sufficient for identifying a rock or mineral. A better method consists of comparing your specimen with the specimens in a fairly large and correctly labeled study collection. You will probably be welcome to use such a collection at your nearest university or natural history museum, but you may prefer to have your own. Inexpensive student reference collections with small specimens of common rocks and minerals are available through some of the larger rock and mineral dealers.

REFERENCE COLLECTIONS—Send for catalog to the nearest of these dealers (addresses on page 329): Ward's (N. Y.); Schortman's (Mass.); Shipley's (Colo.); W. H. Wright (N. Mex.); Minerals Unlimited (Calif.).

TESTING EQUIPMENT—For testing the physical and chemical properties of geological specimens, you may need some of the equipment described in the following, depending on how deeply you intend to pursue the subject.

HARDNESS—The hardness of a mineral is one of the most important points of identification. The hardness is determined by comparing the mineral with the minerals of Mohs scale (named for the German mineralogist, Friedrich Mohs):

10 Diamond	6 Feldspar	3 Calcite
9 Corundum	5 Apatite	2 Gypsum
8 Topaz	4 Fluorite	1 Talc
7 Quartz		

According to this scale, a mineral of a certain number will scratch a mineral that has a lower number, and will,

A streak plate of unglazed porcelain is used to determine the color of the powder mark a mineral leaves on it.

in turn, be scratched by a mineral with a higher number. A mineral that scratches fluorite (hardness 4) but is itself scratched by apatite (hardness 5) has a hardness somewhere around 4.5.

Mineral supply houses carry inexpensive collections of sample hardness minerals (generally exclusive of diamond—for obvious reasons). They also have available so-called "hardness points," consisting of small mineral points of hardnesses 5 to 10, mounted in the ends of short brass rods.

> *Tip*—An easy and costless test for hardness can be done with fingernail, hardness 2.3; copper penny, 3; knife blade, 5.5; piece of glass, 6.5. A mineral that scratches your knife blade, for instance, but is itself scratched by glass will have a hardness of approximately 6.

STREAK—The color of a mineral's "streak"—the powder mark it leaves when a corner of it is rubbed against an abrasive surface—is another important means of identification. The color of the streak of a mineral will often be found to differ from that of the mineral's surface. Black limonite, for instance, makes a brown to yellow streak, while metallic-yellow pyrite makes a black streak.

"Streak plates" for such testing are made of unglazed porcelain. They are usually hexagonal, 2½ inches wide and ¼ inch thick. They are available by the half dozen and dozen from mineral supply houses.

> *Tip*—The unglazed back of a bathroom tile or the edge of a broken china plate may be used to check the streak of a mineral.

MAGNETISM—A small horseshoe or bar magnet will help to identify such minerals as magnetite and pyrrhotite. They are magnetic and are therefore attracted to the magnet. A number of other minerals are attracted to a magnet after being heated.

DENSITY—Some rocks are heavy to the feel, others comparatively light. It is a matter of their density or specific gravity—the weight of the rock in relation to the weight of the same volume of water. To determine the density of a rock, a balance is used on which the rock can be weighed first in the air, then submerged in water. For most amateur purposes, an estimate is enough: very heavy, medium heavy, light, very light.

FLUORESCENCE—The ability of a rock or mineral to glow in the dark when exposed to "black" light can be determined through the use of a lamp giving off ultraviolet rays. See page 342.

RADIOACTIVITY—The radiation of radioactive minerals can be tested with a Geiger or scintillation counter. See page 318.

REACTION TO HEAT—Some minerals can be made to fuse (melt) in the heat from a match flame, others when heated in a hot gas flame. The metal in the chemical composition of certain minerals colors an almost colorless flame with a characteristic color and also colors distinctively a small bead of melted borax or of salt of phosphorus. For such tests you will need a Bunsen burner or a pocket blowtorch, a blowpipe, charcoal blocks, a nichrome or platinum wire mounted in a glass rod, borax and salt of phosphorus (sodium ammonium phosphate).

CHEMICAL REACTIONS—Dilute hydrochloric acid is commonly used for testing rocks and minerals; it causes fizzing of carbon dioxide bubbles when dropped on limestone, chalk, marble, and other mineral carbonates. Numerous other chemicals are used in the testing of rocks and minerals. The methods are described in advanced books on mineralogy; few of them are within the scope of the amateur geologist.

PREPARING YOUR SPECIMENS

When a specimen has been identified, you prepare it for inclusion in your collection, by trimming it to final size, marking it and cataloging it.

TRIMMING—ROCKS—The more uniform the size of your rock specimens, the easier it is to compare their physical features and the more attractive your collection. Decide on a standard size and stick to it. The size you pick will be determined by the amount of storage space you have available. Traditionally, rock specimens are cut

Most collectors like to trim their rock specimens into uniform size and to cut them into pillow-like shape.

to a thickness of about 1 inch and trimmed to a rectangular pillow shape, about 3 inches wide, 4 inches long—so-called "hand specimens." You may decide to follow the same dimensions or to make your specimens smaller —2×3 inches, for example.

Cut your specimen to thickness first, then shape it to an even-edged rectangular form. The square end of the head of your geological hammer is particularly suited for trimming the harder rocks, the chisel-edged end for the softer kinds. Hold the piece in one hand and strike sudden, well-planned blows along the edge nearest to you. A number of light taps will usually do the job. When the specimen has become rectangular, break off chips from top and bottom edges to make it pillow-shaped. Trim the back side—the least attractive side—in such a way that the specimen will lie flat without wobbling.

Tip—Protect the palm of the hand in which you hold the rock with a glove or a piece of soft leather.

Tip—A pair of pliers may be found helpful in the final shaping of a specimen.

After trimming, wash the rock with detergent and water, using a hand scrubbing brush if necessary. Then rinse and dry.

Tip—Persistent rust stains on a rock can usually be removed by leaving the rock for a few hours in a solution of oxalic acid in water—3 ounces to 1 quart. Rinse thoroughly in several sets of water. Dry.

MINERALS—Wash your minerals free of adhering dust, soil, or clay with detergent and water. Rinse. Dry. Then select for your collection the specimens that have the best shape, the most perfect crystal form, brilliancy, transparency, luster.

CAUTION—Do not use water for cleaning water-soluble minerals (such as halite, sylvite, thenardite, epsomite, borax, and a few others) and on minerals that are damaged by water (such as pyrite, marcasite, and other iron-containing minerals). Instead, use alcohol or cleaning fluid.

Loose crystals need no further preparation. In cases where crystals are attached to a piece of rock ("matrix"), you may want to trim this down to a suitable size. Do it with extreme care so that you do not detach the crystals—mineral crystals attached to a matrix are far more valuable than loose crystals.

Tip—An old dental scraping tool is excellent for cleaning minerals from adhering rock.

GEM MINERALS—Gem preparation is an art in itself. Numerous collectors attracted to this specialized branch of mineral collecting—*lapidary*—have become expert "lapidarists," turning their gem minerals into true gems.

Traditionally, such minerals as agate, bloodstone, jade, jasper, and turquoise are classified as ornamental rocks; amethyst, aquamarine, kunzite, topaz, and tourmaline are semi-precious stones; emerald, ruby, sapphire, and diamond are precious stones.

Note—The U. S. Bureau of Internal Revenue classifies minerals of a hardness of 6 or more on Mohs scale as semi-precious and precious stones, subject to excise tax, on purchase, of 10 per cent, unless unsuitable for cutting and polishing into gems.

If you decide to take up lapidary as a hobby, you will need special lapidary equipment to saw, grind or lap, sand, polish and buff your stones.

LAPIDARY EQUIPMENT—Ward's Natural Science Establishment, Rochester 3, N. Y.

East Coast Mineral Corp., 440 Columbus Avenue, New York 24, N. Y.

Rock-a-Teer Enterprises, 4705 W. Edison Road, South Bend 19, Ind.

Lapidary Equipment Co., 1545 W. 49th Street, Seattle 7, Wash.

Get the help of other lapidarists in your locality and learn by doing, by following the instructions in a lapidary manual.

REFERENCES—G. F. Herbert Smith. *Gemstones*. Pitman Publishing Corporation.

Richard T. Liddecoat, Jr. *Handbook of Gemstone*

Identification. Gemological Institute of America, Los Angeles, Calif.

J. D. Willems. *Gem Cutting.* Charles A. Bennett Co., 237 N. Monroe St., Peoria 3, Ill.

Lelande Quick and Hugh Leiper. *Gemcraft: How to Cut and Polish Gemstones.* Chilton Co., 56th and Chestnut Sts., Philadelphia 29, Penn.

PERIODICALS—*Lapidary Journal.* Del Mar, Calif.
Gems and Minerals. Palmdale, Calif.

SOCIETIES—Gemological Institute of America, 11940 San Vincente Blvd., Los Angeles 49, Calif. Periodical: *Gems and Gemology.*

FOSSILS—Obviously, no standard size can be set for trimming fossil specimens. Each of them should be trimmed to such a size that the fossil will show to best advantage.

In trimming fossils, it is important to prop up the rock matrix in which the fossil is imbedded, to prevent the matrix from shifting during the delicate trimming process. For this, a sand bag comes in handy. Fill a small bag of some strong material about three quarters with soft sand, then tie up or sew up the top. Lay your sand bag flat on the table. Set the rock matrix with the fossil firmly on it with the side to be trimmed to the top. Per-

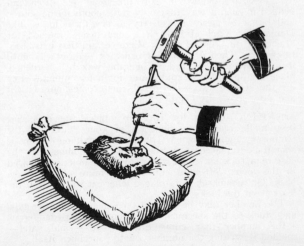

When freeing a fossil from the rock matrix in which it is embedded, prop up the matrix firmly on a sand bag.

336   FIELD BOOK OF NATURE ACTIVITIES

form coarse trimming with chisel and hammer, more intricate trimming and cleaning with an awl.

Tip—If there is little contrast between the fossil and the matrix, you may want to tint the surrounding rock with a water- or alcohol-soluble color, to make the fossil more discernible.

PLASTER CASTS—In many cases, plants and animals have left impressions in rocks and have themselves disappeared. To find out how they looked, make a plaster cast of the impressions. Brush the rock with a thin layer of mineral oil, then make a cast in the same manner in which a positive cast of an animal track is made (page 135).

PLASTER MOUNTING—Fragments of a broken fossil may be mounted in plaster. Cut a piece of plywood to the size of the mount you want to make, then nail a ridge around the edge of it. The ridge should be about as high as the thickest piece of the fossil is thick. Smear the inside of the form with vaseline, then fill it half full of a plaster-of-Paris-and-water mixture (see page 136). When partly set, arrange the fossil sections in the plaster, then pour in more plaster if desired. Smooth the surface before the plaster has hardened completely. When completely set, remove from the form and let dry.

"TURNING"—Shells in soft limestone are often imbedded in such a way that only the smooth inside shows, and break to pieces if you try to pry them loose. The Danish Dr. Carl Malling has suggested a method for "turning" this kind of fossil. Make certain that it is absolutely dry. Then drip into it ordinary sealing wax until it is completely covered. When the wax has hardened, place the specimen in cold water for a few minutes. Pry off the sealing wax—the fossil shell comes out with it and now shows its "right" side.

MARKING—When the rock or mineral specimen has been made ready for inclusion in your collection, the temporary number which you placed on it on finding it should be replaced with its permanent number. In the case of a rock specimen, the number is sometimes placed in the lower left-hand corner, but more often on the back. On a mineral, it is placed where it will detract the least from the looks.

The number may be written on paper or adhesive tape and stuck to the specimen. But this method is dangerous —the number may come off. A better—and safer— method is writing the number on the specimen itself.

Using white, quick-drying enamel, paint a small rectangular or oval spot about $\frac{1}{4} \times \frac{3}{8}$ inch, at the proper location. When completely dry, write on this marking spot, with India ink, the number you have given the specimen in your collection. Let dry. Then cover the India-ink number with clear nail polish to protect it.

Tip—For the sake of simplicity and uniformity, you may want to make a stencil of your standard-size marking spot and use this, with a stencil brush, when marking your specimens.

CATALOGING—For each numbered specimen, prepare a file card, 3×5 inches, or a page of a loose-leaf notebook, with all the pertinent information.

Minimum information should contain the following items (compare with list on page 328) : 1. number of the specimen in your collection; 2. name of the specimen; 3. topographic location where found; 4. geological environment and associations; 5. date collected; 6. source if obtained by barter or purchase; 7. date received—purchase price, if any.

To add to the interest of yourself and others, you may further wish to include some of the following information, extracted from a book on rocks and minerals: 8. number in Dana system of mineralogy; 9. distinguishing characteristics; 10. physical properties; 11. chemical composition; 12. interesting facts: industrial uses, etc.

STORING YOUR SPECIMENS

Store your specimens so that they are protected from damage and dust, and so that they can be readily studied. This means keeping them in separate compartments in suitable containers.

TEMPORARY STORAGE—Cigar boxes may be used for temporary storage of the small collection. Divide the box into compartments by notched strips of heavy cardboard, pieces of a dismantled cigar box, or ⅛-inch plywood.

PERMANENT STORAGE—ROCKS—The best way of storing your rock specimens permanently is in individual cardboard trays of suitable size, arranged in shallow drawers of the proper depth, fitted in some kind of cabinet. The complete facilities for this type of storage are available from mineral supply houses. They are expensive, so you may prefer to make your own.

INDIVIDUAL TRAYS—Start by figuring out the size of the individual trays you need. Consider the idea of settling on a standard size for large specimens, half that size for medium specimens, quarter size for small specimens. With this system, it is possible to fill up a drawer in such a way that no space is wasted.

Pasteboard trays that fit this system may be purchased from mineral dealers at a reasonable price. The most popular sizes are: $2^{15}/_{16} \times 3^{15}/_{16}$ inches, $1^{15}/_{16} \times 2^{15}/_{16}$ inches and $1^{7}/_{16} \times 1^{15}/_{16}$ inches. They have the standard height of $\frac{5}{8}$ inch.

You can easily make similar trays yourself from stiff cardboard and masking tape. Draw a rectangle of the proper size on the cardboard. Draw another rectangle with its sides $\frac{5}{8}$ inch from the first. Cut out this rectangle. Remove a small square from each corner. Use this first cutout as a template for cutting out the others. To form the tray, score the sides, then bend them up and secure the corners with strips of masking tape. For extra strength, you may decide to run the masking tape the full length around all four sides of the tray.

DRAWERS—Rocks and minerals are heavy, therefore don't attempt to make the drawers of your projected cabinet too large. Also consider the most effective way of fitting the largest number of individual trays into the drawers.

Drawers commercially available are made to the following inside dimensions which many collectors consider ideal: $20\frac{1}{4} \times 13\frac{1}{4} \times 1\frac{3}{4}$ inches. A drawer of this size will

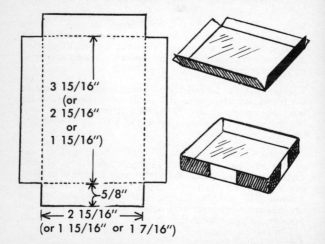

3 15/16"
(or
2 15/16"
or
1 15/16")

5/8"

2 15/16"
(or 1 15/16" or 1 7/16")

You can make your own trays for individual rocks from strong cardboard. Diagram indicates the three most popular sizes.

Cabinets for rock collections are available commercially through dealers of rocks and minerals.

take 36 standard-size pasteboard trays, 72 medium-size, 144 small-size.

You can make up such drawers yourself from ¼-inch plywood and strips of ½×1¾-inch lumber. Assemble the pieces with nails and flathead screws.

CABINET—The cabinet, fundamentally, is a strong wooden box, placed on its side. It should, of course, be of sufficient width to fit your trays. Its height depends on the number of trays you expect to use—you should figure on a height of 3 inches for each tray.

To support the drawers, use pieces of ½-inch angle iron or ½-inch aluminum corner molding, as long as the cabinet is deep. Screw these supports horizontally onto the inside of the cabinet sides, 3 inches apart.

The illustration (page 341) will give you a general idea of the simplest kind of cabinet possible. If you are any kind of a cabinetmaker you will be able to work out your own embellishments.

> *Tip*—To keep out dust, make doors for the cabinet, or provide each drawer with a front, 3 inches wide, that will completely cover the open space between the drawer and the one above it. Drawers made up in this way will need pulls.

PERMANENT STORAGE—MINERALS—In a storage cabinet containing a mixed collection of rocks and minerals, the minerals will find their way into the pasteboard trays intended for small specimens. If you are mainly a mineral and gemstone collector you may prefer a less elaborate storage arrangement.

MINERAL COLLECTION BOXES—Rather than having a cabinet with drawers, many mineral collectors make use of separate shallow boxes with hinged or lift-off lids. Such boxes are easily moved around and can be readily stacked on a bookshelf or in a sideboard or kept in a file drawer.

Mineral collection boxes of this type are obtainable from most mineral dealers. Two common sizes are 16½ × 13×1¾ inches (with space for 45 2½×1¾-inch trays) and 13¼×10¼×1¾ inches (with space for 36 2×1½-inch trays).

It is quite a simple matter to make up similar boxes at home from ¼-inch plywood and ½×1¾-inch lumber, assembling them along the same lines as the drawers for a rock cabinet. An overlapping lift-off lid may be made in the same fashion, cutting the plywood 1 inch longer and wider and using ½×1-inch lumber instead of ½× 1¾-inch.

The box may be partitioned by strips of heavy cardboard or ¼-inch plywood. But the use of separate specimen trays (see page 337) is preferable to permanent partitions.

METAL DRAWER CABINETS—Metal drawer cabinets for minerals are available from mineral dealers—but you may be able to find just what you need locally in a hardware store (metal chests for small tools), in an office supply house (legal blanks cabinets, "junior" blueprint cabinets), in a jewelry store (drawer cabinets for silverware), in a photographic shop (35 mm negative files, Microfilm files), in a drygoods store (spool cabinets).

PLASTIC BOXES—Plastic boxes of all sizes and shapes are on the market. You may be able to find small plastic boxes of just the right size to hold your individual mineral specimens and cabinets of crystal-clear Lucite or Plexiglass for storing your entire collection.

DISPLAYING YOUR SPECIMENS

Some day you may want to put your collection—or parts of it—on display in your home or at a hobby show or special exhibition.

DISPLAY TRAYS—The simplest way of showing off your rock and mineral specimens is to use the regular trays and drawers in which you store them. Place in each specimen tray a label with just enough information on the specimen to be of interest to the general public. If desirable, provide each drawer with a glass top.

DISPLAY SHELVES—An old book shelf may be used for

displaying large specimens—so-called "cabinet specimens," 4×5 inches or larger; or "museum specimens," 5×10 inches or more. Even better is a case with adjustable glass shelving. If desired, appropriate lighting may be installed.

Tip—A local show-case company may have suitable secondhand show cases on sale at reasonable prices.

DISPLAY CHARTS—A small number of specimens may be displayed on a piece of ⅛-inch plywood. Cut the plywood to desired size and arrange the specimens on it. Drill small holes through the plywood to each side of the specimens and fasten them in place with thin wire.

INDIVIDUAL MOUNTINGS—Especially beautiful mineral specimens may be mounted on bases of ⅛- or 3/16-inch clear plastic or squares of Styrofoam. Attach the specimens with plastic cement.

MICROMOUNTS—"Micromount boxes," ⅞×⅞-inch, made of plastic, are available through many mineral supply houses, for displaying tiny mineral crystals.

PLASTIC EMBEDDING—Minerals make excellent objects for plastic embedding, as described on page 212. Before embedding, clean them thoroughly in carbontetrachloride to remove finger marks, then let them dry completely.

FLUORESCENT MINERALS—Fluorescent minerals should be displayed in such a way that they can show off their remarkable qualities. To do this, two kinds of lighting

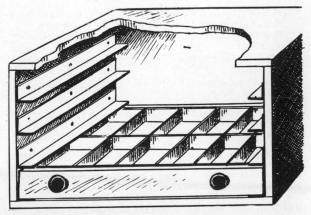

For a simple, homemade rock cabinet, use angle irons to support the drawers. See description on page 339.

You can make a cardboard viewing box for studying fluorescent minerals. Provide it with viewing slit and two socket holes.

are necessary—the ordinary light of a common electric bulb and the ultra-violet light from a special light source.

LIGHT SOURCES—The *argon bulb* is the cheapest source for the special light required. It screws into the ordinary lamp socket and emanates light in the range between 3,300 and 3,700 Angstrom units. Other light sources are the long-wave-light *mercury vapor tube* (with a range of 3,600 to 3,650 Angstrom units) and the short-wave-light *quartz tube* (of 2,540 Angstrom units).

SUPPLIES—Argon bulb may be in stock at your local electrical dealer. If not, he can order it for you.

Ward's Natural Science Establishment, Rochester 3, N. Y.

Ultra-Violet Products, Inc., 5305 Santa Monica Blvd., Los Angeles 27, Calif.

East Coast Mineral Corp., 440 Columbus Avenue, New York 24, N. Y.

Tip—Ward's catalog FM-12 contains a chart of the more important fluorescent minerals and the way in which they react to the three different light sources.

SETTING UP THE DISPLAY—For greatest effectiveness, the display of fluorescent minerals should be arranged in a room that can be darkened completely. Set it up on a table around which your audience can move and arrange the two light sources directly overhead, and in such a way that they can be turned on and off alternately. Or display your specimens in a "shadow box," arranging your lights accordingly.

Tip—If conditions do not permit any elaborate arrangement, fluorescent minerals may be studied in a simple viewing box made of cardboard or wood. Paint the inside of the box with a dull black paint and cut in the lid a viewing slit and two socket holes—one for an ordinary electric light bulb, the other for an argon bulb. See illustration page 342.

Rock and Mineral Photography

Of all the photographic models with which you have to deal in nature photography, rocks and minerals are the easiest to handle. They stay put where they are or where you place them. Nothing disturbs them. They patiently wait for you to adjust your lights, if necessary, and take their picture. And the results are often breath-taking—they range from the gigantic sweep of a mountain range through the intricate texture of a rock specimen to the colorful brilliance of an almost microscopic crystal.

Geological photography challenges you to roam the country for shots of the granite rocks of Acadia National Park, Maine; the stalactites and stalagmites of Carlsbad Caverns, New Mexico; the opalized wood of the Petrified Forest, Arizona; the geyserite formations at the mouth of Old Faithful in Yellowstone National Park, Wyoming; the red sandstone cliffs in the Garden of the Gods, Colorado; the crumbling slate of the Delaware Water Gap, Pennsylvania and New Jersey—and hundreds of other photogenic, geological wonders.

And when you are tired of roaming, geological photography gives you the chance to spend many quiet evenings at home shooting the specimens of your collection.

Stills

EQUIPMENT—Any camera you would use for taking the ordinary pictures of landscapes and members of the family will do for taking long shots of distant geological formations and medium shots of outcrops. When it comes to taking close-ups of rock details and of minerals, you will require the same features in your camera as are needed for insect photography (see page 195).

Your hands are probably steady enough to permit you to take long and medium shots with a hand-held camera. But for close-ups you need a tripod. For indoor shots you further need suitable lighting and various props for placing and posing your specimens.

WHAT TO PHOTOGRAPH—In your travels you will soon build up a *series* of photographs of geological formations. At home, you will be developing further series of shots of the rocks and minerals you have gathered.

As a record of each of your excursions, you may decide that a *sequence* is in order—several shots of the geological formation in question: the formation as a whole, details of its structure (bands, folds, faults, dikes, etc.), close-ups of its component parts (minerals and mineral-like matter).

> *Tip*—To make it possible to determine comparative size, you may want to include an object of known size in your photographs—in your medium shots, your mineral hammer or a pick; in close-ups, a ruler, a coin or other familiar subject. Pough, in his *Field Guide to Rocks and Minerals,* very cleverly had his specimens posed on pieces of wide-wale corduroy of about 5½ stripes to the inch (each stripe approximately 5 mm).

OUTDOOR PHOTOGRAPHY—In taking photographs of geological formations, consider composition, light, and sky. A routine head-on photograph of a mountain, taken on a dull day against an overcast sky, may be all right for a record shot—but how much more effective the shot if taken from the most attractive angle, with sunlight and shade emphasizing rock texture, and with a dark sky sharply outlining the silhouette.

Back-lighted geological formations photograph poorly. For best effect they should be front- or side-lighted. The time of day suggested for finding rocks and minerals (see page 322) is also the time of day for getting the best lighting for your photographs.

> *Tip*—In black-and-white photography, a yellow filter will increase the contrast and add crispness to a medium shot. A yellow or orange filter will darken the sky in a distant shot. Always use a haze filter when taking color shots of distant objects.

INDOOR PHOTOGRAPHY—Your indoor photographs will all be close-ups of rock and mineral specimens. Posing, background, and lighting become your main considerations.

POSING—Study the specimen you want to photograph from all angles and decide on its most photogenic side. Then place the specimen on the background you intend to use with the chosen side to the lens. Use blobs of modeling clay to prop it up if necessary.

BACKGROUND—For background, use a piece of material or a sheet of cardboard—of a neutral gray if you are shooting in black-and-white; of a contrasting color if you are using color film. Arrange the material or curve the cardboard against an upright support in such a way that the background completely fills the negative.

LIGHTING—Use two floodlights and one spotlight for bringing out the shape, texture, and color of the specimen to greatest advantage and for illuminating the background. Modify the light arrangement for each specimen. Take your light-meter reading by substitution, against a piece of gray cardboard.

Tip—For shadowless photography, arrange your setup as follows: Lay the background material on the floor and place two boxes (1 foot high) on it, 1 to 2 feet apart. Lay a sheet of glass as a "bridge" between the two boxes. Pose your specimen on the glass. Light it so that the shadows fall outside the section of the background that fills the negative.

Be especially careful with minerals that are translucent or have a lustrous surface—you may have to use a polarizing filter to eliminate light reflections. Crystals may show up especially well if illuminated from below. The cat's-eye effect (chatoyancy) of certain minerals and the "star" (asterism) of certain gemstones may be brought out with a spotlight focused to a pin point.

In the case of fluorescent minerals you will want to take two photographs: 1. under ordinary light; 2. under ultra-violet light to show their fluorescence. Your light meter will give you the correct exposure for the shot under ordinary light. Only experimentation will give you the correct exposure for the shot under ultra-violet light —your light meter will probably not even register.

MOVIES

OUTDOORS—All landscape shots may be considered parts of a geological movie—they cannot help but show some of the geological features of the area photographed. But they will make up a geological movie only if tied together with medium shots, showing forms and structures, and close-ups, showing textures and colors.

A wide-angle lens makes it possible for you to photograph a geological feature from a location much closer to the object than the usual 1-inch lens permits. A telephoto lens at the proper distance will give you your medium shots and can also be used for taking the close-ups.

In shooting a landscape, beware of the tendency, so prevalent among movie amateurs, of "spraying the hose" on it—of moving the running camera across it from side to side. Instead, focus on the left part of the landscape and, while holding the camera still—on a tripod, preferably—run it for approximately 5 seconds. Stop the camera. Shift its position until the view finder is framed on the section to the right of the first shot. Shoot again for 5 seconds. And so on until you have covered the whole subject.

It is only in very special cases—such as making a horizontal sweep of the Grand Canyon or a vertical sweep of the Devil's Tower—that you are justified in VERY SLOW "panning."

INDOORS—In taking movies of rocks and mineral specimens indoors, use the same technique as for photographing stills indoors (see above).

Add movement to some of the shots by having a helper turn a specimen in his hand, or by placing the specimen on the slowly turning turntable of a record player, or by moving the light source that illuminates it.

PART III

CONSERVATION PROJECTS

11.   GENERAL CONSERVATION

CONSERVATION of natural resources is the watch-word of everyone interested in nature. It should be the watchword of every child, adolescent and adult in our own country and around the world. Conservation, or the lack of it, can be the difference between abundance and scarcity, between a high standard of living and an ever-decreasing standard.

Until the beginning of this century, there was little realization in America of the need for conservation practices. Virgin forests still spread their vast expanses over wide sections of our country, the soil was fertile, wildlife abundant, our mineral wealth seemingly inexhaustible, our scenic wonders enduring. But forests were cut, soils depleted, wildlife destroyed, mineral resources wastefully tapped, scenic areas defaced. And for each natural resource diminished, all the others were affected.

The voices raised in warning went unheeded for a long time.

But their echoes reverberated. Slowly other voices were added, until today every intelligent person realizes the importance of conservation and earnestly desires to do his or her share.

The way a farmer tills his soil in Kansas, or an engineer builds a dam in Tennessee, or a hunter kills a predator in Maine, or a forester cuts his trees in Oregon used to be the private concern of each of them. Not any more—the way they go about it may ultimately influence all of us by the processes they set in motion. A flood in Missouri, a drought in Texas, a dust storm in Oklahoma, used to be local matters. Not any more—they may be symptoms of poor resource-use practices that may ultimately affect us all.

"Never send to know for whom the bell tolls: It tolls for thee!"

To the world at large, conservation has come to mean "the wise use of natural resources for the greatest good of the most people for the longest time."

To each individual person, the term "conservation" has taken on its own meaning. To some, conservation is a Hoover Dam, to others a compost heap in the garden. To some it is planting a thousand trees, to others refraining from throwing a burning cigarette out of a car window. It is obeying game laws and willow-planting a stream bank. On a farm it is the contour planting of a field, in the city the salvaging of scrap metal.

Conservation is all of those things and many more: Conservation is an area of learning, an attitude of mind, a way of living in harmony with nature.

By making conservation a part of your everyday thinking and acting, and by working with others for the acceptance and use of proper conservation practices you are helping to make a richer and better country and world.

BOOKS ON CONSERVATION—GENERAL—J. Russell Whitaker and Edward Ackerman. *American Resources*. Harcourt and Brace.

R. L. Parson. *Conserving American Resources*. Prentice-Hall.

C. H. Callison. *America's Natural Resources*. Ronald Press.

Guy-Harold Smith, ed. *Conserving Natural Resources*. John Wiley & Sons.

YOUR PERSONAL APPROACH

To a great extent, the personal contribution of the average person toward conservation is *not doing* certain things: *not* throwing trash or a burning cigarette butt from a car, *not* damaging trees on a hike, *not* building your picnic fire on a spot from which it may spread, *not* ditching your tent when you are camping in an area subject to erosion—*not* wasting, *not* destroying.

If you own land, or have access to land—whether a suburban garden, a farm, a camp, or a country estate— you will want to be *doing* things with it: you will want to use it to the best purpose, you will want it to produce to the height of its capability, you will want to improve it. To this end, a great number of people stand ready to help you—they are as close to you as your telephone.

WHERE TO GET HELP—Open up your telephone book to "U. S. Government." In most cases, you will find here the telephone numbers of local representatives of the Department of Agriculture—soil conservationists, regional and district foresters—and of the Department of Interior—wildlife technicians. Under the name of your state, you will find the telephone numbers of your county conservation agent, district forester, game manager. These people will help you determine what *can* be done, plan with you what *should* be done, and, in many cases, give you active assistance to *get* it done.

In addition to federal and state government personnel, you will find many others willing to help you: local school science teachers or college instructors, municipal or county park departments, nature or conservation clubs, sportsmen's groups, local chapters of national organizations (Garden Club of America, Audubon Society, Izaak Walton League, Boy Scouts and Girl Scouts, Camp Fire Girls, 4-H, Future Farmers of America).

INCREASING YOUR KNOWLEDGE OF CONSERVATION—WORKSHOPS—Within recent years, many states have established conservation workshops or "resource-use" workshops—outdoor study sessions where teachers, youth leaders, and others may spend from two weeks to a month learning about our natural resources and their relationship to the daily lives of all Americans, and ways and means of making use of the knowledge thus gained. If your time permits, you may want to participate in such a workshop.

REFERENCES—*Some Conservation and Resource-Use Workships and Courses.* Yearly list by states prepared by U. S. Forest Service, Washington, D. C.

AUDUBON CAMPS—Each summer, the National Audubon Society runs camps with a program combining general nature study and conservation in each of its four nature centers—in Maine, Connecticut, Wisconsin, and California. The camp period occupies two weeks and gives each camper a chance to take part in a thoroughly enjoyable experience and to meet nature enthusiasts from many parts of the country.

REFERENCE—For information about the Audubon Camps, drop a line to National Audubon Society, 1130 Fifth Avenue, New York 28, N. Y.

CONSERVATION BY PEN—In working for conservation on a personal basis, do not underestimate the power of the pen. A letter to a congressman or state legislator showing a well-informed interest and presenting a constructive suggestion may have an important bearing on his vote for or against a bill dealing with a public issue involving conservation.

To write an intelligent letter of this type, you need not only to keep up to date, through periodicals and the daily press, on bills before the Congress of the United States or your state legislature, but also to weigh carefully, in your own mind, the pros and cons before you put your thoughts on paper. Be realistic in your approach —sentimentality and conservation do not always coincide. A major conservation project which, at first glance, seems destructive to natural resources may, in the long run, prove to be the very opposite. On the other hand, a project of moderate scale only might have to be sharpened and expanded to produce the greatest possible future benefit—or might, on investigation, be found to be an attempt, that should be resisted, at establishing a toe hold for some kind of undesirable development.

WORKING WITH OTHERS

The individual attitude and actions of each of a hundred and eighty million Americans are of tremendous importance in the conservation of our country's resources. But those alone are not sufficient. There is much to be done that can only be accomplished by concerted action, by working with other people as interested as yourself in the welfare of our country.

Every locality has its own resource problems, each with its own solution. In addition, there are state-wide and country-wide conservation problems which can only be solved by the active co-operation and intelligent voting of an informed citizenry.

In working with others, set out first to know and to help the local people who are engaged in conservation work (see page 351). They, in turn, will be more than happy to co-operate with you and to assist you in your activities.

Take part, as well, in local study groups, training sessions, round tables, and town meetings where conservation is the subject.

MEMBERSHIP IN CONSERVATION SOCIETIES
—Some of your work on behalf of conservation can best be done through membership in and financial support of one of the many national conservation societies and organizations, and by taking part in the deliberations and field work of their local branches or chapters.

Among such groups, you may decide to join one that covers the general field of conservation, or one that concerns itself with the phase of conservation in which you are particularly interested.

CONSERVATION SOCIETIES—GENERAL—National Audubon
Society. Hdqrs.: 1130 Fifth Avenue, New York 28,
N. Y. Periodical: *Audubon Magazine*.

Izaak Walton League of America. Hdqrs.: 1326 Wau-
kegan Road, Glenview, Ill. Periodical: *Outdoor
America*.

General Federation of Women's Clubs. Hdqrs.: 1734
N Street, N.W., Washington 6, D. C. Periodical:
General Federation Clubwoman.

Garden Club of America. Hdqrs.: 298 Madison Avenue, New York 22, N. Y. Periodical: *The Bulletin*.

CONSERVATION SOCIETIES—SPECIALIZED—For conservation
societies in the fields of outdoor areas, soil and water,
forestry, and wildlife, see the sections that follow.

CONSERVATION LEADERSHIP—If you have the
chance and inclination to undertake education in conservation—whether as a parent, a youth leader, a camp
counselor, or a teacher—you will find that the suggestions
on pages 33–37 relative to establishing a general interest
in nature apply equally well to conservation. With those
as a basis you can take the needed steps that lead into
actual performance of a conservation activity:

Appreciation comes first. The more you know about
nature and conservation yourself, the better able you are
to make others appreciate nature and the importance of
conserving our natural resources. Almost all the activities in the preceding chapters of this *Field Book* can be
used to this end: to stimulate an interest in nature and
to instill in those with whom you work the necessary
enthusiasm for undertaking specific conservation projects.

Investigation comes next, in order to establish a clear
understanding of the relationship between everything in
nature—between soil and water, between animals and
plants, between man and everything around him. Investigation will serve to answer numerous questions as, for
example: Some fields have a deep layer of topsoil, others
haven't—why the difference? In some places wildlife
thrives, in others it doesn't—why and why not?

Experimentation follows. Are there ways, for instance,
of determining the comparative fertility of different soils?
Find out by experiments. Are there methods for stopping
erosion? A small model of a hillside will tell you. Experiments on a small scale can help solve problems in
the field.

Application is "the proof of the pudding." It is not just
a matter of accepting for yourself and encouraging others

to accept the *Conservation Pledge,* as a personal obligation:

> I give my pledge as an American to save and faithfully to defend from waste the natural resources of my country, its soils and minerals, its forests, waters, and wildlife.

It is even more important to *do* something about conservation. It is toward this point that the suggestions on the following pages are directed—some of them in the whole vast area of conservation, others more specifically in activities that will result in the

> Protection and improvement of our country's OUTDOOR AREAS; Wise use and planned maintenance of our SOILS and WATERS; Proper utilization and systematic perpetuation of our FORESTS and GRASSLANDS; Intelligent management of our WILDLIFE.

YOUTH WORK—If you are a teacher, your curriculum may include conservation. In such case, your state or community will have developed the necessary teaching helps. In using them, one of the most important things to remember is that nature—and consequently the need of conserving nature—begins right outside the school door: in schoolyard or playground.

BOOKS ON CONSERVATION EDUCATION—*Handbook for Teaching of Conservation and Resource-Use.* Richard L. Weaver, ed. National Association of Biology Teachers, P.O. Box 2073, Ann Arbor, Mich.

A. Reginald Whittemore. *Conservation and Nature Activities.* Audubon Society of Canada. Toronto, Canada.

B. Ashbaugh and M. Beuschlein. *Things to Do in Science and Conservation.* Interstate Printers and Publishers, Danville, Ill.

If you are interested in working with young people, you may decide to make yourself available as a camp counselor or on a year-round basis to one of the existing youth movements that sponsor conservation—the Boy Scouts, Camp Fire Girls, 4-H, and others.

REFERENCES—For information in regard to the conservation activities of these movements, drop a line to the national headquarters. For addresses, see page 39.

Effie G. Bathurst and Wilhelmina Hill. *Conservation Experiences for Children.* Bulletin No. 16, 1957. Office of Education, U. S. Department of Health, Education and Welfare, Washington 25, D. C.

Or you may want to establish a conservation club along the lines of the general nature club described on page 37, but specifically dedicated to conservation and with a program of meetings and field trips featuring seasonal conservation activities.

REFERENCE—*Junior Conservation Clubs.* Pennsylvania Game Commission, Harrisburg, Penn.

Some states run a summer program of Junior Conservation Camps for boys of high-school age who are leaders in their schools and interested in conservation. These camps combine a rich camping experience with thorough training in conservation education, for the purpose of developing leadership for local work. Boys participating are generally sponsored by some conservation group in their community. If such a Junior Conservation Camp is in existence in your state, you should find it worth while to arrange with some local group to sponsor some boys from your community.

SPECIAL ACTIVITIES— In co-operation with local agencies, many special events may be organized for the education of young people and adults in the importance of conservation and for undertaking general conservation activities.

CONSERVATION FIELD TRIPS—A field trip for a general study of conservation problems and practices may be run along the same lines as the usual nature field trip (see pages 39–41). For suggestions in regard to field trips for investigating special phases of conservation, see pages 366-70 for soil and water conservation, pages 386-90 for forest conservation, pages 402-04 for wildlife conservation.

CONSERVATION TRAIL—A small group of conservation enthusiasts can easily establish a conservation trail in a local park or nearby camp area. Such a trail is built in the same manner as a regular nature trail (see pages 46–51). The difference is that the wording of the trail markers is specifically aimed at opening the eyes of the trail user to the features around him directly related to conservation—along this line:

It took Nature about 5,000 years to form these 8 inches of topsoil. The wrong use of the land can cause them to be lost in a few years.

Look up. This hollow tree makes a perfect apartment house for squirrels and raccoons.

Notice the tracks around this brush pile. How many do you recognize?

When raindrops fall and run away
They can't be used another day.

This willow planting prevented the stream bank from being washed away.

CONSERVATION EXHIBIT—In promoting an increased interest in conservation, you may want to put up an exhibit in a location where a fairly large number of people will have a chance to view it: a school or club room, a camp nature lodge, or possibly, for a seasonal display of certain conservation practices, a store window. For suggestions for setting up an exhibit, see pages 52–54.

A great number of the collections and demonstration items described in this *Field Book* would fit naturally into such an exhibit. So would photographs of local areas showing good conservation practices. In addition, a large amount of colorful exhibit material in the form of posters, charts, maps, and literature is available from federal and state agencies—much of it free of charge, some of it at very nominal cost.

SOURCES OF EXHIBIT MATERIALS—U. S. Department of Agriculture, Washington 25, D. C. Various agencies: Federal Extension Service, Soil Conservation Service, Forest Service. Write for lists of material. Or get in touch with your local Soil Conservation District Supervisor or County Agent.

U. S. Department of the Interior, Washington 25, D. C. Various agencies: Fish and Wildlife Service, Bureau of Land Management, Bureau of Reclamation, Geological Survey. Write for lists of materials.

State Departments of Conservation, Forests and Waters, Fish and Game, Education, Planning and Development. Charts, photographs, pamphlets.

CONSERVATION NIGHT— An evening program may be developed around general conservation or one of its many phases, or reporting on the activities of your group, with some local conservationist as the main speaker or master of ceremonies, and with the showing of a movie or a slide series on an outdoor subject as a special feature.

SOURCES OF MOVIES AND SLIDES—U. S. Department of Agriculture, Office of Information, Motion Picture Service, Washington 25, D. C.

U. S. Department of Agriculture, Forest Service, Division of Information and Education, Washington 25, D. C.

U. S. Department of the Interior, Fish and Wildlife Service, Film Loan Library, Box 128, College Park, Md.

Complete Listing of Free Movies for Sportsmen's Clubs. Outdoor Life Magazine, 353 Fourth Avenue, New York 10, N. Y.

National Audubon Society, 1130 Fifth Avenue, New York 28, N. Y.

Encyclopaedia Brittanica Films, Wilmette, Ill.

CONSERVATION FAIR—A conservation field day may be set up in a local park or campsite, along the lines of a country fair, with exhibit booths and demonstration areas with opportunities for "learning by doing." Such a fair may cover: *soil conservation*—soil types, erosion models, demonstration of gully control; *forestry*—tree nursery, tree planting, tree enemies and their control, forest fire fighting; *game management*—live and stuffed game birds and upland game, birdhouses, feeding stations, shrubs and other plants that encourage game birds and upland game; *fish and pond management*—stuffed fish and fish in aquariums, exhibits of rods and reels, teaching of casting methods, creel census. See index for detailed instructions for most of these activities.

CONSERVATION CAMP—The program suggested above for a one-day conservation fair may be turned into a weekend activity. In such case, more emphasis should be placed on projects involving the active participation of all the campers—in actual tree planting and other forestry practices, erosion control and other soil management procedures, stream improvement and fishing, and so on. Some of these activities may be developed on a competitive basis, for increased interest.

CONSERVATION GROUP PROJECTS—The deeper your group's understanding of conservation, the more eager it will be to undertake various projects to protect and perpetuate our country's natural resources. But the clearer also will be the realization of the interrelationship of all living things and their dependence on soil and water for their existence, and therefore the importance of anticipating how a project will fit into the scheme of things.

Where nature is untouched there is a balance between animate and inanimate things, between ecologic, economic, esthetic, and recreational values.

Whenever man takes over, he invariably upsets nature's balance—often deliberately for his gain, sometimes unthinkingly to his loss. When he drains a marsh, for instance, to establish a field for cultivation, the balance is upset in the direction of economic gain—ecologically the land will suffer through the elimination of wildlife food and shelter, esthetically through the destruction of its natural attractiveness, recreationally through the reduction of its use for hunting and fishing. When a man turns a forest into a picnic ground or camping area, he enhances its recreational appeal and possibly its economic worth, but diminishes its ecologic and esthetic values. Conversely, when he turns a wood lot into a wildlife preserve or a cultivated field into a farm pond, he is helping nature re-establish a natural balance.

Most of the conservation projects in the following

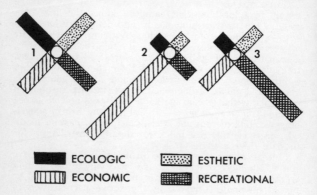

ECOLOGIC   ESTHETIC
ECONOMIC   RECREATIONAL

Diagram 1 suggests an area in nature where there is a balance between ecologic, economic, esthetic and recreational values. In 2, economic considerations have thrown nature out of balance. In 3, recreational considerations have upset the balance.

chapters of this *Field Book* can be safely undertaken by the amateur without fear of upsetting nature's balance. But before entering upon a large-scale conservation project, you and your group need to consider and weigh carefully the probable ultimate effects. Such a project should be done only with the advice and active assistance of experts in the field of conservation.

12. CONSERVATION OF
OUTDOOR AREAS

THE way the average American behaves in our country's outdoor areas is probably the most easily read evidence of his attitude toward conservation and his exercise of conservation practices.

Within the last sixty years almost two hundred million acres of government land and many more million acres of state property have been set aside for the outdoor enjoyment of all the people of the United States. They provide homes for wildlife, preserve water, furnish pasture land, and produce timber, but their main purpose is to make recreational facilities available for millions of visitors annually.

They are for the pleasure of every American citizen—today and for generations to come. They are under the protection of each American citizen—and that means you and I.

REFERENCES—NATIONAL AREAS—Maps of National Parks, list of National Monuments, and information pamphlets. National Park Service, U. S. Department of the Interior, Washington, D. C.

Maps of National Forests and Wilderness Areas, and information pamphlets. Forest Service, U. S. Department of Agriculture, Washington 25, D. C.

Devereux Butcher. *Exploring Our National Parks and Monuments.* Also *Exploring the National Parks of Canada.* Oxford University Press.

STATE PARKS—Write to your state park director or superintendent, at your state capital, for maps and informative pamphlets.

In spite of the fact that all of these outdoor areas belong to each American citizen, how does he protect them?

Have you ever traveled behind a car from which was flipped a burning cigarette butt? Have you ever stopped at a wayside area littered with paper and empty cans? Have you ever visited a "beer-can beach" or a "smashed-bottle lake shore"? Have you ever come upon a public picnic site with tables and fireplaces deliberately destroyed? Have you ever passed a birch grove with the bark ripped off every tree? Have you ever seen the empty hooks from which some park sign was stolen by a souvenir-hunting thief? Have you ever seen a park bench, a beech tree, a marker, defaced with some fool's initials?

Have you ever asked yourself, "How is this possible?"

The sad fact is that irreplaceable values are destroyed and millions of dollars' worth of damage done each year to our national and state parks through the sloth, the carelessness, the lack of consideration, and the deliberate vandalism of visitors.

What can be done about it? The situation can be resolved if every American will set for himself a gentlemanly code of outdoor behavior and live up to it.

LIVING THE OUTDOOR CODE

The *Outdoor Code* developed and promoted by the Boy Scouts of America might well be the code of outdoor behavior for all Americans. By following it yourself and teaching others to follow it you can make a major contribution to the conservation of our outdoor areas. This code is simple and to the point:

As an American, I will do my best to

BE CLEAN IN MY OUTDOOR MANNERS— I will treat the outdoors as a heritage to be improved for our greater enjoyment. I will keep my trash and garbage out of America's waters, fields, woods and roadways.

BE CAREFUL WITH FIRE—I will prevent wildfire. I will build my fire in a safe place, and be sure it is out before I leave.

BE CONSIDERATE IN THE OUTDOORS—I will treat public and private property with respect. I will remember that use of the outdoors is a privilege I can lose by abuse.

BE CONSERVATION-MINDED— I will learn how to practice good conservation of soil, waters, forests, minerals, grasslands, and wildlife; and I will urge others to do the same. I will use sportsman-like methods in all my outdoor activities.

This *Outdoor Code* speaks for itself. Nevertheless, some of its points may need amplification.

BE CLEAN IN MY OUTDOOR MANNERS—Rubbish has no place in the American landscape. Make "Leave No Trace" your slogan and dispose of rubbish properly.

TRASH—Candy wrappers, cigarette packages, and similar *"pocket trash"* belong in your pocket until you can throw them into a waste container or your home wastepaper basket. Trash along roadsides is a national problem requiring the expenditure of millions of dollars a year in clean-ups—help solve the problem by keeping a *trash bag* in your car in which to accumulate trash that collects during a ride.

GARBAGE—When camping, deposit *garbage* in a waste container. If none is available, dispose of burnable garbage by burning and carry unburnable garbage out with you.

CONTAINERS—Never break *bottles* and *jars* and never throw them in a fire—hundreds of first-aid cases are caused annually in our parks by broken glass. Never throw *cans* about and never bury them—at best it will take several years for cans to rust to powder and, if buried, animals dig them up in short order. Instead, deposit bottles, jars, and cans in a waste container. If none is at hand, take them with you—if you had room to pack in the full containers, you have room to pack out the empty ones for proper disposal.

BE CAREFUL WITH FIRE—Nine out of ten fires in our outdoor areas are caused by thoughtless and careless smokers and campers.

MATCHES—After using a *match,* break it in two before disposing of it. This is an old-timer's trick. The breaking is not the point—the point is that you can't break a match without touching the burned part, and you will then know quickly enough whether or not the match is out.

SMOKES—Never, never, never flip a glowing cigarette or cigar out of a car window—use the ash tray. Never

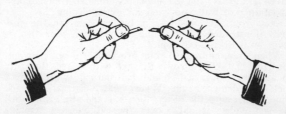

"The Broken Match" is a symbol of the good outdoorsman. Your feel will tell you whether the match is DEAD OUT or not.

smoke in areas where a fire danger exists. Carefully follow smoking rules of the outdoor area you are visiting.

Extinguish a *cigarette* by crushing out the burning ember completely against mineral dirt or rock; then field-strip the butt: tear open the paper, scatter the tobacco, roll up the paper in a tiny ball. Crush out the ember of a *cigar* in the same manner; then break the butt apart. Knock out *pipe* heels on mineral dirt protected from the wind, so that the wind will not carry away sparks; then crush out embers.

CAMPFIRES—Follow the park rules for the lighting of campfires. In many parks open fires may be used only in certain areas, or in permanent stone or metal fireplaces.

Sprinkle water on the remains of a campfire until all embers are extinguished. Then "garden" the wet ashes into the soil.

Where no fireplaces are available, clean a fire spot down to mineral ground—sand, gravel, clay, or rock—and remove all flammable materials for a safe distance. Never build a fire on duff—dry, decaying vegetable matter, leaves and grass: the fire may spread underground. Have a container of water on hand for extinguishing.

Keep your fire small—just big enough for the job. Keep it attended all the time. "Chaperone your fire"—never let a fire go out alone!

When used, extinguish your fire until it is not just out, but DEAD OUT! Drown the fire with water, then stir up and turn over ashes and half-burned twigs with a stick and drown again. Where water is scarce, work mineral dirt into the ashes, then stir and stir again until the last ember is out. Cover the extinguished remains with mineral dirt and do some "gardening" in the soil to help heal the fire scar.

BE CONSIDERATE IN THE OUTDOORS—Treat property and other people the way you would want to have your own property treated and the way you would like to be treated by other people. Be considerate, in your behavior, of other people's feelings and desire for privacy.

PRIVATE PROPERTY—Never trespass private property— get permission. Don't cross planted fields—crops are valuable. Don't climb fences—use gates; close them after you if you had to open them; leave them open if that was the way you found them. Leave animals undisturbed. Don't destroy private property—whether stone fences or windowpanes in an empty building.

PUBLIC PROPERTY—Heed the advice of "the man with the badge"—the park ranger, forest ranger, or game warden. Follow rules for the use of the picnic spot or camping area you are using. Refrain from damaging park furniture and fixtures. The innocent-sounding "souvenir hunting" spells T-H-E-F-T in plain English and should be pronounced that way! Spare the wildflowers. Do not deface living trees. Use available toilet facilities, or bury human wastes. Clean up after you so that the place looks the way you would like to have found it yourself—even though it wasn't that clean when you arrived. If you make use of firewood already cut and stored, replace it, with interest, for the party that follows you. Keep trails open and in good condition.

BE CONSERVATION-MINDED—The more you travel in the outdoors, the more will grow your desire to protect our natural resources for your own use and for the future, and to do your part in their conservation. The pages that follow contain specific suggestions for activities in all these fields.

WORKING WITH OTHERS

In addition to living up to an outdoor code yourself and encouraging others to do the same, you can do much for the conservation of our outdoor areas by working in close contact with sportsmen's clubs, youth groups, societies promoting the protection and development of parks, camp grounds, and wilderness areas, and with local, state and federal agencies.

SOCIETIES—Wilderness Society. Hdqrs.: 2144 P Street, N.W., Washington 7, D. C. Periodical: *Living Wilderness.*

National Parks Association. Hdqrs.: 1300 New Hampshire Ave., N.W., Washington 6, D. C. Periodical: *National Parks Magazine.*

Nature Conservancy. Hdqrs.: 2039 K Street, N.W., Washington 6, D. C. Periodical: *Nature Conservancy News.*

GOVERNMENT AGENCIES—National Park Service, U. S. Department of the Interior, Washington 25, D. C. (National parks, national recreation areas, national monuments.)

Forest Service, U. S. Department of Agriculture, Washington 25, D. C. (National forests.)

Your own state's Division of Parks, Park Service, or Park Commission.

Field Projects in Conservation of Outdoor Areas

CLEAN-UP CAMPAIGNS—In numerous instances, a youth group or a sportsmen's club is able to organize a clean-up of a local area, in co-operation with the local authorities. The area involved may be a roadside park, a picnic ground, the town square, a beach or a lake shore—even the roadside along a highway leading into town.

Secure the co-operation of local newspapers to publicize the project and get public support for it.

DEVELOPING AN OUTDOOR AREA—You and other civic-minded people may decide to get together to work for the creation of a local *community forest* or to help in the development of the *camping areas* of your local Boy Scout or Girl Scout council, or other youth group. For suggestions, see section on forestry (pages 390-92).

TRAIL BUILDING—Wilderness trails have been constructed or are in construction in many of our states, for use of adventure-seeking hikers. The most famous of these trails are the Appalachian Trail, extending for two thousand miles from Mount Kathadin in Maine to Mount Oglethorpe in Georgia, and the equally long Pacific Crest Trailway from Canada to the Mexican border.

Work on these trails combines an interesting outdoor experience with a lasting conservation Good Turn. It involves clearing new trails with axes, machetes, and hoes; keeping old trails open by removing windfalls and rockslides; constructing log bridges over mountain streams and ravines; putting up trail signs; building or repairing shelters; and numerous other things.

REFERENCES—*Wilderness Trails,* published by Boy Scouts of America, New Brunswick, N. J., lists and describes the main trails of the United States by states.

Appalachian Trail Conference, 1916 Sunderland Place, N.W., Washington, D. C. Brochures and guides to the Appalachian Trail.

Pacific Crest Trail System Conference, Hotel Greene, Pasadena, Calif. Periodical and guides to the Pacific Crest Trail.

13. SOIL AND WATER
CONSERVATION

SOIL and water are inseparable—conservationally speaking. Without water, soil is sterile, unproductive. With sufficient water, soil is able to bring forth the plant life on which man and animals depend.

Without soil and water the whole human race would perish. Yet experts on soil and water conservation estimate that one-third of the top soil of our country has been lost since the founding of America, through improper uses of the land, and tell us that the pollution of our streams and lakes by erosion, sewage, and industrial wastes is steadily worsening.

Today, at a time of greatly accelerated population growth, the dangers of soil depletion and water pollution are recognized by every thinking citizen. The problem of keeping soil healthy and water plentiful and clear is being attacked on every level—federal, state, municipal, as well as by individual farmers and landowners.

By learning the principles of soil and water conservation and finding out what is being done in your community, you will be in a position of helping in the battle to conserve our country's soils and waters.

BOOKS ON SOIL AND WATER CONSERVATION—Hugh Hammond Bennett. *Elements of Soil Conservation.* McGraw-Hill Book Company.

J. H. Stallings. *Soil: Use and Improvement.* Prentice-Hall, Inc.

M. D. Butler. *Conserving Soil.* Van Nostrand.

Soil: Yearbook of Agriculture 1957 and *Water:* Yearbook of Agriculture 1955. U. S. Department of Agriculture.

WORKING WITH OTHERS

Most of the soil and water conservation projects described in the following pages can easily be accomplished, without special technical knowledge, by a group of youngsters or adults. For some of the more advanced projects, secure the advice of your local representatives of the federal and state government agencies dealing with the conservation of soil and water.

GOVERNMENT AGENCIES—FEDERAL—U. S. Department of Agriculture. Soil Conservation Service. Periodical: *Soil Conservation.*
U. S. Department of Agriculture. Extension Service.
STATE—Department of Agriculture.
Agricultural Experiment Station.
College of Agriculture: Extension Service.
COUNTY—County Agent.

SOCIETIES—Soil Conservation Society of America. Hdqrs.: 838 5th Avenue, Des Moines 14, Iowa. Periodical: *Journal of Soil and Water Conservation.*
Friends of the Land. Hdqrs.: 1368 North High Street, Columbus, Ohio.
Also general conservation societies, page 353.

Field Observation in Soil and Water Conservation

EROSION STUDY—The loss of topsoil through erosion constitutes one of the greatest dangers to our land. Of different kinds of erosion, *gully erosion* and *stream bank erosion* are most readily recognizable. *Sheet erosion,* in which the top layer of soil of a large area is washed away, is the most insidious and most difficult to recognize. *Wind erosion* occurs when strong winds sweep over dry, bare soil, *splash erosion* when rain falls on bare soil.

The best time to study the first three types of erosion is during or immediately after a heavy rainfall. Look particularly for the following:

GULLIES—Are gullies present? If "yes," are efforts being made to stop them or are they still eating their way uphill? If possible, follow a gully to its starting point. What caused it? How can it be stopped?

STREAM BANKS—Is stream bank erosion cutting into the land and carrying soil away? Since most severe cutting takes place at the outer bends of the loops made by a stream, have measures been taken to protect these outer bends? Is there any indication—by muddiness—that land upstream is being eroded?

CULTIVATED FIELDS—Study a level patch of land at the foot of a cultivated slope. Has any silt been deposited there? What is the depth of the silt as compared to the top soil left on the field? Looking up over the field, do you see rill marks and other signs of erosion?

REFERENCE—*Our Productive Land.* Agriculture Informative Bulletin No. 106. U. S. Department of Agriculture, Soil Conservation Service.

WATERSHED STUDY—A watershed or drainage basin is an area of land from which the water drains to a given point. A watershed in good condition holds the water from rain or melting snow. It stores some of it in the soil, permits the rest to run off the surface at a slow rate. A watershed may be small, taking in only a part of a single farm. Or it may be large, covering the hills and valleys, forests and ranges, farms and even cities of a great area. It may provide only for the watering of a small herd of cows—or it may be a source of your city's drinking water and the water that makes your community's industries possible.

In investigating a watershed area, pay especial attention to these nine points, as enumerated by the U. S. Department of Agriculture:

1. Is the ground well covered with grasses, shrubs, or trees?
2. Does the use the land now receives allow the plants to reseed and reproduce young plants?
3. Do the plants look strong and healthy?
4. Is there a layer of dried grass or leaves over the ground?
5. Does the ground feel soft and springy underfoot?
6. Where gullies are present, are they eroding?
7. Are the stream banks receding and washing away?
8. Do the streams run muddy during and after rains?
9. Is there evidence of stream pollution that could endanger the welfare of towns and cities below?

If you can say "Yes" to questions 1 through 5 and "No" to questions 6 through 9, your watershed is in good condition. If you must answer "No" to questions 1 through 5 and "Yes" to questions 6 through 9, your watershed is in poor condition and may require the most urgent attention of yourself and other conservation-minded citizens of your community—

REFERENCE—*Know Your Watershed.* U. S. Department of Agriculture, Forest Service Leaflet No. 282.

LAND JUDGING—Take a field trip over a farm of which a land capability map or conservation survey map has been prepared, for the purpose of investigating and understanding the eight capability classes into which various types of land are grouped. Secure permission in advance from the owner of the property, and arrange to have a local Soil Conservation Service technician accompany you and your group. If at all possible, have the technician demonstrate the methods he used for determining the land classifications:

LANDS SUITED FOR CULTIVATION—CLASS I: Very good land, with little or no erosion; nearly level and easily worked. Can be cultivated safely with ordinary good farming methods.

CLASS II: Good land, with moderate erosion. Can be cultivated safely with easily applied conservation practices.

CLASS III: Moderately good land, with moderate to severe erosion. Can be cultivated safely with intensive treatments and conservation measures:

CLASS IV: Fairly good land, best suited to pasture and hay. Can be cultivated occasionally with careful erosion prevention practices.

LANDS UNSUITED FOR CULTIVATION—CLASS V: Land suited for grazing or woodland use with few limitations. Nearly level, with little or no erosion, but too wet, stony, or otherwise not suited to cultivation.

CLASS VI: Land suited for grazing or forestry with some limitations. Too steep, eroded, shallow, wet or dry for cultivation.

CLASS VII: Land suited for grazing or forestry with extreme care to prevent erosion or other damage. Usually too steep, rough, shallow or dry to be seeded to grass.

CLASS VIII: Land suited only for wildlife, recreational or watershed purposes. Usually extremely steep, rough, stony, sandy, wet or severely eroded.

REFERENCE—Edd Roberts. *Land Judging*. A field method study of soil and water conservation. University of Oklahoma Press, Norman, Okla.

SOIL CONSERVATION PRACTICES—Secure the assistance of the technician of your nearest Soil Conservation District to arrange a field trip to a local farm where up-to-date conservation measures are used. Arrange to have the technician act as a guide, with the farmer himself accompanying you and your group, to point out and explain the different practices that have been applied:

CONTOURING—Plowing, planting, cultivating, and harvesting sloping fields "on the level"—that is, along contour lines instead of along up-and-down-hill lines—in order to conserve water and reduce erosion.

CONTOUR FURROWING—Plowing furrows along contour lines to hold water.

COVER CROPS—Growing plants with dense tops and strong roots to protect soil from water and wind erosion.

FERTILIZATION—Adding plant food in the form of manure or commercial fertilizer to stimulate plant growth. GREEN MANURING is the adding of organic matter to the soil by turning under green grass crops, grain, or legumes.

CROP ROTATION—Alternating various crops on a piece of land, from year to year, to keep the soil productive and to improve it.

STRIP CROPPING—Growing strips on the contour of close-growing plants (such as grass or clover) between strips of row crops (such as corn or beets) to hold water and to catch soil eroding from the row crop strips.

TERRACING—Ridging the land nearly on the contour to hold rainfall and slow down runoff water.

STUBBLE MULCHING—Leaving soil-improving crops and crop residues (such as grain stubble, straw, cornstalks, lespedeza) on the ground without turning them under, to protect the soil from erosion and baking.

PASTURE DEVELOPMENT AND IMPROVEMENT—Developing new pasture with selected grasses and legumes, increasing growth by such measures as fertilization, liming, drainage, irrigation, fencing, weed control, fire protection.

PROTECTED WATER DISPOSAL OUTLETS—Stabilizing waterways for carrying off excess water, by grasses, legumes, and vines.

DRAINAGE—Providing ditches or tile drains for the removal of excess water from wet land.

IRRIGATION DEVELOPMENT AND IMPROVEMENT—Bringing in water by canals and ditches and managing it for most effective use in growing crops.

GULLY CONTROL—Using plants and mechanical means to prevent and stop the formation of gullies. Protecting eroded land from further damage by planting it with trees, shrubs, grasses or vines.

PONDS AND POND MANAGEMENT—Establishing ponds by impounding water by dams or digging and protecting it against siltation.

WATER SPREADING—By the use of dikes and dams spreading runoff water from slopes and gullies over land that needs it.

WINDBREAK AND SHELTER BELT—Planting living trees and shrubs to reduce the force of the wind, thereby cutting down wind erosion and creating better growing conditions.

Wood lot management—Using land primarily suitable for tree growing for the production of a wood crop.

reference—Albert B. Foster. *Approved Practices in Soil Conservation.* Interstate Printers and Publishers, Danville, Ill.

ABANDONED FARM—Take a field trip to an abandoned farm. On the basis of having studied proper conservation practices on a well-run farm, determine what might have caused the deterioration of the abandoned farm and the farming methods that might have saved .it.

Field Experiments in Soil and Water Conservation

The most effective use of land and the proper conservation of soil and water depend on the nature of the soil, the way it absorbs water, its fertility, the slope of the land, the amount of rainfall it receives, and several other things.

Some of the methods used for determining the quality and capability of soils involve simple experiments that can be performed by a single person or a group.

SOIL INVESTIGATION—Soil profile—One of the items of the greatest importance to a person investigating a piece of land is to know the thickness and composition of the layers of different kinds of soil that make it up. These layers—or soil "horizons"—can be found by digging a hole in the sampling area and investigating the "profile" of the excavation.

Dig a hole in the ground, wide enough so that you can

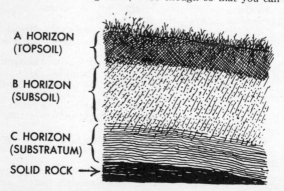

A HORIZON (TOPSOIL)

B HORIZON (SUBSOIL)

C HORIZON (SUBSTRATUM)

SOLID ROCK →

A hole in the ground will lay open the soil "profile" so that you can study the layers—"horizons"—of the soil.

squat in it and can see the various layers the whole way
down to the bottom. Dig down through the *A horizon*
(the topsoil containing organic matter), the *B horizon*
(the subsoil consisting of mineral matter only), and the
C horizon (the substratum of soft rock) to solid rock.
Use a sharp spade so that you can smooth off at least
one side of the hole to make the horizons clearly visible.

> *Tip*—If you are interested solely in learning the gen-
> eral aspects of a soil profile, you can save yourself a
> lot of work by finding a roadbank or a gully where
> it may be only necessary to slice off the weathered
> front to establish a clearly delineated perpendicular
> surface. Also excavations for water lines, basements.

After having cut the profile, measure the different
horizons and take notes of their color (from deepest black
to whitish gray or yellow), their texture (from clay and
silt to coarse sand), their structure (from single grains
to distinctly defined aggregate masses), their consistency
(from crumbly to stiff).

SOIL SAMPLING—When it is not feasible to dig out a
soil profile, you can use a soil auger to bring up soil

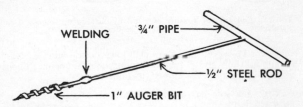

An inexpensive soil auger may be made by welding an old auger
bit to a steel rod and providing this with a crossbar.

samples from various depths. The soil auger consists of
an iron rod ending in a 6-inch-long auger bit, of a diameter of 1 to 1½ inches. The opposite end of the soil auger
is provided with a crossbar for ease in driving it into the
ground.

> *Tip*—Instead of buying a regular soil auger, have a
> local welding shop weld an old 1-inch auger bit to
> one end of a 30-inch length of ½-inch steel rod. Weld
> a 1-foot length of ¾-inch pipe crosswise to the other
> end to provide a handle. Make file marks on the steel
> rod, 1 inch apart, for measuring purposes.

Push the soil auger straight into the ground to the

desired depth. Then screw it 6 inches farther down into the soil layer you want to sample. Now pull the rod straight up—the soil sample will come up in the auger.

Soil texture—The texture of a soil can be determined by settling the soil in water.

Fill a 1-quart screw-top jar two-thirds full of water. Add soil to be studied to almost fill the jar. Screw on the top. Shake the jar vigorously, then set it aside.

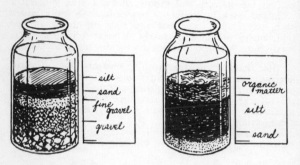

You can find out the texture of a soil by shaking up some soil in water, then letting it stand until it settles.

Tip—To speed up the settling process, add ¼ teaspoon alum and 1 teaspoon household ammonia. Then shake. Settling is almost instantaneous.

After the soil has settled, measure the various layers into which the particles have settled and note your findings.

Tip—Simplest way of recording your findings is to note them on a 3×5-inch file card placed next to the jar. Mark off on the card the various layers, with a designation of their consistency: silt, sand, pebbles.

Soil testing—Various tests can be used to find the chemical reaction of the soil and to determine whether or not certain important elements are present.

The chemical reaction of the soil can be ascertained by the use of long-range pH test paper on a moistened sample, as described on page 257. Acid soil will have a reaction of 6.5 pH or less, neutral soil between 6.6 and 7.3 pH, alkaline soil 7.4 pH or more.

Note—For a complete soil analysis, ask your local County Agricultural Agent or drop a line to the

Extension Service of your state's Department of Agriculture for information on how and where to send samples for testing.

SOIL CONTENTS—The higher the organic contents, the better the soil. On the spot where you want to investigate the contents of the soil, trim off all the aboveground vegetation down to the soil surface with a pair of grass clippers. Then dig out ¼ cubic foot of soil, by making a hole 8½ inches square, 6 inches deep. Or simpler, dig out enough to fill a No. 10 tin can (1 gallon).

Spread out the soil on heavy wrapping paper or newspaper, a small amount at a time, and carefully separate the parts of it into the following groupings: organic matter—decaying leaves, stalks, roots, seeds; animal life —worms, grubs, insects, spiders, others; mineral matter —large pebbles, small pebbles, finer particles.

Tip—By using sieves of various mesh—½-inch, ¼-inch, ⅛-inch, ¹⁄₁₆-inch—you can separate the soil particles into even more exactly measurable parts.

If you like, you can place the components of a soil sample in a number of screw-top jars to make possible a comparison with the contents of samples taken from other localities

SOIL FERTILITY—The fertility of a certain soil is generally evident from the plant cover that grows on it: rank, healthy, sparse.

If you want to study comparative fertility of various soil samples, bring enough of each sample home with you to fill a small flower pot. Plant a few beans in each pot and water regularly with the same amount of water to each sample. Compare the growth of the plants sprouting from the beans.

LOCAL LOSS OF TOPSOIL—Locate in your community an old stone or rail fence running up a hillside. Using a soil auger (see page 371), find the depth of the topsoil close to the fence. Next determine the depth of the topsoil of the field next to the fence. What is the difference?

Similarly compare the depth of topsoil of nearby field that has not been tilled for years, a well-seeded pasture, woodland, and so on.

DEGREE OF EROSION LOSS—After a heavy rain, collect runoff water from different types of land in 1-quart screw-top jars. Cover the jars and set them aside for a few hours, or until sediment has settled and water above is clear. Measure amount of silt in the different water samples. Compare the silts from runoffs from a gully in cultivated land, a meadow stream, a woodland brook, and so on.

DETERMINING SLOPE—The greater the slope of a piece of land, the greater the danger of loss of topsoil through erosion. The slope of land is measured in per cent. This per cent of slope, by definition, is the "rise" (the difference in height between two points), divided by the "run" (the horizontal distance between the two points), times 100.

To determine a slope, use two yardsticks and a carpenter's level. Make a mark on one yardstick at the 33⅓-inch point. Place this yardstick horizontally, with its zero end touching the slope. Place the level on the stick and move the stick's free end up or down until the bubble of the level indicates that the stick is horizontal. With the second yardstick measure the distance to the ground from the bottom edge of the horizontal stick at the 33⅓-inch mark. The number of inches, multiplied by 3, gives the per cent of slope.

If the "rise," for instance, as measured with the vertically held yardstick, is 8 inches, and the "run" is 33⅓

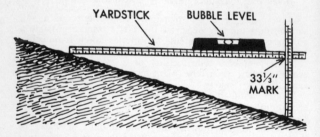

Two yardsticks and a bubble level make it possible for you to determine the degree of a slope.

inches, as measured on the horizontal yardstick, the per cent of slope is

$$\frac{8}{33\frac{1}{3}} \times 100 = 8 \times \frac{100}{33\frac{1}{3}} = 8 \times 3 = 24 \text{ per cent}$$

WATER-SOIL INVESTIGATION—WATER ABSORPTION—To test the ability of different soils to absorb water, secure as many No. 5 tall tin cans (fruit-juice or tomato-juice cans) as you have soils to test. Remove both ends of each can. Scratch a mark with a nail on the side of each can, 2 inches from the edge. In addition to these marked cans you need a 5-inch square of 1-inch board, a hammer, a watch, a ruler, a 1-quart can or other quart measure, and a gallon jar with water.

Place a can on a test spot, with the end closest to the 2-inch scratch mark on the ground. Place the board on top of the can and hammer on the board until you have driven the can into the ground to the 2-inch mark. Measure out 1 quart of water and pour it into the can. Jot down in your notebook the time of the pouring. Then take further notes on the water absorption: measure the

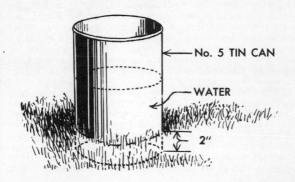

← No. 5 TIN CAN

← WATER

2″

Use a tin can with both ends removed to learn the way in which different soils absorb water.

distance from the edge of can to water surface every minute for the first 10 minutes, then every 10 minutes, or until all water has been absorbed, depending on the type of soil.

In this manner, test the following soils and learn their comparable rates of water absorption: woodland soil with litter of dead leaves on top, bare woodland soil, tramped-down woodland path, grassland, cultivated field, cultivated field eroded down to subsoil.

WATER-HOLDING ABILITY—With a heavy nail, punch a number of holes in the bottom of two or more coffee cans or No. 10 tin cans. Pack the cans half full of soil from different localities: woodland, grassland, cultivated field, and so on. Prop each can over a glass container. Pour two cups of water into each can. Determine from the amount of water coming through, the degree of water-holding ability of each soil.

Demonstrations of Soil and Water Conservation

A number of easily arranged exhibits can be used to demonstrate to a group of interested people various problems connected with soil and water conservation and their solutions.

WATER EROSION DEMONSTRATIONS—To show different kinds of erosion, make up two erosion demonstration trays. The 25×12-inch bottom may be cut from ½-inch plywood or made from scrap wood. The two sides are made from 4-inch-wide strips of ½-inch wood, 25 inches long. One end piece is $½ \times 4 \times 11$ inches, the other $½ \times 3 \times 11$ inches. After assembling the boxes, nail a strip of tin cut from a No. 10 can or coffee can under the shallow end of each of them. Shape the tin in such a way that it will act as a spout to carry water flowing over the 3-inch endpiece in a narrow stream into a glass jar. Line the trays with aluminum foil or sheet plastic to make them watertight.

CROP COVER AND EROSION—To demonstrate how crop cover cuts down erosion, place a 3-inch-thick sod, cut to size, from a lawn or pasture in one tray; fill the other tray with a 3-inch layer of soil from the same place, but without grass or any other crop. Set the two trays on a table with the tin spouts protruding beyond the edge. Place an empty quart jar below each spout. Prop up the opposite end of the trays with blocks of wood to create a slope.

> *Tip*—According to the formula on page 374, a 1-inch-high prop ("rise") under the edge of a 25-inch-long tray ("run") will give a 4 per cent slope. Steeper slopes can be established as follows: 2 inches—8 per cent; 3 inches—12 per cent; 4 inches—16 per cent; 5 inches—20 per cent.

With the trays in position, sprinkle over them simultaneously 1 pint of water from each of two plastic squeeze-bottle clothes sprinklers. In the tray with the sod much of the water will be retained—the runoff will be slow and the water flowing into the jar will be almost clear. In the tray with the bare soil the water will create sheet erosion and miniature gullies—the runoff will be fast and the water flowing into the jar will be muddy.

MULCHING AND EROSION—Using the two erosion demonstration trays, fill both of them with the same kind of soil and flatten down the surface. Cover the soil in one tray with a layer of grass cuttings or straw; leave the other uncovered. Again use the clothes sprinklers as rain makers and "rain" down over the two trays. Compare the difference in runoff from the mulched and unmulched soil.

FURROW LINES AND EROSION—Again, fill both trays with the same kind of soil and flatten down the surface. In

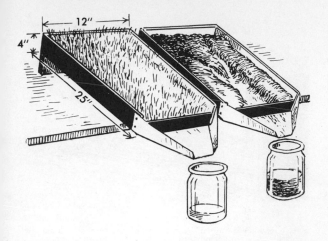

Two erosion demonstration trays can be used to demonstrate the effect of flowing water on bare soil, mulched soil, crop land.

one tray, make crosswise, horizontal furrow lines with a finger or stick; in the other, make up-and-down-hill furrow lines. Pour water over both trays. Study effect and compare amount of soil washed off each tray.

Tip—Instead of using the erosion demonstration trays, the effect of furrow lines may be shown on two even mounds of firmly packed soil. Make circular furrow lines with your finger around one mound; make lines from top to bottom of the other mound. Then sprinkle water from a sprinkling can on top of each mound and study the result.

SPLASH EROSION—Beating rain breaks up the surface of the soil before carrying it away. To show this splash erosion, prepare two "splashboards" from pieces of ½-inch wood, 4 inches wide, 18 inches long, pointed at one end to make it easy to drive them into the ground. Paint the boards white and mark them with inch marks, starting 6 inches from pointed end. Nail a piece of tin, 4×6 inches, as a protecting roof to the unpointed end of each board (see illustration page 378).

Drive the two boards, to a depth of 6 inches, into two locations with different kinds of cover. After a rain, compare the amount of soil splashed onto each board and the height the splashes reached.

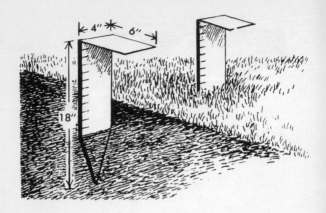

Splash erosion is caused by rain falling on bare soil. Make two "splashboards" to demonstrate the danger of splash erosion.

Tip—By tacking 2-inch strips of blotting paper to the splashboards, a permanent record can be made of the splashing.

Instead of going into the field, you can set up the splashboards in conjunction with two erosion demonstration trays containing different kinds of soils. Use a sprinkling can to simulate rain. Sprinkle the same amount of water from the same height (about 4 feet) the same distance from each board (about 1 foot). Then compare the splashes.

WIND EROSION DEMONSTRATION—Fill two erosion demonstration trays with dry sand. Place them in a level position on a table or on the floor. Place a cardboard shield around one end of each tray. These shields may be made by cutting the top and one end off two cardboard boxes of appropriate size.

Leave one tray of sand untouched. Crosswise in the other, stick a row of short, leafy branches (to suggest a windbreak), and a row of evergreen twigs (to suggest a hedgerow), and place a layer of cut grass (to suggest mulching).

Put up two electric fans at the unshielded ends of the two trays.

Start up the fans and watch the effect. After a few minutes, stop the fans and compare the amount of sand blown onto the two cardboard shields.

Field Projects in Soil and Water Conservation

"Charity begins at home." So does soil and water conservation. It begins with an opening of the eyes to features around the home grounds that involve conservation and a determination to do something about those practices that are inconsistent with good conservation. With the home conditions taken care of, the next steps may be the school grounds, the Scout camp, and, eventually, the local watershed or other public lands.

HOME PROJECTS

LAWN CONSTRUCTION—The level-surfaced lawn generally presents no problems beyond mowing and watering. The lawn on the sloping surface is a different matter. To establish it, it may be necessary to lay a strip of sod along the top of the slope and another at the bottom of the slope and to sow deep-rooting grass mixtures between them. To keep the soil and seeds from washing down before the grass roots are formed, the area may have to be covered with a mulch of straw or even with burlap held down along the edges with sods. A particularly steep slope may have to be sodded in its entirety rather than seeded.

Even after being established, the sloping lawn has to be watched. If it shows signs of sheet erosion, it will need to have its soil replenished and its surface mulched.

SOIL IMPROVEMENT—If the plants growing around your home grounds seem healthy and thriving your soil is in good condition. If the opposite is the case, it is evident

Wind erosion can be shown with a tray filled with dry soil, and an electric fan. Catch dust in shield made from cardboard box.

that the soil is deficient in some of the nutrients that ensure healthy growth. It may be lacking in organic matter or in any of a number of chemical elements.

Rather than attempting to guess at the needs of your soil, have a test made of it as suggested on page 372. Then follow the recommendations of the soil specialist.

COMPOST HEAP—The addition of humus will enrich any soil. Some of this humus you can manufacture yourself by establishing a "compost heap." In such a heap, all kinds of vegetable matter is decomposed into a rich, friable soil supplement. Instead of burning leaves, discarding lawn clippings, throwing out dead flowers and kitchen vegetable refuse (potato peels, melon rinds, wilted lettuce, pea shells, etc.), you salvage them to improve your garden soil.

Pick a suitable, inconspicuous corner of the garden for your proposed compost heap. Here, dig up and turn over the soil over an area about 4×6 feet. Cover the area with a 3- to 4-inch layer of manure if you can get it easily. If not, simply start dumping cut grass, leaves, and other vegetable matter on the area. When a 4-inch layer has built up, sprinkle it lightly with hydrated lime, bone meal, commercial fertilizer or one of the garden products specifically developed for compost heaps. Cover with a 2-inch layer of topsoil. Continue in this manner with alternate layers of vegetable matter, fertilizer, and topsoil, slanting the sides slightly toward the middle, until the pile has reached a height of about 3 feet. Then start another.

Keep the top of the heap somewhat concave so that it will collect whatever rain falls. If the weather is dry, wet down the heap regularly.

If the heap was started one spring, the compost should be decomposed sufficiently by the following spring to be spaded into your garden soil.

WATERING—Any householder knows enough about conservation of water to have faucets fixed as soon as they start leaking. But a great many of them waste water through improper watering practices. Here are three simple rules for watering:

Water only as needed. Do not water until the ground has become fairly dry and the plants show an actual need of water by drooping slightly. To most plants, too much water is as bad as too little.

Water generously when you do water. Surface sprinkling encourages shallow roots, susceptible to the slightest drying out of the topmost layer of the soil; it also wastes water through a high evaporation loss. Instead of sprinkling, soak. Remove nozzle or sprinkler. Replace with perforated hose or canvas hose, or permit water to flow in a gentle stream from the end of the hose. When one spot has been soaked, move the hose to another area.

Tip—Place end of hose on a board or a piece of canvas to prevent the water from washing a hole in the ground.

Water in the evening. The evaporation loss is less in the evening than in the middle of the day. Also the water is retained far better after the soil has cooled, therefore benefits the plants for a longer period.

GROUP PROJECTS

A group of adults interested in conservation or an organized youth group, such as Boy Scouts or Girl Scouts, can often perform a valuable service to their community by discovering areas in need of conservation practices and giving their time and efforts to remedy the situation. Projects suited for group action involve certain types of erosion control, gully fighting, and stream bank protection.

EROSION CONTROL—Volunteer groups in many parts of the country have helped salvage watersheds whose natural cover had been destroyed by fire. Others have rescued overgrazed hillsides from erosion. Still others have reconditioned recreational areas. Sometimes seeding with grass did the job; at other times planting was necessary.

JOHNNY GRASS SEED—In 1949, the Grand Valley Chapter of the Izaak Walton League of America in Grand Junction, Col., conceived the Johnny Grass Seed idea as a modern counterpart of Johnny Appleseed. The plan was to popularize as a community project the reseeding of overgrazed range lands in the area. The members of the chapter put on a publicity campaign, secured contributions toward the purchase of grass seed and did the seeding with a large army of volunteer helpers. The idea has since been picked up by a long list of youth and adult organizations. It can be undertaken by any group of people from seven to seventy strong enough to bend over and scratch up a little soil with a stick.

For a Johnny Grass Seed project to be a success, these steps need to be taken: Establish an enthusiastic and vigorous committee to spearhead the project. Secure the technical assistance of local experts: County Agent, Soil Conservation Service technician, state conservation officer, or other qualified person. Decide on the type and extent of the project. Publicize the project thoroughly. Secure the necessary amount of seed and line up the needed equipment. Make arrangement for packaging and

distributing the seeds, with clear instructions to be followed. Plan and run the program of the actual field
project.

REFERENCE—*Johnny Grass Seed—A Conservation Action
Project.* Izaak Walton League of America, 1326 Wau-
kegan Road, Glenview, Ill.

PLANTING—Where tree planting rather than seeding is
indicated to prevent erosion, follow the suggestions on
pages 298-99 and page 392.

GULLY FIGHTING—Gullies carry away good topsoil,
reduce crop yield of adjacent fields, endanger livestock,
reduce the value of a farm—may undermine farm buildings and highways and create other havoc. The fight
against gully formation is a relentless one. It can only be
won through vigilance and speedy action.

Farmers keep a wary eye on their farmland. They try
to prevent gullying through proper farming methods. But
gullies may form many other places. An unprotected road
cut, a path from a campsite down to the swimming area,
a short cut across the school grounds, the ruts of truck
tires up over a field—and a gully may get a start. The
best way to fight it is to eliminate the cause and to check
the damage already done.

PLANTING—The most satisfactory method for stopping
a small or medium-sized gully is by diverting the water
that may flow into it, at least temporarily, and by planting it to grasses and legumes, shrubs and trees suitable
to the location in which you live.

GRASSES AND LEGUMES—Bluegrass, redtop, Bermuda,
brome, Napier, Kikuyu, clovers, lespedezas.

SHRUBS—Viburnums, dogwoods, chokeberry, wild plum,
sugar sumac, coralberry, multiflora rose, autumn olive.

TREES—Black locust, catalpa, cottonwood, green ash,
hackberry, honey locust, mulberry, Osage orange, pines,
willows.

CHECK DAMS—Where the soil is too poor for planting,
a small to medium gully may be healed with a check dam
that will collect and hold soil carried into it and eventually permit plants to grow.

WOVEN-WIRE DAM—To establish a woven-wire dam, set
a row of short posts across the gully, with a slight curve
toward downstream. Dig a small ditch, about 6 inches
wide and 6 inches deep, on the upstream side of the row
of posts. Place heavy-gauge woven wire against the posts,
with the coarse mesh in the ditch. Staple wire to the
posts. Form an apron from brush by pushing the butt
ends through the wire mesh from the downstream side
and anchoring them in the mesh. Then pack fine brush,

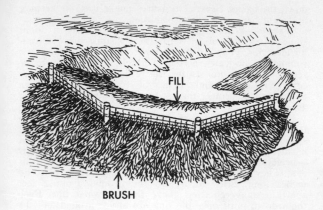

A check dam made from heavy-gauge woven wire, brush, and fill can be used to heal a gully.

straw, earth and sod against the upstream side of the wire mesh to the height you want the dam to be. •

BRUSH DAMS—Where plenty of brush is available, this may be used for a gully dam. Place a thin layer of straw, about 10 feet wide, across the gully. Pack brush on top of the mulch, with butt ends pointing upstream, until the brush layer has reached the desired height. Place stakes upright in among the brush, in rows that run crosswise to the gully. Drive them only part way down, then stretch galvanized wire along the rows and fasten it to the stakes. Continue driving down the stakes until the wire holds the brush layers.

LOOSE-ROCK DAMS—Where rocks are in good supply, a rock dam is easily built. Make a ditch across the gully, about 12 inches deep, 2 feet wide or wider. Place a rock foundation in the ditch. Then build up the rocks in over-lapping layers until the dam has reached the proper height. The flatter the rocks the better. Keep the middle of the dam lower than the sides to form a spillway. Below the spillway, make an apron by sinking a number of rocks into the ground in such a way that the top of them is flush with the surface. Pack fill and sod against the upstream side of the dam.

STREAM BANK PROTECTION—Many stream banks are exposed to erosion from seasonal floods that turn the stream into a soil-eating torrent and form gullies tearing down the banks. Several measures can be used for keeping a stream bank in healthy condition.

SEEDING—Where the stream bank has only a slight slope it may be seeded with the "pasture mix" recommended for your area. Perform this task during the summer's low-water period. Scratch up the area to be seeded with a rake, scatter the seeds, then rake again to cover with soil. A light mulch of straw, manure or lawn clippings will protect the seeds from blowing or washing away.

PLANTING—Willows are particularly suitable for protecting a stream bank. Their strong water-seeking root system will quickly stabilize the bank. Cut a number of hardwood cuttings from last year's growth of a willow —preferably purple osier, black, brittle or weeping willow. They should be from $\frac{3}{16}$ to $\frac{1}{2}$ inch thick, 12 to 18 inches long. Stick them into the ground about 2 feet apart in staggered rows above the low-water line. Push them down until only the tips are above ground and the butt ends are below water level. Use a planting bar if necessary. If planted in the spring or early summer the cuttings will soon sprout roots.

A stream-bank willow planting requires regular maintenance. For greatest effectiveness the plants should be cut down periodically to keep the shoots thin and pliable so that they will flatten over the stream bank during high-water periods.

RIPRAP—If heavy, angular stones are available, these may be used to protect a sloping stream bank. Place the first rows of stones, masonry fashion, against the "toe" (lower portion) of the bank, starting from the bottom of the stream. Continue up the bank to the possible flood height. For further protection, plant willow, dogwood, alder above the stone setting. Their roots will help keep the stones in place.

FARMING AND LARGE AREA PROJECTS—It is not the province of this book to deal with large-scale soil and water conservation problems. If you happen to be a farmer or other landowner, a camp director or a manager of a recreational area, you should secure technical advice and assistance through your local Soil Conservation District. You can get this help by contacting your County Agricultural Agent (for address and telephone number, see your telephone book).

14. FORESTRY AND FOREST
CONSERVATION

TO a great number of people, a forest is simply a collection of trees. They like the forest for its greenness, its coolness—as a recreation area. They know that trees provide them with timber and fuel wood and a great number of other products. But few of them realize the other values of the forest: as pantry and shelter and living space for wildlife, as protection for a watershed, as a windbreak against the forces of the wind

When the early settlers came to America, the timber resources of the country seemed inexhaustible, the land occupied by forests highly desirable for farming. And so, thousands of square miles of forest land were stripped—to the detriment of the generations that followed. It is only recently that a semblance of balance has again been restored—of trees being planted where trees were being cut, in order to provide for a continuous supply of forest products and to perpetuate forest preserves for wildlife, watershed protection and human recreation.

BOOKS ON FORESTRY—Charles H. Stoddard. *Essentials of Forestry Practice.* Ronald Press.

John F. Preston. *Developing Farm Woodlands.* McGraw-Hill Book Company.

H. A. Meyer, ed. *Forest Management.* Ronald Press.

Trees: Yearbook of Agriculture 1949. U. S. Department of Agriculture.

WORKING WITH OTHER PEOPLE

As in the case of other conservation projects, a large number of forestry projects can be undertaken by people having little technical knowledge but large amounts of enthusiasm. For best results, it pays to seek the help of federal and state forestry experts.

GOVERNMENT AGENCIES—FEDERAL—U. S. Department of Agriculture. Forest Service.
STATE—Department of Forestry.
COUNTY—County forester or forest ranger.

SOCIETIES—American Forestry Association. Hdqrs.: 919 17th Street, N.W., Washington 6, D. C. Periodical: *American Forest.*
American Forest Product Industries. Hdqrs.: 1816 N Street, N.W., Washington 6, D. C. Periodicals: *Forestry Digest; American Tree Farmer.*
Western Forestry and Conservation Association. Hdqrs.: 712 U. S. National Bank Building, Portland 4, Ore.
Also general conservation societies, page 353.

REFERENCES—*Bibliography of Forest Industry Educational Materials.* Available free from American Forest Products Industries—for address, see above.

Field Observation in Forestry

STUDY OF YOUNG FOREST—Locate an area where a forest is in the process of establishing itself or is regenerating after fire, storm or cutting. Look particularly for the following:

OLD FIELDS—What trees are coming up? Were their seeds brought in by wind (ash, basswood, maple, birch, sycamore, spruce) or birds (red cedar, wild cherry) or animals (hickory, walnut, butternut, oak, beech)? Which have made the greatest growth?

BURNED-OVER AREAS—Has a large number of trees been burned? Did any trees survive the fire? What kind were they? Do they have fire scars at base? What did the fire do to the forest floor? Evidence of erosion? What kind of plants have made a start?

PASTURED WOODLANDS—Compare a pastured woodland with one that is kept free of grazing. Note especially the effect of grazing on young trees and on the forest floor. Is a "browse line" apparent? Do seedlings show healthy growth or are they stunted and deformed? Is there evidence of erosion?

TREE DISEASES—Determine evidence of tree diseases. What kind are they? What causes them? Can they be cured or prevented from spreading?

INSECT ENEMIES—Evidence of insects eating leaves or inner bark, insects cutting twigs, insects boring in bark or wood? What damage have they done? Can they be eliminated?

STORM DAMAGE—Presence of windfalls? Damage caused to other trees and to undergrowth? Fire danger from broken limbs?

CLEAR-CUT AREAS—Find out from stumps the age of the trees at time of cutting. What kinds of trees were they? Do height of stumps show evidence of good forest practices? Are piles of slash in evidence? Has any effort been made toward replanting area? What new trees have come into the area? Of what does the undergrowth consist? Evidence of erosion?

PARTIALLY CUT AREA—Find out from stumps what trees were cut and their age. Does cutting show evidence of good forest practices? Were enough saplings left to completely regenerate the area?

ESTABLISHED FOREST—Take a field trip to a properly managed, established forest—such as a local forest experiment station or a private forest area where correct methods of forestry are practiced. Secure permission in advance from the forester in charge or the owner of the property, and arrange to have a local forest technician accompany you and your group. As far as possible, familiarize yourself with terms used in forestry and observe the practices that have been applied.

TYPE OF FOREST—Is it a hardwood forest, a conifer forest, or a forest of mixed hardwoods and conifers? What are the principal species? Are the trees of an even diameter and height or are trees of varying sizes distributed throughout the area?

TREE SIZES—A tree not yet 3 feet high, grown from a seed, is called a *seedling*. A sprout from an old tree, not yet 3 feet high, is a *shoot*. A *small sapling* is a young tree between 3 and 10 feet high. A *large sapling* is a tree more than 10 feet high but less than 4 inches in diameter at breast height (d.b.h.). A *small pole* is a tree 4 to 8 inches in diameter. A *large pole* is a tree 8 to 12 inches thick. A *standard* is a tree 1 to 2 feet thick. A *veteran* is a tree more than 2 feet thick.

STANDS OF TREES—A stand of seedlings is a *seedling growth*. Saplings form a *brushwood* or *thicket*. Poles make up a *polewood*. A stand of saplings is a *young timber*; of veterans, an *old timber*.

IMPROVEMENT CUTTINGS—CLEANINGS OR WEEDINGS—Removing undesirable "weed trees" (trees of little or no commercial value), as well as diseased, insect-infested, and decayed trees.

THINNINGS—Reducing the number of trees in an immature stand when they have become overcrowded, to

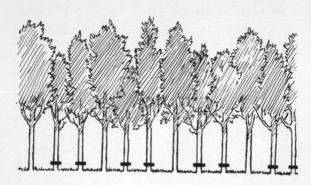

Thinning is the process of cutting out a number of trees to permit the remaining trees to get an added spurt of life. For suggestion about number of trees to remove, see page 393.

improve the composition, quality and rate of growth of the remaining trees.

LIBERATION or RELEASE CUTTINGS—Removing "wolf trees" (large trees with wide-spreading crowns over-topping and stunting the growth of more desirable younger trees), as well as poorly formed trees no longer growing at a profitable rate, and salvaging trees damaged by storm or fire.

PRUNING—Removing the lower branches, living or dead, from a tree to produce higher quality of timber with fewer knots. Usually confined to coniferous trees.

GIRDLING—Killing a tree without having to cut it down by making, with an ax, a complete ring of hacks ("frills") around the trunk through the bark and cambium at least ½ inch into the sapwood.

HARVEST CUTTINGS—Removing trees for use as timber. In *selective cutting* (the recommended method for harvesting a mixed-age forest) selected, mature trees are removed as single, scattered trees or in small groups, leaving a growing stand for a future cut. In *clear cutting* all "merchantable trees" (trees over 6 inches in diameter at breast height) are removed in one cut. In *seed-tree cutting* at least ten healthy, vigorous trees are left on each acre to reseed the area. In *diameter-limit cutting* trees of a certain diameter at breast height are removed.

REFERENCES—*Managing the Small Forest*. Farmers' Bulletin No. 1989. U. S. Department of Agriculture.

John Frederick Preston. *Developing Farm Woodlands*. McGraw-Hill Book Company.

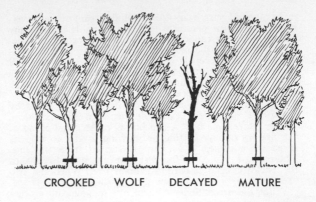

CROOKED   WOLF   DECAYED   MATURE

In liberation or release cuttings, "wolf trees" and deformed trees
are removed and mature trees are harvested.

FOREST FIRE CONTROL—Find out from your state
forestry service how forest fires are controlled in your
state. If possible, have a local forester, or forest ranger,
or fire warden arrange for a demonstration, in which
you can have your group take an active part, of the controlling of a small fire.

KINDS OF FIRES—Most common fire is the *surface fire.*
In this, the flames sweep through litter on the forest
floor, ignite the underbrush, destroy young trees, lick up
the trunks of older trees and scorch the lower branches.
If the flames should jump up into the treetops, the fire has
become a *crown fire*—the most destructive of all and the
hardest to extinguish. A *ground fire* (or turf or duff fire)
may burn unnoticed under the forest floor for several days
and then suddenly break into a surface fire. A *stem* or
tree fire involves a single tree, ignited by lightning, by a
spark from an engine or some other way.

A forest fire usually spreads in an oval shape, its head
broad or acute, depending on wind, fuel, and slope of
ground. It may eventually assume a V shape.

FIRE-FIGHTING TOOLS—Find out what tools are best
suited for fighting a small fire in the woods of your area
and learn to use them in controlling a fire. These tools
may include hoe or rake for cleaning firebreaks, ax for
chopping down burning snags, shovel to throw dirt on the
fire, fire swatter for beating out the flames (pine top, burlap bag, special swatter), back tanks with hand pumps.

Tip—An effective fire swatter may be produced by
attaching a piece of old belting to a hoe handle.

ATTACKING THE FIRE—A small fire can often be extinguished by the person who discovers it. If there is any chance that you cannot handle it alone, report it immediately: rush to the nearest telephone and tell the operator, "I want to report a forest fire!" The operator will connect you with the local fire warden. Tell him the exact location of the fire. While waiting for his arrival, do what you can to prevent the fire from spreading.

Generally, a fire is attacked at its head and flanks by the *direct method* of beating it out or wetting it down. In the *indirect method,* a fire line is constructed ahead of the fire by raking, cutting or plowing a trail to stop its spread. Sometimes, a *backfire* is started from this line. The updraft created by the heat from the main fire makes the backfire burn toward the main fire. When the two fires meet they both die out through lack of fuel.

When the fire is under control, the mopping-up process follows, of completely extinguishing smoldering stumps and forest debris. This work continues until every ember is killed, until the fire is dead out.

The fighting of a large fire is a job for professional fire fighters using special equipment. Nevertheless, an informed amateur may be able to render great assistance.

Field Projects in Forestry

More and more, small and large communities throughout the country realize the importance of forest areas within their borders for recreational purposes, for watershed protection, for the production of forest products, for providing outdoor laboratories for schools, youth groups and clubs. In addition, the Boy Scouts, Girl Scouts, and other youth movements continually seek to expand and improve their camp holdings in order to provide the opportunities for outdoor living which their programs call for.

Working with other people in your community and in close touch with your County Agent and extension forester you may be instrumental in establishing and maintaining a community forest area or in helping local youth movements develop their forest areas.

REFERENCES—*Community Forests.* U. S. Department of Agriculture, Forestry Service. Cat. No. A13.2:C73/9. *Town Forests.* Free. American Tree Association, 1214 16th Street, Washington 6, D. C.

ARBOR DAY—Arbor Day would be an appropriate day on which to undertake a community forestry project.

Each state observes Arbor Day on its own date, according to the best local time for tree planting. In three states, Arbor Day is a legal holiday: Florida (third

Friday in January), Nebraska (April 22), and Utah (last Friday in April).

For program material and suggestions for ceremonies for Arbor Day, check with your state's conservation department or your state forester.

REFERENCE—*Arbor Day*. American Forestry Association, 919 17th Street, N.W., Washington 6, D. C.

FOREST PLANTING—PREPARATION OF SITE—Generally, the site for a forest planting requires little or no preparation. If it is partly covered by shrubs some of these may have to be removed, but normally shrubs will protect the young trees rather than interfere with their growth. If the planting is on grassland, turn back a turf, 12 to 15 inches square, where a tree is to be planted to hold back encroaching grass and weeds until the tree has become established.

SPACING AND ALIGNMENT—In some instances, uneven spacing and no alignment of the trees being planted are preferable in order to give the forest-to-be a "natural" look. If, on the other hand, the planting is designed for the purpose of eventually producing harvestable trees, the seedlings should be properly spaced and aligned to assure straight, long boles.

USING MARKERS—The lines can be laid out as described on page 298, using three markers for each. Working a two-man team, the first man makes the hole, lines himself up with the marker ahead, steps forward the agreed number of feet (two long paces for 6 feet, for instance), makes another hole and continues. The second man of the two-man team takes out a seedling from the pail in which he carries the plants, puts it in the ground, stamps the

A planting line with streamers of bright cloth tied to it can be used to assure even spacing of seedlings. See text next page.

dirt firmly around it, proceeds to the next planting hole, and so on. Any number of two-man teams can plant in this manner along marked lines.

USING PLANTING LINE—Another way of assuring regular spacing is through the use of a planting line. This is a long cord with streamers of bright cloth tied on it at proper interval of spacing. At each end, the cord is fastened to a stake. To start with, the two stakes are hammered into the ground with the cord taut between them. A seedling is then planted opposite to each colored streamer. When the first row is completed, the planting line is moved forward the proper number of feet and the second row of seedlings planted. And so on.

NUMBER OF TREES REQUIRED—For general planting, trees are set 6 feet apart in parallel rows 6 feet distant from each other. Slow-growing trees may be placed at 4-foot and fast-growing at 8-foot intervals.

The following table shows the number of trees that need to be ordered for planting 1 acre, depending on the spacing:

Spacing in feet	Number of trees per acre
4×4	2,722
5×5	1,742
6×6	1,210
6½×6½	1,000
7×7	889
8×8	680

PLANTING PROCEDURE—Plant the seedlings at the proper time (early spring or late fall) while the trees are dormant. For the actual procedure of planting follow the instructions on pages 298–99.

For a large planting, the process may be speeded up somewhat by using a special planting tool—planting bar or dibble—instead of the customary mattock. The dibble has a strong, straight blade, 3 inches wide, 10 inches long.

When planting, the dibble is pushed into the ground at an angle, pushed forward to upright position and removed. The seedling is placed in the hole with root collar at ground level. The dibble is now pushed straight down into the ground 2 inches from the plant, pulled back to firm the soil at the bottom of the roots, rocked forward to firm the soil at the top of the roots, then removed. Finally firm the dirt with the foot.

REFERENCES—Farmers' Bulletin 1123F *Growing and Planting Hardwood Seedlings* and Farmers' Bulletin 1453 *Growing and Planting Coniferous Trees on the Farm.* U. S. Department of Agriculture.

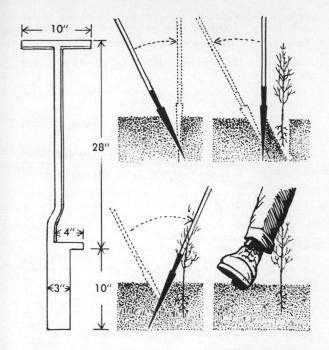

A planting bar or dibble simplifies the task of making planting holes and firming soil around the planted seedlings.

CARE OF FOREST—A few field trips with a forest technician through a properly managed forest will provide you with general information on the various practices for keeping a forest in good condition (see page 387). Of these, thinning and pruning require special care.

THINNING—When the crowns of the trees in a community forest, a camp, a wood lot are interlocking or when dying branches begin to appear, the time has come for a thinning operation—for cutting out a number of the trees to permit the others to get an added spurt of life. How extensive should such an operation be? How far apart should the trees be spaced after thinning?

The U. S. Forestry Service suggests using a simple rule for spacing hardwoods and southern pines after thinning called the "D+6" rule—in which D stands for the same number of feet as the number of inches of the average diameter of the trees involved. According to this rule, a tree 6 inches in diameter and another 8 inches in diameter should be spaced 13 feet apart $(\frac{6+8}{2}+6)$. A 7-inch and a 10-inch tree should be about 14½ feet apart.

Note—For western species, a similar rule—"D+4"—applies. Check with your farm forester.

Cut down the trees to be removed with ax or saw, leaving short stumps.

Tip—Chop some of the smaller trees halfway through only and bend down their crowns, as suggested on page 408, to create food and shelter for wildlife.

PRUNING—In pines and spruces, each side limb causes a knot in the trunk. The removing of the lower branches by pruning when the young trees have reached a diameter of 3 to 6 inches at breast height will assure at least one length of log from which clear lumber can be sawed when the trees reach maturity.

Do the pruning just before the growing season begins in the spring—and do a careful job so as not to injure the tree. Cut off the branches with a sharp pruning saw or with clippers—*never* with an ax. Make the cut flush with the bark, leaving no protruding stub. Use a pole saw for branches that are out of reach or get up on a ladder set firmly against the tree. Do not prune more than two-thirds of the total height of the tree.

INSECT AND DISEASE CONTROL—Most control methods for preventing insect and disease damage to a forest are expensive and hard to apply, even by professionals. Only a few projects are suitable for amateurs:

TENT CATERPILLARS—Tent caterpillars, under natural conditions, do little damage but fit into nature's scheme by providing food for certain birds. In recreational areas and orchards, their presence is undesirable—they defoliate the branches and thereby weaken the trees.

The simplest way of preventing tent caterpillar damage is to destroy the eggs during the winter or early spring before the caterpillars have a chance to emerge. The egg masses are found on twigs of apple and cherry —wild and cultivated—in the form of tight bands, about ½ inch wide, rounded at the ends and covered with a protective "varnish." Simply peel off the bands with your fingers and drop them in kerosene. Or cut off the twigs with a sharp knife and burn them.

If the "tents" have already been established, remove

them by twisting a stick up into them and pulling them down. Since the caterpillars are out feeding in the daytime, the job of removing their nests should be done in early morning or at dusk when the caterpillars are "home." Squash the caterpillars underfoot, or drop them in a pail of kerosene.

CANKER WORMS—Canker worms—also known as measuring worms, inchworms and loopers—may cause damage to certain shade and fruit trees by skeletonizing the leaves.

The female canker worm moth, emerging from her pupa in the ground, is wingless and must climb up a tree trunk for her egg laying. A ½ inch-wide band of sticky material around the trunk will trap her and smother her before she gets a chance to lay her eggs. Several brands of material suitable for the purpose are available through hardware stores and garden shops.

Since the fall canker worm moth emerges from its pupa in the ground in the fall and the spring canker worm in early spring, the bands should be applied in October and kept on until May to be effective.

WHITE PINE WEEVIL—In almost any planting of white pine a number of the young trees will be found to suffer from "leader trouble": the leader (the upright top shoot) is deformed and drooping—it looks like a shepherd's crook—because of the work of the grubs of the white pine weevil. The only way to overcome this leader trouble is by removing the damaged leader and establishing a new.

To do this, first cut off the deformed leader and burn it Then prune off all but one of the branches in the whirl directly under it. The branch that is left will eventually grow upward and form a new leader.

WHITE PINE BLISTER RUST—Millions of white pine trees are killed yearly by blister rust—a fungus disease spread by tiny, rust-colored spores carried by the wind from a host plant to the needles and twigs of the trees. The hosts are currant and gooseberry bushes, wild and cultivated. The only way to stop the blister rust is by eradicating the host plants within the traveling area radius of the spores of any stand of white pines—900 feet for common currants and gooseberries, one mile for European black currant. This job is performed by professional foresters in many parts of the United States. It can easily be done by interested volunteers.

Familiarize yourself with the looks of currant and gooseberry and teach your helpers to recognize them. Then spend some time in late spring or early summer pulling the plants up by the roots. Protect your hands with heavy gloves. Use a wrecking bar to help uproot especially persistent plants. Burn the plants.

Tip—In an area with a heavy infestation of currant and gooseberry, stake off small, square plots with wooden stakes and binder twine and go over every square inch of the area to be positive that all plants are pulled out.

ESTIMATING STANDING TIMBER—To estimate the lumber in a tree, a forester measures its diameter at breast height (d.b.h., 4½ feet) and its height in feet or in 16-foot-long lengths, then uses a special table that turns diameter and height into board-foot volume.

MEASURING DIAMETER—DIAMETER TAPE—When it is a matter of measuring the diameter of a few trees only, use a regular tape measure, as suggested on page 287, and divide the number of inches found by 3.1416 (π) to get the diameter in inches.

If you have to measure a number of trees, turn your tape measure into a diameter tape by marking it at approximate 3.1416-inch intervals. When the tape measure is wrapped around the tree, you can then read the diameter directly at the point where the zero end of the tape reaches the rest of the tape.

Tree diameters are measured to the nearest inch only. This means that while, obviously, a 6-inch tree will have a diameter of 6 inches, any tree with a diameter spread from 5½ to 6½ inches is considered a 6-inch tree. So to measure a 6-inch tree, make a line in India ink or thinned paint right across the tape measure at the 1'5¼" indication (for a 5½-inch diameter), a second at 1'8½" (for a 6½-inch diameter), and write the figure "6" halfway between the two lines to indicate that any tree measuring between the two marks is a "6-inch tree." Continue marking the tape in similar fashion until you come to the end of it. A 5-foot tape will measure trees up to 19 inches in diameter if marked as follows (the figures in parentheses are the diameter measurements in inches written onto the tape) :

1'5¼"—(6)—1'8½"—(7)—1'11½"(8)—2'2¾"—(9)—2'5¾"—(10)—2'9"—(11)—3'0"—(12)—3'3¼"—(13)—3'6½"—(14)—3'9½"—(15)—4'¾"—(16)—4'3¾"—(17)—4'7"—(18)—4'10"—(19)—5'1¼".

CRUISER STICK—When it is a matter of finding the diameter of a large number of trees, a forester uses a cruiser stick. This is a stick with markings graduated in such a way that, when held against the tree, the user can read the tree's diameter directly.

To make a cruiser stick, secure a piece of 1-inch lath, about 3 feet long. At a distance of 3.72 inches from one end, make a mark and write the figure "4." At a distance

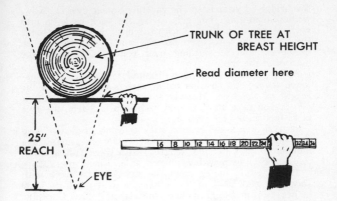

A cruiser stick or "Biltmore stick," made from a piece of lath,
makes it easy to determine the diameter of a tree.

of 5.39 inches from the end, make a second mark and
write the figure "6." Continue marking the stick in similar fashion, until it is marked as follows (the figures in
the parentheses are the diameter measurements) :

3.72 (4)—5.39 (6)—6.96 (8)—8.45 (10)—9.87 (12)—
11.21 (14)—12.50 (16)—13.72 (18)—14.91 (20)—16.04
(22)—17.14 (24).

To use the cruiser stick for measuring a tree diameter,
hold the stick horizontally against the tree at breast
height (4½ feet above ground) at a distance of 25 inches
from the eye, so that the zero end of the stick and one
side of the tree coincide. Read the diameter of the tree at
the marking that coincides with the other side of the tree.

REFERENCE—The Forest Service has developed templates
    for making cruiser sticks (or "Biltmore sticks") for
    arm reaches of 23, 24, and 25 inches. Drop a note to
    U. S. Forest Service, Washington 25, D. C., and ask
    for one of the Biltmore stick templates.

MEASURING HEIGHT—PLAIN STICK—You can measure a
tree's height in feet by using a plain stick approximately
3 feet long. Measure the length of your average step in
advance, then proceed as follows :

Grasp the stick near one end and hold it vertically in
front of you in your outstretched arm. While adjusting
your hold on the stick but keeping your arm outstretched,
swing the tip of the stick toward your face until it touches

the bridge of your nose (be careful of your eyes!). Now, without changing your grip, swing the stick back up into vertical position. Walk backward until in sighting over the tip of the stick you see the top of the tree to be measured, and in sighting over your fist you see the bottom of the tree.

Since you are working with similar triangles, the distance from your position to the tree is now equal to the height of the tree. Measure this distance by stepping it off. If you take 15 steps and each step is 3 feet, the tree is 45 feet high (15 times 3).

CRUISER STICK—A cruiser stick is often graduated (on the side not marked for diameters) for measuring the number of logs (16-foot lengths) in a tree. This graduation consists in markings placed at 6.15-inch intervals.

Measure 6.15 inches from one end. Make a mark with India ink and label it "1." Make the next mark at 12.30 inches (2 times 6.15 inches) and label it "2." Continue marking the stick in similar fashion until it is marked as follows (the figures in the parentheses are the 16-foot lengths):

6.15 (1)—12.30 (2)—18.45 (3)—24.60 (4)—30.75 (5).

To use the cruiser stick for measuring a tree height, walk 66 feet away from the tree (22 steps if you have adjusted your walk to taking 3-foot steps). Face the tree. Hold the stick vertically at arm's length—25 inches from

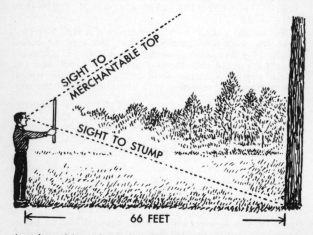

SIGHT TO MERCHANTABLE TOP

SIGHT TO STUMP

66 FEET

A cruiser stick can be graduated in such a way that you can read on it the number of logs in a tree.

the eye—so that the zero end of the stick and the merchantable top (uppermost log) of the tree coincide. Read the number of 16-foot logs at the marking that most nearly coincides with the stump of the tree.

> *Tip*—Biltmore stick templates mentioned in reference on page 395 also contain measurements for determining the number of 16-foot logs in a tree and for obtaining number of board feet.

RULER—You can also measure a tree's height with an ordinary ruler by using the method described on page 287.

ESTIMATING BOARD-FOOT VOLUME—With the diameter and the height of a tree found, you can estimate the number of board-feet of lumber it is possible to cut from the tree, and thereby the tree's timber value.

To do this, you open up to the table, in the *Volume Tables* pamphlet prepared by the U. S. Forestry Service, for the kind of tree in question. The number of board-feet is read where the horizontal column indicating the tree diameter in inches meets the vertical column indicating the tree height in feet or 16-foot logs.

REFERENCE—U. S. Forestry Service. *Volume Tables.* Tables for estimating board-foot volumes of timber. Catalog No. A 13.2:T48/17.

TIMBER CRUISING—A timber cruise is an inventory of the kinds and sizes of trees growing in a certain area. It is done mostly for determining the marketable value of a wood lot or forest but can also be used as an adjunct

Diameter of tree breast-high (inches)	Shortleaf pine				Loblolly pine				White oak				Black oak			
	1-log	2-log	3-log	4-log	1-log	2-log	3-log	4-log	1-log	2-log	3-log	4-log	1-log	2-log	3-log	4-log
8																
10																
12																
14																
16																
18																
20																

Make up a chart along this line when you plan to count the number of trees of various sizes in a wood lot.

to a general tree survey (see page 290) or for training in forestry practices.

WOOD LOT CRUISE—In the case of a small wood lot, it is fairly easy to make a count of all trees of and above a certain diameter—such as 6 inches. Before setting out, make up a tally sheet on ruled paper along the line shown in the illustration.

For each tree found and measured, make a mark on the tally sheet. For tallying, foresters generally use a "dot and dash" method. In this, one dot means one tree, three dots mean three trees, four dots and two dashes mean six trees, and so on, in this fashion:

Use a piece of carpenter's or lumberman's chalk to mark the trees measured to prevent duplication or missing of trees.

When the cruise is completed, the tally can be used to determine the board-foot volume of the merchantable trees.

FOREST CRUISE—In estimating the trees in a forest covering several acres it is not feasible to make a count of all the trees. Instead, the "line plot" system of cruising may be used. In this, the timber on circular ⅕-acre plots is measured at equally spaced intervals along compass lines laid out at a fixed distance apart.

When tally is completed for all sample plots, the board volume of all the merchantable trees is totaled. By dividing the total by the number of sample plots and multiplying by 5 you arrive at the average board volume per acre. You then multiply the figure found by the number of acres the forest covers to get the grand total of the whole area.

A forest cruise is a rather complicated project. It involves following exact compass directions and taking correct measurements. If you are interested in making such a cruise, secure the help of a local forest technician.

15.   WILDLIFE CONSERVATION

W HEN conservationists speak of "wildlife," they
mean the animals with backbones that inhabit our
fields and forests, our lakes and streams: birds and
mammals, fish, reptiles and amphibians.

The creatures of the wild are important to the balance
of nature. Most of them are important to man as well:
many of them are of direct help to the farmer by controlling injurious insects and rodents, some provide recreation in the form of hunting and fishing, a number of
them furnish us with fur and food, others contribute to
our esthetic enjoyment of nature.

While America was still a wilderness with almost unlimited living space for wild creatures, the amount of
wildlife depended on the ability of the species to reproduce and to survive. Today, when man has taken over
the land, the amount of wildlife is determined by the
"carrying capacity" of man-managed areas—the capacity
of the land to provide adequate living conditions for the
wildlife on it.

Wildlife conservation and management have become a
matter of conserving and managing and improving the
areas where wildlife lives through proper soil and water
and forestry practices that will ensure cover for protection, food and water for sustenance, and adequate living space.

BOOKS ON WILDLIFE CONSERVATION—Durward L. Allen.
    Our Wildlife Legacy. Funk & Wagnalls Company.
    Edward H. Graham. *The Land and Wildlife*. Oxford'
    University Press.
    L. W. Wing. *Practice of Wildlife Conservation*. John
    Wiley and Sons.
    Reuben Edwin Trippensee. *Wildlife Management*.
    Charles Scribner's Sons.

Working with Others

Many of the projects described in the previous sections on soil and water conservation and forestry provide the necessary indirect first step toward successful wildlife conservation. The next step is the undertaking of projects that will directly affect wildlife by providing food and cover for the largest possible population of birds, mammals, and fish compatible with the other uses of the area.

Most of the wildlife conservation projects in the following pages are readily organized and performed. For some of them you will be better off if you secure the advice and assistance of local wildlife technicians.

GOVERNMENT AGENCIES—FEDERAL—U. S. Department of the Interior. Fish and Wildlife Service.
STATE—Fish and Wildlife Commission.
COUNTY—Game manager or game wardens.

SOCIETIES—National Wildlife Federation. Hdqrs.: 1412 16th Street, Washington 6, D. C. Periodical: *Conservation News*.
Wildlife Management Institute. Hdqrs.: 709 Wire Building, Washington 5, D. C. Periodical: *Outdoor News Bulletin*.
Wildlife Society. Hdqrs.: Remington Farms, Chestertown, Md. Periodical: *Journal of Wildlife Management*.
Ducks Unlimited. Hdqrs.: 165 Broadway, New York 6, N. Y. Periodical: *Ducks Unlimited*.
Also general conservation societies, page 353.

Field Observation in Wildlife Conservation

WILDLIFE SURVEY—Make a thorough study of a farm, a camp, a public recreation ground, or a specific wildlife area (forest, dry upland, wet lowland, and so on) for the purpose of determining its wildlife population —species and estimated number based on sight records or sign of presence. Use a large map of the area under investigation. Divide map into squares and investigate each square of land. Mark especially significant wildlife areas on the map.

WILDLIFE SEEN—Make list of animals and birds actually seen. Are they residents? Migrants?

DENS—Make a thorough search for dens in the ground, among rocks, under tree roots, in hollow trees, in down trees (see pages 108–9). Determine inhabitants, if not seen, from tracks, claw marks, adhering hairs.

NESTS—How many nests and where located? Scan

trees, penetrate thickets, traverse fields to locate nests (see pages 68–70). What kind are they?

SIGN OF WILDLIFE—Look for tracks, scat or droppings, feathers, feeding sign, scent posts, scratch hills, runways and other sign (see page 109). Also—depending on where you live—for lookout posts of hawk, dusting beds of quail, dancing hills of prairie chicken, drumming logs of grouse, and other special features.

COVER—Is adequate cover available for type and size of area? Look for *concealment cover*—ground litter, weeds, shrubs among which a bird or an animal could hide against its enemies; *emergency cover*—brush piles, hollow logs, rock heaps, brier patches to assure a quick getaway if pursued; *shelter cover*—windbreaks, hedges, thickets that will protect against the heat of the sun and inclement weather; *travel-lane cover* (especially important for quail) of brush or high weeds for safe traveling between feeding grounds and concealment cover; *resting cover* for roosting, sleeping and loafing between feedings; *nesting cover* for raising a family in comparative safety.

FOOD—Is adequate food available to support the wildlife population on a year-round basis? What kinds of fruit- and seed-bearing shrubs and trees are found? What grasses and legumes suitable for wildlife food? Evidence of overbrowsing by deer?

WATER—Does the area contain ponds, lakes, streams to provide drinking water for wildlife? Is the water clear or is there evidence of pollution or erosion?

IMPROVEMENTS NEEDED—On the basis of your finding, what measures should be taken for improving the wildlife population? Indicate location of proposed improvements on map.

REFERENCES—*Improving the Farm Environment for Wildlife.* Conservation Bulletin No. 12. U. S. Department of the Interior, Fish and Wildlife Service.

Making Land Produce Useful Wildlife. Farmers' Bulletin No. 2035. U. S. Department of Agriculture.

WILDLIFE MANAGEMENT—Make a field trip to a federal, state or private wildlife reservation or refuge or some other area—farm, camp, park—where good wildlife management procedures are followed. Arrange for a local wildlife management technician to come along as a guide to point out and explain what is being done.

In making such a field trip, keep in mind the three basic concepts for a sound wildlife conservation program promulgated by Ira N. Gabrielson, former director of the U. S. Fish and Wildlife Service:

1. Soil, water, forest, and wildlife conservation are only parts of one inseparable program.

2. Wildlife must have an environment suited to its needs if it is to survive.

3. Any use that is made of any living resource must be limited to not more than the annual increase if the essential seed stock is to be continually available.

On the basis of these concepts, look particularly for the following:

SOIL CONSERVATION—Are proper soil conservation practices carried out? Is best possible use made of the land according to its capability? Is there effective erosion control?

PLANTINGS—Do erosion-controlling plants provide food and cover for wildlife? Are waste areas improved for wildlife? What seed- and fruit-bearing plants suitable for wildlife are growing in the area? Is food adequate and available at all seasons of the year?

WATER—What water facilities are present? What is condition of water—clear, murky, silt-laden? What fish are found? Any shallow-water areas for waterfowl? Are stream banks protected, streams themselves improved for wildlife?

FOREST AREAS—Is there evidence of good forestry practices? Are forest edges suitable for wildlife cover? Is cut brush disposed of or is it turned into brush shelters? Are hollow den trees left standing? Does evidence of browsing indicate that the number of deer are within the area's "carrying capacity" of adequate living space?

HARVESTING—How is surplus of wildlife harvested? Is the area posted or is it open for hunting and fishing? Any special limitations in addition to the state's regulations in regard to length of season, bag limits, methods of harvesting?

Field Projects for Improving Open Land for Wildlife

PLANTS FOR WILDLIFE—FOOD PATCHES—The simplest way of providing food for game birds is to leave uncut a couple of rows of corn along the edge of a cornfield or a strip of grain unharvested along a fence close to natural cover. For a farmer, this is a simple matter. A group of non-farmers—such as a sportsmen's group—may co-operate with a farmer in establishing food patches for wildlife by providing the seed and doing some of the seeding in places that will not interfere with effective farming practices: along fences, and roads, at the margins of wood lots, in corners of fields, around gullies and ditches or wet spots.

For general purposes, corn tops the list. It supplies a large amount of food for the space it occupies and its strong stalks withstand adverse weather. Sudan grass, sorghum, and millet provide cover in addition to food. Legumes such as alfalfa, clover, vetch, cowpeas, soybeans have high wildlife food values.

REFERENCE—*Plants Useful in Upland Wildlife Management and Upland Game Management*—see page 94.

ODD AREAS—Any farm, camp or outdoor recreational area is certain to have a number of plots of idle land that could be changed into cover and feeding grounds for songbirds and small mammals. These plots—generally referred to as "odd areas"—may be eroded slopes or gullies, knobs or sinkholes, gravel or borrow pits, abandoned logging roads or old building sites, or even stretches of good land cut off from the main fields by a stream or gully. To be of value to wildlife the area should be at least 50 feet across—preferably ¼ acre (104 feet square; 118 in diameter) or larger.

In planting, plant first a well-spaced clump of 20 to 30 trees or tall-growing shrubs in the middle of the area. Then surround this center planting with three or four rows of smaller shrubs. Use fruit-bearing trees and shrubs that will thrive in your locality (see list on page 93).

REFERENCE—The pamphlet mentioned on page 93, *Fruits Attractive to Birds,* lists suitable trees and shrubs by states.

The plantings on an odd area need a certain amount of maintenance. Permit only a few trees to turn into full-fledged trees. Trim the rest so that they remain bushy for maximum cover. Pile up the trimmed-off branches into brush shelters (see page 407).

WINDBREAKS AND HEDGEROWS—In parts of the country where windbreaks have been established or where hedgerows are common, these may be improved for wildlife by planting fruit-bearing shrubs on each side of them—such as Tatarian honeysuckle, American wild plum, silverberry (autumn olive), high-bush cranberry, buffalo berry, elderberry, Russian olive.

In Southeastern United States and up into the Central States, bicolor lespedeza—a perennial shrub growing to the height of 8 feet—has been found of great value for attracting quail and encouraging their increase. A planting of bicolor lespedeza may be started from seed but it is more easily established from 1-year-old seedlings. Seedlings may be available through your Local Soil Conservation District or from a nursery. Plant the seedlings 2 feet apart in rows at 3- to 4-foot intervals. Cover the plants to about 2 inches above the root collar.

Tip—Bicolor lespedeza is also suitable for a field border next to a wood lot, for a planting on top of a stream bank, for odd areas in quail territory.

REFERENCES—*Shrub Plantings for Soil Conservation and Wildlife Cover.* Circular 887. U. S. Department of Agriculture.
Bicolor Lespedeza for Quail and Soil Conservation. Leaflet No. 248. U. S. Department of Agriculture.

LIVING FENCES—Within recent years, the multiflora rose has gained an increasing popularity for forming a "living fence" which is not only effective for keeping livestock within bounds but also for wildlife cover. In good soil, multiflora roses reach a maximum height of 10 feet and approximately the same width. Their red fruits ("hips") are highly prized as wildlife food.

Secure nursery-grown, 1-year-old seedlings. Select plants with a stem diameter of ⅛ to ¼ inch, of an erect growth and with stiff thorns. Before planting, trim the canes to a length of 2 to 3 inches, limiting the new growth to three or four buds. Clear a small area for each seedling by scalping off a 1-foot square. Make the planting hole large enough to permit proper spreading of the root. Pack the soil firmly around the plant.

For a living fence of only incidental value to wildlife, multiflora roses are usually planted 1 foot apart in a single row. For a more adequate wildlife cover, they should be planted at 3-foot intervals in two or more rows, 6 to 8 feet apart.

REFERENCE—*Multiflora Rose for Living Fences and Wildlife Cover.* Leaflet No. 256. U. S. Department of Agriculture.

WATER FOR WILDLIFE—Water is no problem where an area contains brooks and rivers, ponds and lakes, marshes and swamps. In areas with little water, the existing supply may need to be improved or increased. *Wildlife needs water—without water, no wildlife.*

A small spring or a seep may be enlarged by cleaning with a spade or a shovel and walling the sides with rocks. A small gully may be provided with a small dam of earth or rocks that will trap and hold water to last between rains.

In some of the arid parts of the West, a device that catches rain is used to provide water for quail and small mammals during dry spells. It is known as a "gallinaceous guzzler" (from *gallinae*, the bird order that includes quail, partridge, prairie hen and others). It consists of an apron made of a nonporous material that collects and funnels the rainwater into an underground reservoir, easily reached by small species of wildlife by use of a ramp. If you live in the arid West and are interested in the construction of guzzlers as a conservation project, contact your state conservation department.

Field Projects for Improving Woodlands for Wildlife

BRUSH AREAS—RELEASE CUTTINGS—Since birds and animals prefer brush areas rather than dense woods for living quarters, the simplest way to improve a woodland for wildlife is to turn some of it into brushland.

A brush border may be established by cutting down the trees over a strip of 15 to 30 feet along the edge of a forest, preferably on the side protected against the prevailing wind. A large, solid stand of trees may be improved for wildlife by clear-cutting one or more small areas in it, 1 to 2 acres in size.

In each case, the marketable timber should be pulled out and the lopped-off branches stacked into brush shelters.

BRUSH SHELTERS—It takes little effort to turn branches lopped off trees into a brush shelter for ground birds and small mammals.

Use some of the thickest branches for a foundation to keep the rest off the ground, thereby slowing the rotting. Place the large branches side by side or crisscross over a stump or a log. Then pile on slash generously. To be most effective, the pile should be at least 15 feet across and 6 feet high. Place a few heavy branches on top to prevent the wind from blowing the pile apart.

Tip—Instead of burning old Christmas trees, collect them on a community basis and use them for estab-

Brush shelters are a boon to small animals and birds. They are easily made by piling up lopped-off branches.

lishing brush piles. You may get the co-operation of your city officials in taking collected trees to a suitable wildlife location rather than to the city dump for burning. Stack the trees butt-end-up against a small tree or post. Wire them together, if necessary, to keep them in place.

Wildlife will immediately take possession of the brush shelter. Within a year it will be overgrown by vines and berry brambles started from seeds dropped by birds. To speed the process, plant cuttings of wild grape, bittersweet, Virginia creeper around the pile.

BROWSE TREES—In thinning a wood lot, do not chop down all the inferior trees to the ground. Turn some of

"Browse trees" provide shelter and food for wildlife. They are saplings cut halfway through and bent to the ground.

them into a benefit to wildlife by chopping them halfway through only, 3 to 4 feet up, and bending their tops to the ground. The trees will go on growing, providing browse for deer and buds for grouse. Suckers may also form around the roots, providing yet more browse.

DENS AND NESTS—With modern forestry and farming methods, a number of animals and birds are deprived of their natural nesting places—particularly those that normally make use of hollow trees: squirrels, raccoons, opossums, flying squirrels, owls, and wood ducks.

DEN TREES—When making a woodland cutting, leave as many hollow den trees as possible—a minimum of 2 per acre, but preferably as many as 10 to take care of the mixed wildlife population.

DEN BOXES—SQUIRRELS AND RACCOONS—Where no trees with natural den cavities are available, you may be able to entice squirrels and raccoons into using den boxes.

These boxes may be made to the general design of the bluebird birdhouse shown on page 91, but to these dimensions: 12 inches square, 24 inches high, with a hole near the top, 6 inches in diameter if intended for squirrels,

8 inches if for raccoons. Drill several ½-inch holes in the bottom for drainage.

Tip—A nail keg makes a good den box if provided with a well-fitting roof.

A squirrel box should be placed high in a tree, near the top. A raccoon box may be placed in a crotch at least 15 feet above the ground.

WOOD DUCK BOX—Wood ducks are especially in need of nesting boxes because of the scarcity of hollow nest trees in the vicinity of water. They take readily to boxes made of rough unplaned 1-inch lumber.

Make the wood duck box to the general design of the bluebird birdhouse on page 91, but to these dimensions: 10 inches square, 24 inches high, with the back board extending 2 inches above and 2 inches below the box to facilitate the job of nailing it up. The hole, located 4 inches from the top, should be 4 inches in diameter. Drill a few ½-inch holes in the bottom for drainage. Fill the box with 4 inches of clean pine shavings.

A wood duck box may be erected profitably in a tree at a height of 15 to 20 feet aboveground, as much as half a mile or more from water, but it is preferably placed not more than 100 feet from a lake or a stream. It is even better if you can fasten the box to a post put up in an open marsh or in a lake a few feet from the shore. By having it surrounded by water, you prevent squirrels

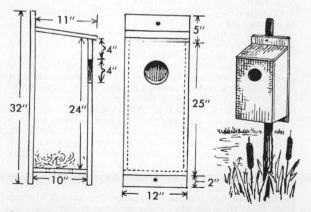

A wood duck nesting box can be made from pieces of scrap wood. It should, preferably, be put up a few feet from shore.

from taking it over and protect the birds against marauding predators.

Use a cedar post, 4 to 6 inches in diameter and long enough to project 6 to 8 feet above the water when driven firmly into the marsh or lake bottom. Nail the wood duck box to the pole close to the top with galvanized spikes. To keep out raccoons, it may be necessary to nail a metal guard to pole below box.

REFERENCE—*Better Nest Boxes for Wood Ducks.* Wildlife Leaflet 393. Fish and Wildlife Service, U. S. Department of the Interior.

Field Projects for Improving Streams and Lakes for Fish

STREAM IMPROVEMENT—Fish living in streams —trout specifically—require water that is well aerated and kept at the lowest possible temperature, with swift riffles for feeding and deep pools for resting. Nature her-self, in many instances, provides these stream features. Where she skimps on them, an individual or a sportsmen's club or a youth group may supply them by introducing a few simple measures that will greatly improve the stream for fish and fishing. If you have particularly ambitious plans in mind, consult your local conservation officer or fishing biologist.

Generally speaking, stream improvement by amateurs should be undertaken only on streams up to approximately 15 feet in width with a relatively stable flow of water— the improvement of larger streams and streams with great water fluctuations involves the use of heavy equipment, experienced workers and, often, the expenditure of large amounts of money.

STREAM BANK PROTECTION—Before attempting to improve a stream, take a good look at the water in it. You will have no luck improving the stream itself if eroding banks keep the water muddy and silt up the bottom. If this is the case, your first job will be the stabilization of the stream banks by seeding, planting or riprap, as described on page 384. The planting of trees is valuable beyond the bank protection: Overhanging foliage from willow trees, for instance, will attract insects for fish food and will provide shade against the summer sun, thus helping to keep the water temperature down.

DEFLECTORS—Deflectors built from rocks or consisting of single logs jutting from the stream bank can be used for directing the current, speeding up the flow and scouring out pools. If made from rocks, these should be firmly set in the stream bed and slanted against the current. If made from logs, these should be dug into the stream bank and securely anchored. If a deflector is set where the stream bottom is soft, a bar will form on the downstream side

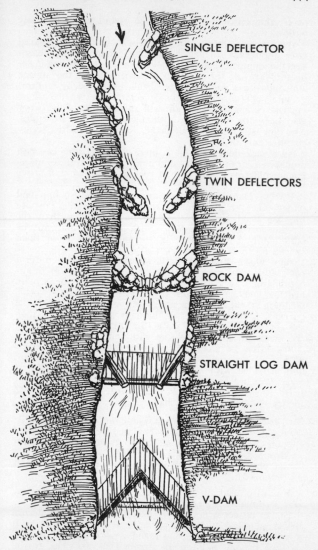

SINGLE DEFLECTOR

TWIN DEFLECTORS

ROCK DAM

STRAIGHT LOG DAM

V-DAM

Various deflectors and dams. Distances greatly foreshortened.

of it; this bar may eventually be stabilized with a few willows.

SINGLE DEFLECTORS—Single deflectors must be placed with great care so that the deflected water will not damage the opposite bank. The best locations for single deflectors are on the inside of a long bend in the stream and opposite a well-stabilized bank, protected by riprap.

TWIN DEFLECTORS—Twin deflectors constructed from opposite sides of the stream will speed up the flow. They also keep the midstream bottom clean and create riffles. The downstream bars they make will help keep the stream channel narrow.

Two rock deflectors made up of a comparatively small number of large boulders and almost, but not quite, meeting in midstream, will form a rock pool that should prove highly attractive to trout.

DAMS—Dams in a stream are not intended to impound water—they are used for creating pools. For this purpose the top need be only 6 to 10 inches higher than the stream bed in mid-channel. Such dams should not be built singly but in series as, for instance, four of them spaced 50 to 100 feet apart.

ROCK DAMS—Investigate the stream for possible natural rock dams and rock pools and build your own to duplicate nature as closely as possible. Dig out the stream bed for anchoring the first layer. Then build up the rocks, wedging them together and slanting them against the current. Make the sides of the dam slightly higher than the center to force the water toward the middle. Chink the upstream side of the dam with sod.

STRAIGHT LOG DAM—The simplest wooden dam consists of a single, reasonably straight log laid across the stream and provided with a board facing. The log should be at least 7 inches in diameter and long enough to extend at least 2 feet into each bank. The boards should be 6 to 12 inches wide, 4 to 6 feet long.

> *Tip*—Your telephone or power company may be willing to provide you with outdated yet well-preserved poles and may even be willing to arrange to have them dropped where you need them. A local sawmill may let you have random-width boards for facing at small or no cost.

You also need a light tail pole, as long as the main log, and a couple of short logs to act as deflectors.

Start the construction by placing the main log across the stream and anchoring it in the stream banks in such a way that the top is level and at the desired height. Anchor the tail pole on the stream bed, crosswise to the stream, at the correct distance from the main log to fit

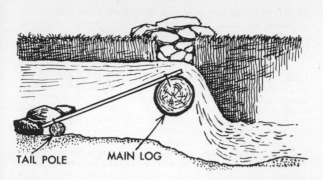

TAIL POLE   MAIN LOG

Side view of a straight log dam. Water flowing over dam creates a pool on the downstream side.

the length of the facing boards. Nail one end of each board to the main log, the other end to the tail pole. Leave a space of ¼ inch between boards to allow for swelling. When completed, pile rocks on the lower part of the facing to strengthen the whole structure.

The water will rise to flow in an even sheet over the entire main log. This flowing may cut into the banks on each side of the stream and cause erosion. To prevent this, reduce the spillway to about 50 per cent, over the middle of the dam, by spiking two deflector logs onto the main log and anchoring the other ends of them in the upstream banks in such a way that they form an angle of 45° to the dam.

V-DAM—The V-dam uses two logs in its construction. The butt ends are sawed off at such an angle that, when spiked together, the logs form the angle of a long V.

Place the log V in the stream with the apex, or point of the V, upstream and with the ends of the arms on the banks, one on each side of the stream. Anchor the ends in the banks in such a way that the top of them is approximately 2 feet above the point of the V resting on the stream bed. Face the upstream side of the two logs with 1-inch boards as described above for a straight log dam.

The water will spill over the V-dam whether it happens to run high or low. Fit an apron into the point of the V to catch the flow and spread it. This apron may be built by driving short logs into the stream bed and topping them with planks, sloped according to the depth you want the pool below the dam to assume. "The less slope, the better the riffle," the experts say.

FISH PONDS—If you and the group with which you are working have access to land which seems promising for the establishment of a fish pond, by all means construct one.

For suggestions on how to go about this, see page 240.

LAKE IMPROVEMENT—REMOVAL OF UNDESIRABLE VEGETATION—Excessive growth of undesirable water plants along the shores and on the surface of ponds and small lakes decreases the number of desirable game fish by providing too generous hiding facilities for the prey fish on which they live and thrive.

Undesirable water plants growing in shallow water—bulrush, spike rush, needle rush, spatterdock, water chestnut, and others—can usually be eliminated by hand-pulling. This should be done early in the summer before the plants have a chance to produce seed or spread further by root growth. To prevent them from returning, it may pay to deepen the shallow areas by shoveling some of the bottom onto the bank.

Free-floating water plants—such as water hyacinth and bladderwort—can be eradicated by raking them out whenever and wherever they appear.

COVER FOR FISH—While a small lake may often be overgrown, giving excess cover to prey fish, many larger lakes do not provide adequate cover for fish. Artificial cover or shelters may alleviate the situation.

UNDERWATER BRUSH SHELTERS—The idea of providing brush shelters for game birds and small animals can be used for fish as well. The main differences in construction are that the brush pile for underwater cover must be held together by wire and weighted.

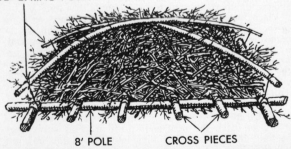

10' SPRING POLES

8' POLE   CROSS PIECES

An underwater brush shelter for fish is made by piling brush onto a wooden frame and sinking the structure into the water.

Stone piles make good shelters for small fish. Nail kegs can provide spawning nests for channel catfish.

Make a square frame by wiring together near the ends four poles of some durable wood—oak, maple, hemlock, tamarack, cedar—8 feet long, 3 to 4 inches thick. Place a number of poles across the frame and wire them in position into a crude platform. Place newly cut brush on the platform to a height of 5 to 6 feet.

Wire one end of a spring pole, about 10 feet long and 2 inches thick, to one corner of the platform. Bend the pole diagonally across the brush pile, pressing down the brush somewhat, and wire the free end to the corner diagonally opposite to the corner where the pole was first fastened. Wire another pole of similar size diagonally across the brush pile, forming an X with the first pole.

Finally wire a cement block or a large rock to each of the four corners of the frame.

Carry or truck the prepared brush pile to the lake and load it onto the stern of a rowboat or onto a raft. Bring it out in the lake to the spot chosen for its location and push it overboard.

Tip—If built during the winter in a low-temperature area, brush piles may be pulled out on the ice and left to sink when the ice melts.

OTHER COVER FOR FISH—If flat stones are readily available, stone piles may be built in water up to 4 feet deep, to provide shelter and nests for small fish.

Nail kegs have been found attractive spawning nests for channel catfish in southwestern lakes if placed on the side in water 2½ to 3 feet deep, with the open end toward deep water. Wire rocks or cement blocks to the nail kegs to weight them down and bore a 1-inch hole in the side that will be to the top, to permit trapped air to escape.

ACKNOWLEDGMENTS

A book of this type is not one man's job. A hundred years of living would not suffice to carry through its many suggestions. The activities described in it have come into being through the work of a great many scientists throughout the years. In gathering them together in a single volume, I have received the help of numerous people—in person and through their writings. The books that are listed throughout this volume have been valuable sources of information and inspiration. I owe to each of their authors a great debt of gratitude. Many of the methods described are standard procedures —originated, tested, and improved by countless nameless scientists; others are the ideas of individuals whose names are known. Wherever possible, I have traced the source of an idea and have given the originator due credit. In the cases where I may have failed, I offer my apologies. Credit would certainly have been given, if I had known to whom it belonged.

For the checking of the manuscript, I have received the willing and generous help of a large number of people. Part I was checked by Raymond L. Taylor, American Association for the Advancement of Science; Harry E. Radcliffe, American Nature Association; Richard L. Weaver, American Nature Study Society. The chapters of Part II were checked as follows: Birds—Carl W. Buchheister, National Audubon Society; Herbert Friedman, Smithsonian Institution. Mammals—A. L. Nelson and William H. Stickel, Patuxent Research Refuge, Fish and Wildlife Service, U.S. Department of the Interior; Donald F. Hoffmeister, American Society of Mammalogists. Reptiles—Roger Conant, Philadelphia Zoological Garden; M. Graham Netting, American Society of Ichthyologists and Herpetologists; Chapman Grant, Herpetologists League. Insects—Cyril F. dos Passos, American Museum of Natural History; Avery S. Hoyt, Bureau of Entomology and Plant Quarantine, U.S. Department of Agriculture. Flowers—Reed C. Rollins, Gray Herbarium, Harvard University; P. L. Ricker, The Wild Flower Preservation Society; Edna A. Clark, The Garden Club of America. Trees—J. P. McWilliams, American Forestry Association; Charles E. Randall, Forest Service, U.S. Department of Agriculture. Photographic sections— R. W. Brown, Eastman Kodak Company. Conservation sections—Ted S. Pettit, Boy Scouts of America. General Conservation and Soil and Water Conservation—Adrian C. Fox, Information Division, Soil Conservation Service, U.S. Department of Agriculture. Forestry and Forest Conservation—Matthew J. Brennan, Division of Information and Education, Forest Service, U.S. Department of Agriculture; Robert A. Wells, Fish and Wildlife Service, U.S. Department of the Interior.

To each of these people I extend my most sincere appreciation for their invaluable assistance.

—WILLIAM HILLCOURT

PROJECT INDEX

While this *Field Book* contains close to 1,000 suggestions for nature activities, the following 400 projects are particularly suitable for group work—school, camp, club, Scout Troop—along the lines indicated on page 42. You may also want to accept some of them as personal challenges. They are graded as follows:

x   Simple projects for beginners, requiring little or no equipment.

x x   Projects involving elementary knowledge; sustained effort; equipment.

x x x   Projects requiring advanced knowledge; extra effort; special equipment.

SUBJECT INDEX